ADIWES INTERNATIONAL SERIES
IN ADVANCED PHYSICS

This book is in the

ADDISON-WESLEY SERIES IN ADVANCED PHYSICS

Morton Hamermesh, Consulting Editor

AN INTRODUCTION TO
PLASMA PHYSICS

W. B. THOMPSON, Ph.D.

Head of the Theoretical Physics Division
Culham Plasma Physics Laboratory of the
United Kingdom Atomic Energy Authority

1962

PERGAMON PRESS

OXFORD · LONDON · NEW YORK · PARIS

ADDISON-WESLEY PUBLISHING COMPANY, INC.

READING, MASSACHUSETTS · PALO ALTO · LONDON

Copyright © 1962
PERGAMON PRESS LTD.

U.S.A. Edition distributed by
Addison-Wesley Publishing Company, Inc.
Reading, Massachusetts · Palo Alto · London

Library of Congress Card No. 62–9184

Printed in Great Britain

ERRATA

p.13	line –3	for	$\operatorname{curl}\mathbf{B}\dfrac{4\pi}{c}\mathbf{j}$	read	$\operatorname{curl}\mathbf{B}=\dfrac{4\pi}{c}\mathbf{j}$
p.15	,, –2	,,	$0J_0$	,,	$0, J_0$
p.26	,, 4, 6, 8, 12	,,	$\boldsymbol{\nu}$	,,	$\mathbf{v}$
p.27	,, 3	,,	$\boldsymbol{\nu}$	,,	$\mathbf{v}$
p.30	,, 22	,,	$v(v_0)$	,,	v_0
,,	,, 26	,,	$v_+^2(v_0)$	,,	v_0^2
,,	,, 29	,,	$\dfrac{n_0 v(v_0)}{\sqrt{[v^2(v_0)-2(eV(x)/M)]}}$	,,	$\dfrac{n_0 v_0}{\sqrt{[v_0^2-2eV(x)/M]}}$
p.65	,, 15	,,	$\dfrac{\partial\boldsymbol{\nu}}{\partial t}$	,,	$\dfrac{\partial\mathbf{v}}{\partial t}$
p.79	,, –2	,,	are Gaussian units	,,	are, Gaussian units,
p.137	,, 19	,,	KIEPENHAUR	,,	KIEPENHAUER
p.167	,, –5	,,	$C_A{}^2$	,,	$C_A{}^{-2}$
p.210	,, 11	,,	$\mathbf{b}x\{$	,,	$\mathbf{b}\times\{$
,,	,, 12-14	,,	cx, cy, bx, by, Vx, Vy	,,	$c_x, c_y, b_x, b_y, V_x\cdot V_y$
p.211	,, 11	,,	$c_\perp{}^2$	,,	$c_\perp{}^2, c_\parallel{}^2$
p.217			Doubt has been cast on the interpretation of this experiment. cf. COENSGEN F. *et al. Nuclear Fusion* supplement paper 61, p. 125, 1962.		
p.231	,, 18	,,	0.22	,,	0.42
p.238	,, 10	,,	$\rho_0\ddot{\boldsymbol{\xi}}$	,,	$\rho_0\ddot{\boldsymbol{\xi}}$
p.239	,, –4	,,	$(8\pi p'/Bg^2)$	,,	$(8\pi p'/B_z{}^2)$
p.241	,, 2	,,	$(\mathbf{v}\cdot\mathbf{k})\mathbf{k}$	,,	$(\mathbf{v}\cdot\hat{\mathbf{k}})\hat{\mathbf{k}}$
,,	,, 8	,,	$\gamma=\omega_p{}^2\Omega/(\omega^2-\Omega^2)$	,,	$\gamma=\omega_p{}^2\Omega/\omega(\omega^2-\Omega^2)$
,,	,, –5	,,	$w_n=w+$	,,	$\omega_n=\omega+$
,,	,,	,,	w_0	,,	ω_0
p.242	,, 10	,,	$w(\mathbf{k})$	,,	$\omega(\mathbf{k})$

CONTENTS

PREFACE

THE following chapters are a somewhat expanded version of a course of lectures given at A.E.R.E. Harwell, at the Clarendon Laboratory of Oxford University and to the Department of Theoretical Physics, Imperial College, London. My intention had been merely to duplicate the notes prepared for these lectures; however, on reflection these appeared both too incomplete and too unconvincing to serve as a reader's introduction to the subject, and I felt it necessary to clarify and, with some regret, to expand them.

The original lecture course was directed toward graduate recruits in Harwell's scientific grades, and at the universities to graduate students in physics. The book is aimed at this same level. While by no means sophisticated, it is intended for readers with some training in theoretical physics; however, those whose education is deficient will find helpful auxiliary reading in elementary texts on hydrodynamics, electromagnetic theory and the mathematical methods of physics—indeed, such a work as Joos' *Theoretical Physics* contains all that is required.

I have been somewhat abrupt in my treatment of experimental results, my ambition having been limited to a presentation of the theoretical language in which plasma physics is discussed, so that experiments have been described only in so far as they bear on theoretical prediction. To have given a complete account of many of these experiments would have required an extensive excursion into advanced engineering practice, for which I lack both space and knowledge. A more complete treatment of many of the experiments mentioned herein will be found in the book of Glasstone and Loveberg, as well as in the original papers cited.

The subject of plasma physics has aroused such interest, holds forth such golden promises and has generated such a mountain of technical papers that some "child's guide" is called for. My own knowledge of the subject has been developed in an attempt to assist in the quest for a method of controlling the release of thermonuclear energy, and the bias may be obvious; nevertheless I feel, possibly with prejudice, that it is this research which has produced the most significant recent advances in the subject and that an introduction developed in this context should provide a reasonable basis for a study of the literature.

One unfortunate aspect of controlled thermonuclear research is that until 1958 most of it was carried out in secret and as a result, much was unnecessarily duplicated. In fact a great deal of the development in this work was carried out independently at Harwell, and the presentation given here is to a large extent a personal one. Furthermore, in giving references I have completely ignored the delicate question of priorities, and insufficiently equipped with either erudition or tact have made no attempt, even by implication, to suggest an assignment of laurels.

A personal acknowledgement however; these pages would have been poorer without the work of Spitzer's theoretical group at Princeton under Frieman and Kruskal, the analytical presentations of Grad and his colleagues, and the elegant achievements of M. N. Rosenbluth. The energy principle of Ch.6 § 3 comes directly from Princeton, while that of Ch.8 § 11 is due to Rosenbluth. Nearer home, I must thank my colleagues at Harwell, particularly P. C. Thonemann who provided the major inspiration for the thermonuclear effort, and R. J. Tayler who has contributed particularly to my understanding of magnetohydrodynamic stability. I am grateful also to Mrs. R. Jackson and her aides at Harwell who translated the manuscript into type, to my wife who read much of the typescript and to Dr. Bruce Robinson of the University of California, San Diego who has read the galleys. Finally, in spite of this help, a word of apology and of caution; if a statement appears unusually outrageous examine it with care—it may be a misprint.

La Jolla, December 1961

CHAPTER 1

AN INTRODUCTION TO PLASMA PHYSICS

1. INTRODUCTION

WHEN a gas is raised to a sufficiently high temperature, the atoms and molecules of the gas may become ionized, electrons being stripped off by the violent collisions consequent on the thermal agitation of the particles. When this happens, the dynamical behaviour of the gas may be dominated by the electromagnetic forces acting on the free ions and electrons, and its properties become sufficiently different from those of a normal unionized gas to merit the introduction of a new name, the "plasma", to denote a gas in such a highly ionized state. This name was derived from the expression "plasma oscillation" introduced by LANGMUIR to denote characteristic oscillations of a very high frequency (1000 Mc/s) which a plasma can support even in circumstances where normal sound is strongly damped.

The most important distinction between a plasma and a normal gas lies in the ability of the former to sustain an electric current, the plasma being a fairly good electrical conductor, whereas normal gases are insulators. The dynamical consequences of this are particularly important in a magnetic field, where the motion of the gas is often dominated by the electromagnetic body force $\mathbf{j} \times \mathbf{B}$ and it is in interaction with a magnetic field that the plasma displays its most novel and spectacular behaviour.

The study of ionized gases is of respectable antiquity and has proved a most fruitful branch of physics; indeed, the modern study of molecular, atomic and nuclear physics had its origin largely in the study of the conduction of electricity through gases. However, the very fruitfulness of the subject in these fields directed interest away from the nature of the plasma itself toward the information about atomic structure produced by the study of discharges. Aside from the intrinsic interest of atomic structure, another fact directed the course of research in electrical discharges; the discovery that the electrical properties of a slightly ionized gas are dominated by the complex processes of ionization, excitation, inelastic and resonant scattering that may occur when an electron strikes an atom. Since, as we shall see, a highly ionized gas can be produced and observed only with considerable difficulty, it was natural that the study of ionized gases should be largely a study of atomic collision processes.

In recent years interest in the plasma itself has been revived. This revival was initiated by the astronomers who were stimulated by the behaviour of ionized gas on the sun's surface, on the surface of stars, in interplanetary and interstellar space, and by geophysicists studying the dynamics of the ionosphere. More recently, the technological possibilities of the plasma have attracted attention, most spectacularly in the research directed toward the controlled release of energy from the thermonuclear fusion of light elements.

These notes, which were stimulated by controlled thermonuclear research, are directed toward the study of pure plasma dynamics and as far as possible will avoid discussing those branches of the subject in which atomic collision processes play an important role. In particular, they are concerned chiefly with an idealized plasma composed of electrons and ions in which inelastic processes including ionization and recombination are unimportant.

This idealized subject has considerable theoretical interest. From a macroscopic viewpoint the plasma interacting with a magnetic field can often be considered as a magnetohydrodynamic fluid, an electrically conducting fluid subject to electromagnetic forces. The properties of such a fluid, which must be described by a combination of the hydrodynamic equations for the fluid, and Maxwell's equations describing the field, are extremely interesting, and, as may be expected, magnetohydrodynamic flow exhibits a wider range of phenomena than normal fluid motion. Microscopically, the plasma consists of an assembly of particles interacting through known forces and appears as the ideal subject for the methods of classical kinetic theory. The plasma, however, proves even more interesting than this, for since the forces of interaction are long-range the simple picture of a diffuse gas in which the interaction can be represented by scarce binary encounters is never valid and the microscopic dynamics of a plasma must be understood as a study in many-body physics. This means that plasma physics has connections with a wide range of interesting physical problems. In the presence of a large magnetic field, the dynamics of the plasma can be at least partially understood by neglecting the local interactions altogether and considering the particles as moving independently in the macroscopic fields, which, of course, are in turn produced or modified by the mean motion of the particles. Even in this case it proves possible to describe the plasma by hydrodynamic-like equations.

In addition to its intrinsic interest, the study of plasma attracts attention by the range of its application. The sun and stars and much interstellar matter are ionized and as magnetic fields have been shown to be quite common in the cosmos it is not surprising that many astronomical phenomena appear to be illustrations of the behaviour of the plasma.

Technologically, possible applications of the plasma are continually suggested, ranging from such specific problems as rapid switching of large currents to more spectacular—and more speculative—suggestions such as the use of ionic drive for interplanetary flight, or the use of magnetic containment in a controlled thermonuclear reactor.

One difficulty with the study of this subject is that contact with experiment is less intimate than could be desired. The chief reason for this is the difficulty of producing and observing plasma in the laboratory. Unless the degree of ionization is high, inelastic collision processes dominate the behaviour of the plasma and even at high degrees of ionization the interchange of matter with the cold walls of the containing vessel cools the gas and determines its condition. It has been hoped to inhibit the latter effect by producing configurations in which the plasma is kept away from the wall by magnetic fields; however, attempts to produce magnetically confined plasma encounter difficulties through plasma instability, and have met with only partial success. A further difficulty in performing experiments arises from short time scales usually required. Typical plasma dynamic behaviour is observed when diffusion effects can be neglected and except for very short periods, or in extremely hot plasmas, these effects are extremely important.

2. THE OCCURRENCE OF PLASMA IN NATURE

A good case can be made for the statement that plasma is the normal state of matter. Except for such unusual places as the earth, most matter is either sufficiently hot or sufficiently diffuse to be ionized. Thus the high temperature of the sun and the stars ensures that they are almost completely ionized, although the dominance of gravitational forces, which are no respecters of charges, suggests plasma dynamic effects have little relevance in stellar interiors. On the surfaces of stars, on the other hand, electromagnetic forces can play a significant part, but since the more characteristic plasma phenomena require a magnetic field, typical plasma behaviour can only be expected where magnetic fields are found. There are several ways of inferring the existence of magnetic fields, of which the most direct is from a measurement of the Zeeman splitting of spectral lines. Unfortunately, the splitting is rather slight except in strong fields and tends to be lost in the Doppler and Stark broadening: hence this method of studying cosmic magnetic fields has a limited application.

The situation is somewhat improved when the polarization in the wings of the line is also measured, opposite polarization in the two wings being a characteristic of the Zeeman effect. By using such methods, BABCOCK has produced detailed maps of the magnetic field on the sun's surface and has shown that although there are usually several magnetically active regions of high field, the general magnetic fields of the sun are less than ~ 2 Gauss. In sun spots, however, the field can reach a magnitude of several thousand Gauss and is sufficiently powerful to have an important effect on the structure of the solar atmosphere. Since the electromagnetic stress $\mathbf{j} \times \mathbf{B}$ acts normally to magnetic field lines we expect matter to flow easily along the field and only with difficulty across it; thus if magnetic forces affect the flow we should expect to see configurations suggestive of magnetic field lines in the solar atmosphere and it is indeed just such configurations which represent the most striking features of solar prominences. Higher in the solar atmosphere, in the corona, no Zeeman splitting has been detected, but the shape of the luminous filaments strongly suggests the presence of a magnetic field. The Zeeman effect, however, has been used to study the magnetic field in certain stars, the magnetic variables, where the magnetic field is not only large (10,000 Gauss), but varies in magnitude and sometimes in sign with a period of a few days.

A less direct method of studying magnetic fields is the analysis of radio emission from celestial objects. This possibility arises from the production of synchrotron radiation by electrons rotating about magnetic field lines. The character of the radiation depends on electron energy; if the energy is low the radiation occurs primarily at the gyrofrequency $\Omega = eB/mc$, where e, m = electron charge, mass, c = velocity of light and B = magnetic field strength; but if the electron energy is high so that the electrons move relativistically, the radiation is continuous and may extend as far as the X-ray region. In any case, the radiation is completely polarized, the electric vector being normal to the field lines. Synchrotron radiation of this kind has been discovered in certain gaseous nebulae, noticeably the Crab (which represents the residue of a supernova explosion), as part of the background radiation of the galaxy, and as the major component of the radiation from certain rather peculiar extragalactic nebulae. Radio astronomy gives information about the presence of plasma in astronomical objects arising from the effect of plasma on the passage of electromagnetic waves. As we shall show, plasma acts as a dielectric with a coefficient $1 - \omega_p^2/\omega^2$ where ω_p is the Langmuir plasma frequency and will transmit oscillations only above the plasma frequency. This phenomenon has been used, for example by MARTYN, to infer the distribution of plasma about the sun (v. also PAWSEY and SMERD).

Still less direct evidence of plasma dynamic effects has been obtained from the observations of the polarization of starlight by HILTNER. He discovered that the polarization depends not on the nature of the emitting star, but on its position, particularly on its distance from the earth, hence it must be an effect of the interstellar matter through which the light has passed. At present, it appears most likely to be the consequence of scattering by elongated paramagnetic dust grains which have been aligned by a weak interstellar magnetic field $\sim 10^{-5}$ G. Since there is independent evidence from the spectral lines observed, to indicate that much interstellar material is ionized this raises the possibility of plasma processes playing an important role in interstellar space. One most important consequence may be the acceleration of cosmic ray particles by the electric fields associated with the motions of interstellar matter.

Nearer home, studies of the transmission of radio waves have revealed the presence of an ionized layer, the ionosphere, in the outer part of the earth's atmosphere and its structure has been studied in some detail. The dynamic effects of the ionosphere are displayed in the fading of radio signals and in the diurnal variation of the earth's magnetic field. More spectacular changes in the earth's field, the magnetic storms, have been attributed to the disturbance of the earth's field by an incoming beam of plasma from the sun. Another spectacular effect associated with these beams is the aurora, with which magnetic storms are frequently correlated.

Recently, rocket- and satellite-borne counters have detected belts of energetic radiation, electrons and ions, high above the earth's atmosphere. These are the van Allen belts, which appear to be charged particles trapped in the earth's magnetic field.

Thus we see that throughout the universe, in the sun, the stars, in interstellar matter and in the distant galaxies, as well as in the upper atmosphere, plasmas are common, and an understanding of plasma dynamics may render intelligible many astrophysical phenomena.

3. TECHNOLOGICAL ASPECTS OF PLASMA PHYSICS

In addition to its natural occurrence, the unusual dynamical properties of a plasma have suggested interesting technical applications of highly ionized gases. Electric discharges have been in use for a considerable time either as switch elements in the thyrotron or dekatron, where the low inertia and the high current capacity of the plasma constitute a great advantage, or as rectifiers, in the ignitron. Discharges have also been used as flexible sources of light and are probably most familiar in this form. These devices, however, essentially make use of the relative rapidity with which a gas can become ionized, the peculiar nature of its interaction with solids, or the effectiveness with which it can be heated electrically.

Only recently have the characteristic dynamical properties of a plasma attracted attention and has intensive research begun on the possible applications of these properties. At present most of the actual technological applications lie in the future, but several possible developments are of sufficient interest to merit a great deal of attention. Of these, it seems probable that the direct conversion of the kinetic energy in a gas to electricity will be developed first. This scheme is based on the fact that an ionized gas satisfies a local Ohm's law—i.e. the current density $\mathbf{j}$ in a gas is determined by

$$\mathbf{j} = \sigma(\mathbf{E^*}) = \sigma\left(\mathbf{E} + \frac{\mathbf{v}}{c} \times \mathbf{B}\right)$$

where σ is the electrical conductivity and $\mathbf{E^*} = \mathbf{E} + \mathbf{v} \times \mathbf{B}/c$, the electric field in the fluid, that is the force on a unit charge which moves with the velocity $\mathbf{v}$ of the fluid. This relation between current and voltage shows that if a conducting fluid flows across a magnetic field B, a voltage $V = v\,B.L./c$ will appear across a channel of width L. By a measurement of this voltage, it is possible to estimate the flow velocity of the conducting fluid and a device based on this principle, the electromagnetic flowmeter, is used for gauging the flow of liquid metals. The application of this to the direct conversion of heat into electricity makes use of the hot, rapidly moving gas from a jet. In order to produce the ionization the gas is seeded with the vapour of an alkali metal, for which the ionization potential is low, so that significant degrees of ionization may be produced at moderate temperatures. The partially ionized conducting gas then moves through a magnetic field and between electrodes, from which a large electric current may be drawn representing a considerable fraction of the kinetic energy in the gas. Preliminary engineering studies suggest that such a device could act as a significant supplement to a conventional gas turbine.

A second application of plasma dynamics lies in ion jet propulsion which, in a certain sense, represents the inverse of the direct conversion process, since electrical energy is converted into kinetic energy of gas flow. This process may be of great importance in the design of high-performance, long-range space vehicles. A major problem in the design of such vehicles, using chemically-driven rockets, arises from the dual purpose of the fuel: it is burnt to provide the energy needed to drive the rocket, then expelled with some velocity v to provide the thrust. The acceleration given to the rocket is then determined by the rate of loss of mass, by

$$\frac{\mathrm{d}}{\mathrm{d}t}(MV) + \frac{\mathrm{d}m}{\mathrm{d}t} \ (v - V) = 0$$

where M, V are the mass and velocity of the entire rocket and propellents, $\mathrm{d}m/\mathrm{d}t$ is the rate at which the consumed propellents are discharged and v is the exhaust velocity. Since the exhaust velocity v is fixed by the temperature of the combustion products, the impulse given to the rocket is determined by the total amount of matter ejected; but since the propellents must be carried with the rocket and hence accelerated with it, the total initial mass of the rocket together with its propellents rapidly gets extremely large as the performance requirements are increased. If the ejection velocity v could be increased, the amount of fuel needed for any specified performance would decrease rapidly, and interplanetary flight, for example, would appear much more practical. It is at this stage that plasma dynamics enters the picture, for although the velocities attainable by chemical means are limited, an ionized gas can be accelerated by electromagnetic forces to an almost arbitrary velocity. Two principal methods have been proposed for this, one involving the acceleration of positive ions in an electrostatic field and the other the acceleration of an ionized gas by a changing magnetic field. It is not difficult to show that at least the second of these is capable of accelerating reasonable amounts of gas to high enough velocities to overcome the driving fluid problem in a rocket. There remains, however, the question of the energy supply which becomes increasingly serious with increased discharge velocity, the power required being $\sim v^3$. This may be overcome either by drawing on solar energy, or by using some, as yet undeveloped, lightweight nuclear reactor. There are many serious problems to be solved before any such vehicle is built, but much preliminary investigation has been carried out.

The most exciting application of plasma physics at the present time is in controlled thermonuclear research. There is no doubt that energy can be obtained by the fusion of the nuclei of the heavy isotopes of hydrogen and moreover that the cross sections for the energy-producing reactions are extremely favourable. Any reaction between nuclei, however, is opposed by the Coulomb repulsion between the nuclear electric charges, the repulsion dominating their interaction at low energy; thus only if collisions occur with sufficient energy is there a reasonable chance of an energy-producing nuclear reaction. In cold matter, an energetic nucleus is overwhelmingly more likely to give up its energy to electrons than to retain it until making a nuclear encounter; hence it appears likely that in order to produce useful amounts of energy from reactions between light nuclei, the nuclear fuel will need to be raised to such a high temperature that nuclear reactions are produced during the thermal encounters of particles.

In order to heat a gas to such temperatures it must be both contained and thermally insulated from its surroundings, and since temperatures of greater than 10,000,000°K will be required, clearly material containers are out of the question.

At these temperatures, however, the reacting gas will be fully ionized and electromagnetic forces may be used to confine and insulate it. The problem of designing a configuration in which the force $\mathbf{j} \times \mathbf{B}$ is always directed away from the walls of a containing vessel is relatively simple, but most of the simple configurations prove to be unstable, small disturbances from equilibrium growing until the configuration is destroyed.

The discovery of a stable confining configuration is a much more difficult problem and, so far, in spite of a great deal of intensive theoretical work and a good number of large and difficult experiments, there has been little unqualified success. It is probably in the search for a stable contained plasma that the most highly developed theoretical and experimental studies of plasma have been carried out.

Even if the stability problem can be solved, many other problems will remain before controlled thermonuclear power is a practical reality. In particular, the plasma must be heated—and while joule heating by a d.c. current is adequate at low temperatures, heating at high temperatures where, as we shall see, the resistivity of the plasma is very low, presents serious unsolved problems.

Finally, before usable power is obtained, a thermonuclear reactor must be made extremely efficient. There are so many apparently inevitable power losses, such as radiation from the hot gas, synchrotron radiation from the energetic electrons, joule losses in the conductors producing the magnetic fields, that much of the energy produced in the reactor will be needed to replace these losses, and possibly only a modest fraction of the energy circulating in the reactor will be available for other uses. Thus, unless energy is circulated with high efficiency, there might well be no net power production.

The necessary efficiency will almost certainly be achieved only after a long course of research and will require a detailed and precise knowledge of the physics of very hot plasma. If, however, controlled thermonuclear power can be produced, the universal availability of fuel and the probable freedom from dangerous radioactive by-products may produce a revolution in the future supplies of energy with spectacular and unforeseeable consequences. Such a goal well merits the very considerable research effort expended towards reaching it.

BIBLIOGRAPHY

Natural plasmas are the subject of

    ALFVÉN, H. (1950). *Cosmical Electrodynamics*, Oxford University Press, London.
and are discussed in

    COWLING, T. G. (1957). *Magnetohydrodynamics*, Interscience, New York.

and
  DUNGEY, J. (1958). *Cosmic Electrodynamics*, Cambridge University Press.
A brief account of the solar plasma may be found in
  KUIPER, G. P. (ed.) (1953). *The Sun*, University of Chicago Press, Chicago, Ch. 8
  Solar Electrodynamics, by T. G. Cowling,
while an assembly of research reports is collected in
  LEHNERT, B. (ed.) (1958). *Electromagnetic Phenomena in Cosmical Physics*, Symposium
  6 of the International Astronomical Union, Cambridge University Press.
The ionosphere is discussed in
  RATCLIFFE, J. A. (1959). *The Magneto-Ionic Theory and its Applications to the
  Ionosphere*, Cambridge University Press, Cambridge.
Controlled thermonuclear research is the subject of
  GLASSTONE, S. and LOVEBERG, R. H. (1960). *Controlled Thermonuclear Reactions*,
  Van Nostrand & Co., Princeton, N.J.
  SIMON, A. L. (1960). *An Introduction to Thermonuclear Research*, Pergamon Press,
  Oxford,
and a large collection of research papers appeared in
  *Proceedings of the Second United Nations International Conference on the Peaceful Uses
  of Atomic Energy*.
  Vol. 31 "Theoretical and Experimental Aspects of Controlled Nuclear Fusion";
  Vol. 32 "Controlled Fusion Devices",
or
  LONGMIRE, C., THOMPSON, W. B., TUCK, J. L. (1959) *Prog. Nuc. En. XI, Plasma Physics
  and Thermonuclear Research*, **1**, Pergamon Press, London.
Other technological aspects are mentioned in
  CLAUSER, F. H. (ed.) (1960). *Plasma Dynamics*, Addison Wesley, Reading, Mass.
  FRENKIEL, F. N. and SEARS, W. R. (1960). *Rev. Mod. Phys.* **32**, 695.
Referred to in the text are
  BABCOCK, H. W. (1947). *Astrophys. J.* **105**, 105.
  MARTYN, D. F. (1948). *Proc. Roy. Soc.* **A193**, 44.
  HILTNER, W. A. (1949). *Astrophys. J.* **109**, 471.
  PAWSEY, J. L. and SMERD, S. F. (1953). Ch. 7. in KUIPER, *op. cit.*

CHAPTER 2

BASIC PROPERTIES OF THE EQUILIBRIUM PLASMA

ALTHOUGH the most interesting phenomena of plasma dynamics occur only when the plasma interacts with a magnetic field and carries electric currents, we must begin by studying a plasma from which such fields and currents are absent. Even in thermal equilibrium many subtle questions concerning the statistical mechanics of interacting particles require discussion if the plasma is to be fully understood; however at this stage we will consider an extremely simplified description of the plasma from which these subtleties are omitted.

1. QUASI-NEUTRALITY AND PLASMA OSCILLATIONS

Perhaps the most fundamental property of a plasma is its tendency to remain electrically almost neutral, i.e. for the number densities of electrons and ions to remain almost equal to one another at each point in space. This arises from the large value of the charge-to-mass ratio of electrons, any significant imbalance of charge giving rise to an electric field of sufficient magnitude to drag a neutralizing cloud of electrons into the positively charged region. For example, a 1 per cent separation in 1 cm^3 of a diffuse plasma of 10^{11}/cm^3 would produce a surface field of ~ 150 V/cm, sufficient to give the electrons an acceleration of 10^{17} cm/sec^{-2}. Thus any small charge separation is immediately destroyed by in-rushing electrons. Because of their inertia, the electrons will oscillate about the initially charged region but with a very high frequency, so that quasi-neutrality is preserved in the mean.

It is interesting as a first study in plasma dynamics to consider a simple analytical discussion of this process.

We consider a steady initial state in which there is a uniform initial number density n_0 of electrons neutralized by an equal number of ions. The electron density is then disturbed to $n = n_0 + n'(x)$ and we are interested in the subsequent behaviour of the disturbance in density, $n'(x)$. To describe the motion we will first assume that because of their relatively high inertia the ions remain at rest, only the electrons moving. Next we will assume that if the disturbance n' is on not too small a scale the electrons can be represented by a continuous fluid, and further that the effects of the thermal motion of the electrons can be neglected. A much more elaborate analysis in Chapter 8 will show that these assumptions are justified if the scale of the disturbance is large enough. To describe the motion of the electrons we can then use the hydrodynamic equations of motion, the equation of continuity which equates the rate of increase of density in a small volume to the flow across the surface,

$$\frac{\partial n}{\partial t} + \text{div}(n\mathbf{v}) = 0 \tag{2.1.1}$$

and the hydrodynamic equation of motion which equates the rate of change of momentum of an element of fluid to the force acting on that element, in this case just the product of the charge and the electric field,

$$nm\left(\frac{\partial \mathbf{v}}{\partial t} + (\mathbf{v}.\nabla)\mathbf{v}\right) = -ne\mathbf{E} \tag{2.1.2}$$

where e is the electronic charge.

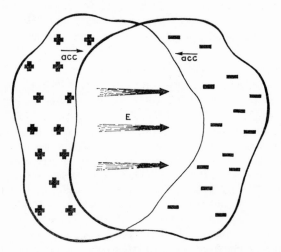

FIG. 2.1. The origin of quasi-neutrality and plasma oscillations. The electric field produced by charge separation accelerates positives and negatives toward each other.

The pressure gradient, which is an effect of the thermal motions, has been neglected in this equation. Finally, we need Poisson's equation relating the electric field to the net charge density

$$\text{div } \mathbf{E} = 4\pi e(n_+ - n_-) \tag{2.1.3}$$

At this stage a further approximation will be made. We assume that the perturbation in density $n'(x, t)$, the velocity $\mathbf{v}$ and the electric field $\mathbf{E}$ are all small, so that eqs. (2.1.1–2.1.3) can be linearized by neglecting the products of small quantities. Then we obtain the linearized, approximate equations,

$$\frac{\partial n'}{\partial t} + n_0 \text{ div } \mathbf{v} = 0 \tag{2.1.4}$$

$$\frac{\partial \mathbf{v}}{\partial t} = - \frac{e}{m}\mathbf{E} \tag{2.1.5}$$

$$\mathrm{div}\,\mathbf{E} = -4\pi e n' \tag{2.1.6}$$

By taking the time derivative of the first of these, and the divergence of the second, we may make the substitutions $\mathrm{div}(\partial \mathbf{v}/\partial t) = -(e/m)\,\mathrm{div}\,\mathbf{E} = 4\pi(e^2/m)n'$, and obtain an equation for the time development of $n'(x)$

$$\frac{\partial^2 n'}{\partial t^2} + \frac{4\pi n_0 e^2}{m}n' = 0 \tag{2.1.7}$$

This shows that any disturbance from equilibrium $n'(x)$ will oscillate with an angular frequency ω_p given by

$$\omega_p{}^2 = \frac{4\pi n e^2}{m} \tag{2.1.8}$$

or at a frequency $\nu_p = \omega_p/2\pi$, $\nu_p = 8920\sqrt{n}$ c/sec (where n is in cm^{-3}) the Langmuir plasma frequency.

Table 2.1. *Plasma Frequencies*

Plasma	Density, n, cm^{-3}	Plasma frequency, ν_p, sec^{-1}	Corresponding free space wavelength	Location in the electromagnetic spectrum
Interstellar gas	1–100	$\cdot89 \times 10^4$–10^5	$3\cdot10^5$–10^6 cm	long wave h.f.
Dense ionosphere Upper stellar atmosphere Tenuous lab. plasma	10^{10}–10^{12}	10^9–10^{10}	3–30 cm	u.h.f. μ-waves
Lower stellar atmosphere Intense lab. plasma	10^{14}–10^{16}	10^{11}–10^{12}	$\cdot03$–$\cdot3$ cm	μ-waves, far infra-red
Dense lab. plasma	10^{16}–10^{18}	10^{12}–10^{13}	$\cdot003$–$\cdot03$ cm	infra-red
Stellar interiors, metals	10^{22}–10^{25}	10^{15}–10^{16}	300–3000 A$^\circ$	visible, far ultra-violet

These oscillations have the unusual character of being non-dispersive: in this approximation a local disturbance does not propagate. Values of the plasma frequency for several plasmas of astronomical and laboratory interest are given in Table 2.1. For comparison, the free space wavelengths of electromagnetic oscillations of the same frequency are given, and it will be noted that electron plasma oscillations are a high frequency phenomenon.

Experimental Evidence for Plasma Oscillations

The theory of plasma oscillations was given by LANGMUIR (1929) who in the same paper presented experimental evidence for the occurrence of these oscillations in electric discharges. His measurements were made on a hot-cathode mercury arc containing a rather complex electrode structure and designed for a survey of the possible oscillations of a plasma. In arc discharges the electron density is 10^{11}–10^{12} cm^{-3} and the plasma frequency ~ 100 Mc/s, so the high-frequency signals were picked up on resonant Lecher wires, rectified by a crystal and detected by a galvanometer. Unfortunately, in the discharge used, it was not possible to make reliable measurements of the electron density, which had to be inferred from measurements of the gas pressure and the electric current, making use of a theory of the arc discharge; thus the published results, while exhibiting oscillations in the correct range with roughly the correct relation between frequency and density, do not permit quantitative comparison of theory and experiment.

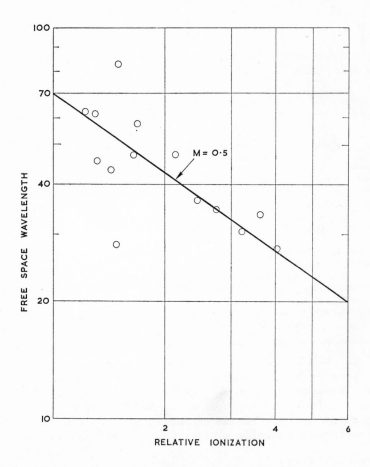

FIG. 2.2. Plasma oscillation. Experiments of Langmuir (*Phys. Rev.* **33**, 195, 1929). Measured free space wavelength vs. the calculated degree of ionization (log log). Theoretical curve has slope $M = -\frac{1}{2}$.

A later series of experiments by MERRILL and WEBB (1939) was performed using a long mercury arc in which the electron density could be measured by the Langmuir probe technique (see Chapter 3). The oscillating signal was again detected by Lecher wires, crystal rectifier and galvanometer.

Their results are presented in the accompanying table.

Table 2.2. Measurements of the Plasma Frequency

n (probe)	ν theoretical $= 8920\sqrt{n}$	ν measured
$1 \cdot 77 \times 10^{10}$	$1 \cdot 2 \times 10^9$	$1 \cdot 18 \times 10^9$
$2 \cdot 56$	$1 \cdot 44$	$1 \cdot 44$
$3 \cdot 33$	$1 \cdot 64$	$1 \cdot 50$
$1 \cdot 93$	$1 \cdot 25$	$1 \cdot 17$
$3 \cdot 09$	$1 \cdot 58$	$1 \cdot 34$

2. THE TRANSMISSION OF ELECTROMAGNETIC RADIATION THROUGH PLASMA

The plasma frequency is important, not only as a characteristic frequency of free oscillations in a plasma, but also as determining the response to a driving force, in particular the way in which electromagnetic oscillations are transmitted through the plasma. To understand this effect, let us first ask what current is induced in the plasma by an electric field which oscillates with a given frequency ω. We can determine the velocity induced in the plasma by using eq. (2.1.5) and writing the driving electric field as $\mathbf{E}(t) = \mathbf{E_0} \exp(i\omega t)$. Then in the steady state

$$\mathbf{v} = -\frac{1}{i\omega}\frac{e}{m}\mathbf{E}$$

and the current induced in the plasma

$$\mathbf{j} = -ne\,\mathbf{v} = \frac{ne^2}{i\omega m}\mathbf{E} \tag{2.2.1}$$

The effect of this induced current on the transmission of oscillations through the plasma can be understood by examining Maxwell's equation for the magnetic field.

$$\text{curl } \mathbf{B} = \frac{4\pi}{c}\mathbf{j} + \frac{1}{c}\frac{\partial \mathbf{E}}{\partial t} = \frac{4\pi ne^2}{i\omega mc}\mathbf{E} + \frac{i\omega}{c}\mathbf{E}$$

$$= \frac{i\omega}{c}\left(1 - \frac{4\pi ne^2}{m\omega^2}\right)\mathbf{E} = \frac{i\omega}{c}\left(1 - \frac{\omega_p^2}{\omega^2}\right)\mathbf{E} \tag{2.2.2}$$

$$= \frac{i\omega}{c}\epsilon(\omega)\,\mathbf{E}$$

Thus the plasma appears as a dielectric with a frequency-dependent dielectric coefficient

$$\epsilon(\omega) = 1 - \frac{\omega_p{}^2}{\omega^2} \tag{2.2.3}$$

If we now consider the propagation of transverse oscillations, which we may assume depend on x as $\exp(i\mathbf{k} \cdot \mathbf{x})$, we obtain first the transmission equation

$$\nabla^2 \mathbf{E}(\omega) + \frac{\epsilon\omega^2}{c^2}\mathbf{E}(\omega) = 0$$

and the dispersion relation for k

$$k^2 = \frac{\omega^2\epsilon}{c^2} = \frac{\omega^2 - \omega_p{}^2}{c^2} \tag{2.2.4}$$

Thus if the frequency ω exceeds ω_p, waves are propagated with a phase velocity $\omega/k = c/\sqrt{(1-(\omega_p{}^2/\omega^2))}$, which is greater than c, the free space velocity of light, and a group velocity, $(d\omega/dk) = c\sqrt{(1-(\omega_p{}^2/\omega^2))}$, less than c. However, if $\omega < \omega_p$, k becomes imaginary and the waves do not propagate, but are attenuated in distances of order $d \simeq c/\sqrt{(\omega_p{}^2-\omega^2)}$, which for low frequencies tends to

$$d \simeq \sqrt{\left(\frac{mc^2}{4\pi ne^2}\right)} \tag{2.2.5}$$

the collisionless screening length.

In carrying out this analysis we have omitted the interaction between particles, and have discovered that the plasma is purely reactive. In fact, collisions between electrons and ions or neutral atoms will introduce a frictional term $-(1/\tau)\mathbf{v}$ on the right of eq. (2.1.5), and will produce an in-phase component to the current which becomes

$$\mathbf{j} = -\frac{ne^2}{m}\frac{\left(i\omega - \frac{1}{\tau}\right)}{\left(\omega^2 + \frac{1}{\tau^2}\right)}\mathbf{E} \tag{2.2.6}$$

and the rate of energy absorption by the plasma becomes, per unit volume,

$$\frac{d\mathscr{E}}{dt} = \frac{1}{2}\frac{ne^2}{m}\frac{1}{\tau}\frac{1}{\left(\omega^2 + \frac{1}{\tau^2}\right)}\mathbf{E}^2 \tag{2.2.7}$$

Since the plasma frequency in arc discharges lies in the microwave region, it is in this frequency range that the most interesting measurements have been made. A typical measurement of the dielectric properties of the discharge is that of ADLER (1949). In this experiment a cylindrical cavity having a small discharge tube along its axis was placed in a waveguide transmission line. By measuring the shift in resonant frequency and the change in attenuation of the transmitted signal on passing a current through the discharge tube, the dielectric coefficient and the a.c. conductivity of

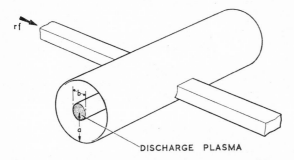

FIG. 2.3. Dielectric properties of a plasma. The principle of Adler's experiment (*J. Appl. Phys.* **20**, 1125, 1949). Microwave resonance of the cylindrical cavity is altered when cavity is loaded by plasma in central discharge tube.

the arc plasma could be calculated. Langmuir probe measurements of electron density were made so that comparison was possible between theory and experiment. To analyse the electrical measurements it was shown that a perturbation treatment could be used. Since the discharge had little effect on the fields in the cavity, it was possible to use the fact that the Lagrangian is stationary at resonance, i.e.

$$\int dv \left(\frac{1}{8\pi}\epsilon E^2 - \frac{1}{8\pi}\mu H^2\right)$$

varies only to second order. Then the induction equation $c\nabla \times \mathbf{E} = -(\partial \mathbf{B}/\partial t) = i\omega\mu\mathbf{H}$ could be used to write the ratio of the resonant frequency in the presence of the discharge ($\epsilon = \epsilon_1$ in the plasma, $= 1$ outside), to that in its absence ($\epsilon = 1$ throughout the cavity) as

$$\frac{\omega_1}{\omega_0} = \left\{\frac{\int E^2 dv}{\int_{discharge} \epsilon_1 E^2 dv + \int_{rest} E^2 dv}\right\}^{\frac{1}{2}} \simeq 1 - \frac{1}{2}\frac{\int_{discharge}(\epsilon_1 - 1)E^2 dv}{\int E^2 dv}$$

and on introducing the resonant form for E appropriate to a cylindrical cavity of radius a; $E \sim J_0(kr)$, where $J_0(ka) = 0$, J_0, a Bessel function obtain

$$\frac{\omega_1 - \omega_0}{\omega_0} = -\frac{1}{2}(\epsilon_1 - 1)\frac{J_0^2(kb) + J_1^2(kb)}{J_1^2(ka)}$$

b being the radius of the plasma column. Experiments were conducted at 8460 Mc/s, and the change in resonance frequency was ∼10 Mc/s. The results were displayed by plotting the electron density *n* derived from the frequency shift and that measured by Langmuir probes as a function of discharge current.

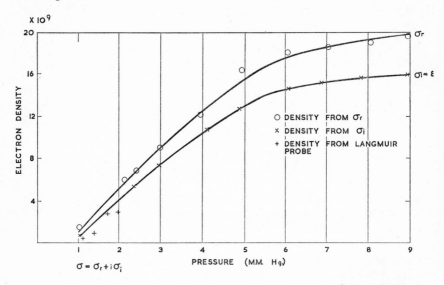

FIG. 2.4. Dielectric properties of a plasma. Results of Adler's experiment. Electron density as calculated from measured real and imaginary parts of the plasma conductivity compared with values measured by Langmuir probes.

In this paper the eq. (2.2.3) is not used explicitly; instead reference is made to MARGANAU's (1946) calculation of conductivity which employs Boltzmann's equation and includes the effect of collisions. Instead of $\epsilon - 1 \simeq n/\omega^2$, Marganau has $\epsilon - 1 \sim n(T/\lambda^2)K_{3/2}(x_1)$ where $x_1 = m(\omega^2\lambda^2/2kT)$ and

$$K_{3/2}(x_1) = \int\limits_0^\infty \frac{x^{3/2}e^{-x^2}}{x+x_1}\,\mathrm{d}x$$

λ being the electron mean free path. For these experiments, however, in a low pressure mercury arc, $x_1 \simeq 120$ and $K_{3/2}(x_1) \simeq 1/x_1$, hence the simpler expression (2.2.3) is recovered.

In recent years the dielectric properties of the plasma, in particular the cut-off in transmission at the plasma frequency has become an important method of measuring electron density in very hot plasmas. If the electron density is too high for μ-wave methods, the effects of ϵ in optical frequencies, in particular its dependence on frequency, may be used to measure *n* by interference techniques.

3. THE DEGREE OF IONIZATION IN A THERMAL PLASMA

Having discussed some of the properties of the fully ionized plasma in equilibrium let us ask how easily such a plasma is realized in the laboratory. In order to ionize an atom it is necessary to add to it an amount of energy most conveniently expressed in electron volts as the ionization potential. Typical values of this are given in Table 2.3. The voltages here are modest,

Table 2.3. Ionization potentials

Element	Ionization potential V_i Volts
H	13·6
N	14·5
O	13·5
He	24·5
A	15·7
Hg	10·4
Fe	7·8
Na	5·1
Cs	3·9

but are well in excess of normal thermal energies. When we observe that a temperature of 11,600°K is needed to give an energy kT of 1 eV so that the mean kinetic energy of a molecule, $\frac{3}{2}kT$, reaches 1 eV only when $T = 7,730°K$, it is apparent that only at extremely high temperatures does the thermal energy exceed the ionization energy. However, if the density is sufficiently low, a considerable degree of ionization can be attained even although the mean thermal energy of particles lies far below the ionization energy. This is possible since at any temperature there are some collisions which are sufficiently violent to produce ionization, hence the equilibrium degree of ionization is determined by the balance between the rate of ionization and the rate of recombination. Since the latter process involves encounters between more particles than the former it decreases more rapidly as the density is dropped. For example, ionization by radiation proceeds at a rate

$$\left(\frac{di}{dt}\right)_{\text{rad}} = \phi n_a p_{ri}$$

where $(di/dt)_{\text{rad}}$ is the rate of production of ions by radiation, ϕ is the radiant flux, n_a the density of neutral atoms and p_{ri} a measure of the probability of ionization being produced by a photon. The inverse process, radiative recombination, proceeds as

$$-\left(\frac{di}{dt}\right)_{\text{rad}} = n_+ n_- p_{rr}$$

where n_+, n_- are the ion and electron densities and p_{rr} the radiative recombination probability. Ionization by electron impact goes at the rate

$$\left(\frac{\mathrm{d}i}{\mathrm{d}t}\right)_e = n_-n_a p_{ie}$$

where p_{ie} is the ionization probability, while its inverse three-body recombination goes as

$$-\left(\frac{\mathrm{d}i}{\mathrm{d}t}\right)_e = n^2_- n_+ p_{re}$$

Using the methods of statistical mechanics it is possible to determine the degree of ionization in a gas in thermal equilibrium without considering the details of the ionization process, simply by observing that the probability of finding a configuration in a state i, in equilibrium at a temperature T is

$$P_i = g_i \exp(-E_i/kT) \tag{2.3.1}$$

where E_i is the energy of the state i, and g_i is the statistical weight to be associated with that state, i.e. the fraction of the total possible configurations that can be associated with the state i. We can then discover

RADIATIVE IONIZATION & RECOMBINATION

IONIZATION & RECOMBINATION
BY ELECTRON IMPACT

Fig. 2.5. Ionization and recombination processes showing origin of the density dependence of thermal ionization.

the fraction of the atoms which are ionized by using eq. (2.3.1) to compare the probability of an electron and an ion existing as an independent pair with the probability of their existing as an atom. Since the number of free particles changes in this process, a prior problem is that of assigning a statistical weight to a free particle. Classically, since a free particle can have any position and any momentum this cannot be done, and it must be tackled as an elementary exercise in quantum mechanics; how many states are available to a free particle?

To determine the number of states available to a free particle, we can either use the uncertainty principle, which states that the number of distinguishable states in the phase space element d^3pd^3x is $dn = (d^3pd^3x/h^3)$, where h is Planck's constant. Alternatively observe that the wave functions of the free particle may be written $\exp(i\mathbf{k} \cdot \mathbf{x})$ where $\mathbf{k} = \mathbf{p}/h$. Further, if the particle is confined to a cube of side L, the vector $\mathbf{k}$ satisfies

$$\mathbf{k} = (2\pi/L)(n_1, n_2, n_3)$$

and to each distinct triad of integers corresponds a single wave function. If the numbers n are large, we may write for the number of wave functions in the momentum range $dp_x dp_y dp_z$

$$dN = dn_1 dn_2 dn_3 = L^3 \frac{dp_x\, dp_y\, dp_z}{h^3}$$

To get the statistical weight of a free particle of any momentum p, at temperature T we write

$$g_i = \frac{L^3}{h^3} \exp\left(-\frac{p^2}{2mkT}\right) d^3p$$

and for the total weight

$$g_i = \frac{L^3}{h^3} \cdot \int \exp\left(-\frac{p^2}{2mkT}\right) d^3p = \left(\frac{2\pi mkT}{h^2}\right)^{3/2} L^3 \qquad (2.3.2)$$

Now if we neglect the small interaction potential between the free ion and electron, the difference in potential energy between the ion electron pair and the atom is just the ionization energy, eV_i. If also we neglect the internal degrees of freedom of all the particles, then the ratio of the probability per unit volume of finding an electron and an ion to that of finding a neutral atom, which is equal to the ratio of the product of ion and electron density n_+ and n_- to neutral density n_0, becomes

$$\frac{n_+ n_-}{n_0} = \left(\frac{2\pi m_+ kT}{h^2}\right)^{3/2} \left(\frac{2\pi m_- kT}{h^2}\right)^{3/2} \left(\frac{2\pi m_0 kT}{h^2}\right)^{-3/2} \exp\left(-\frac{eV_i}{kT}\right)$$

On noting that the ion and atomic masses are almost equal, this is reduced to

$$\frac{n_+ n_-}{n_0} = \left(\frac{2\pi m_- kT}{h^2}\right)^{3/2} \exp\left(-\frac{eV_i}{kT}\right) \qquad (2.3.3)$$

a simple form of Saha's equation. If we express the temperature in electron volts and number densities in cm^{-3}, we may write this as

$$\frac{n_+ n_-}{n_0^2} = r_i^2 = \frac{3 \times 10^{21}}{n_0} T^{3/2} \exp(-V_i/T) \qquad (2.3.4)$$

or in a form more suitable for high degrees of ionization,

$$r_i = \frac{3 \times 10^{21}}{n_-} T^{3/2} \exp(-V_i/T) \qquad (2.3.5)$$

Table 2.4 gives values of the ratio $r_i = (n_+/n_0)$ for hydrogen and for caesium (which is the element with the lowest ionization potential) in a number of interesting plasmas.

Table 2.4. Degree of Ionization from the One-level Saha Equation

Hydrogen: $V_i = 13 \cdot 6$ V

System	Temperature, °K	Density n, cm^{-3}	Ionization ratio $r_i = n_+/n_0$
Hottest furnace best vacuum	3,000	10^{10}	10^{-13}
Solar surface	6,000	10^{16}	$5 \cdot 10^{-4}$
Solar atmosphere	10,000	10^{14}	10
Hot confined plasma	$2 \cdot 5 \times 10^5$	10^{14}	10^7
Solar corona	10^6	10^{10}	10^{12}
Hot gaseous nebula	10^4	10^3	10^{12}
Cold interstellar gas	10^2	10^2	10^{-580}

Caesium, $V_i = 3 \cdot 9$ V

System	Temperature, °K	Density n, cm^{-3}	Ionization ratio $r_i = n_+/n_0$
Vacuum furnace	3,000	10^{10}	20
Solar surface	2,000	10^{12}	$0 \cdot 14$
Solar surface	6,000	10^{16}	40

Note that while in many astrophysical systems the ionization of hydrogen is complete, this is not true on the solar photosphere, where, however, the alkali metals are ionized. Moreover, observe that while it appears impossible to ionize hydrogen by heating the gas, it seems not too difficult to get a reasonable degree of ionization in caesium vapour.

Saha's equation, which represents an application of the law of mass action is valid for any dissociative reaction and has been accurately checked in its chemical context. SAHA himself was interested in explaining the relative line strengths of elements in stellar atmospheres and inferring the chemical composition of the stars. In this context applications are complicated by the fact that light from a star does not come from a uniform isothermal source, but from varying depths in a semi-transparent atmosphere of variable temperature, and the deduction of physical conditions at the source involves an unravelling of the process of line production, a problem in radiative transfer. However, sufficient agreement has been obtained between spectra calculated for model atmospheres and observed stellar spectra for Saha's programme to be carried out.

Laboratory studies of Saha's equation as applied to ionization were first carried out by LANGMUIR and KINGDOM (1925), who considered the equilibrium of caesium in contact with tungsten, where emission from the metal surface is a complicating feature. Ionization was determined by the saturation of the ion current and satisfactory agreement found.

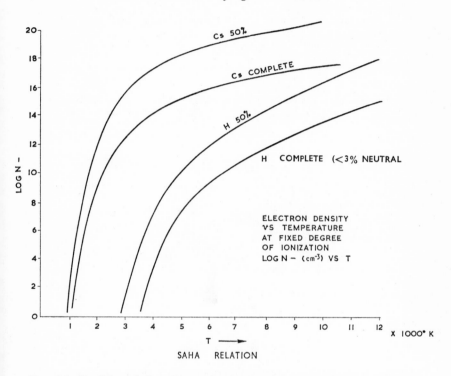

FIG. 2.6. The Saha relation. Curves showing log of electron density vs. temperature for fixed degree of ionization in thermal equilibrium.

4. THE PRODUCTION OF PLASMA BY SHOCK WAVES

Although conventional furnaces are of little use in producing ionization, another method has had some success. This invokes the high temperatures produced when a gas is suddenly compressed by a shock wave. An instrument making use of this is the shock tube, which is simply a strong, usually straight, tube divided into two parts by a thin metal diaphragm. In use, one side of the tube, the compression chamber, is filled with a hot compressed, preferably light gas, while the other side contains a cool, low pressure, preferably heavy gas. When the diaphragm is burst, the compressed gas expands with a speed $v_1 = 2c_1/(\gamma_1 - 1)$, where c_1 is the sound speed in the compressed gas, $c_1^2 = (\gamma_1 p/\rho) = (\gamma_1 k T_1/m_1)$, γ, being the ratio of specific heats, p the pressure, ρ the density, T the temperature and m the molecular weight of the compressed gas. The expanding gas pushes the initially rarefied gas ahead of it with a velocity v_1, the rarefied gas being accelerated to this velocity on passing through a shock, moving with velocity $v_2 = (\gamma_2+1)v_1$, where γ_2 is the ratio of specific heats in the rarefied gas. The increase in temperature of the driven gas is determined by the velocity of this shock,

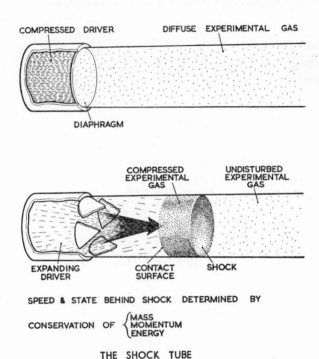

FIG. 2.7. Principle of the shock tube. Conditions in the hot gas ahead of the contact surface with driver gas may be calculated from conservation laws.

and it can be shown that the ratio between the temperature T_2 behind the shock in the driven gas is increased over the initial temperature T_1 of the driver by

$$\frac{T_2}{T_1} = \frac{\gamma_1(\gamma_2-1)}{2\gamma_2}\left(\frac{\gamma_2+1}{\gamma_1-1}\right)^2\frac{m_2}{m_1}$$

where m_2 is the molecular weight of the driver gas. The increase in temperature arises largely from the fact that the molecular velocities $\langle v^2 \rangle$ are similar in the two gases, but the temperature measures the energy associated with the random motion $T \simeq m\langle v^2 \rangle$. If the driver gas is light, e.g. hydrogen, and the driven gas heavy, e.g. argon, then (T_2/T_1) may be large, e.g. $\simeq 250$; and hydrogen at $1000°$K would produce argon at $250,000°$K which would be fully ionized at atmospheric densities. Higher temperatures can be obtained by driving the shock with an explosion, or by a violent electrical discharge. A treatment of the shock will be found in Chapter 5.

Experimental Evidence for the Production of Thermal Plasmas

Before the production of thermal ionization behind a shock can be investigated quantitatively it is necessary to calculate the degree of ionization to be expected. To do this, the Rankine–Hugoniot relations (cf. Chapter 5) (representing the mechanical conservation laws) must be solved together with Saha's equation. For strong shocks the conservation of energy becomes $H = \frac{1}{2}u^2$, where u is the velocity of the incoming gas relative to the shock and H the specific enthalpy of the gas behind the shock. Ionization adds to the specific heat by increasing the number of particles per unit mass, and also by requiring the potential energy of ionization.

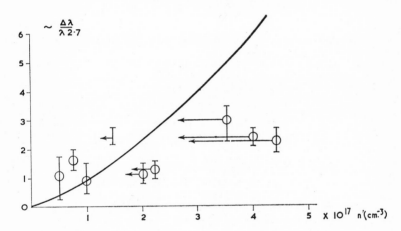

Fig. 2.8. Electron density behind an ionizing shock. Measured Stark broadening of spectral lines plotted as $\Delta\lambda/\lambda^{2.7}$ vs. n calculated from shock speed and initial pressure. Arrows show expected reduction in ionization due to cooling. Solid curve is theoretical value. (After Petscheck, Rose, Glick, Kane and Kantrowitz, *J. Appl. Phys.* **26**, 83, 1955.)

The problem has been solved by RESLER, LIN and KANTROWITZ (1952), and by PETSCHECK, ROSE, GLICK, KANE and KANTROWITZ (1953). In two later papers experiments are described in which shocks having a velocity 17 times the velocity of sound in the gas ahead were produced in argon, and the argon behind the shock was 40 per cent ionized. In these experiments the electron density was too high to be measured by probes or by transmission experiments; instead the Stark effect was used. The spectral lines of argon observed behind the shock were shifted to the red and greatly broadened (at 4300 Å, by ~ 9 Å) and this was shown as due to the combined effect of slowly varying microfields and collisions with electrons. Good agreement was obtained between theory and experiment for the line shape, and the relationship between the measured values of $\Delta\lambda$, and the values calculated using a theory of Stark broadening due to BARANGER (1958) together with the Saha and Rankine–Hugoniot relations, was displayed. When allowance was made for the cooling of the plasma by radiation during the measurement there was satisfactory agreement. Cooling was also described theoretically and checked experimentally.

A second estimate of the electron density and the temperature was made by comparing the intensity of the continuum with that predicted by a theory of UNSÖLD (1938).

BIBLIOGRAPHY

Plasma Oscillations
  LANGMUIR, I. (1939). *Phys. Rev.* **33**, 195.
  MERRILL, H. S. and WEBB, H. W. (1939). *Phys. Rev.* **55**, 1191.
  ADLER, F. P. (1949). *J. Appl. Phys.* **20**, 1125.
  BARANGER, M. (1958). *Phys. Rev.* **111**, 494.
Ionization
For the Saha equation—most texts on statistical mechanics, which however describe it in the context of chemical reactions e.g.
  TER HAAR, D. (1954). *Elements of Statistical Mechanics* Rinehart, New York.
A very full treatment is found in
  FOWLER, R. (1929). *Statistical Mechanics*, Cambridge Ch. V.
  SAHA, M. N. (1921). *Proc. Roy. Soc.* **A99**, 135.
Experiments on shocked plasmas
  RESLER, E., LIN, S. C. and KANTROWITZ, A. (1952). *J. Appl. Phys.* **23**, 1340;
  PETSCHEK, H. E., ROSE, P. E., GLICK, H. S., KANE, A. and KANTROWITZ, A. (1955).
    J. Appl. Phys. **26**, 83.
  MARGENAU, H. (1946). *Phys. Rev.* **69**, 508.
  UNSÖLD, A. (1938). *Ann. Phys.* **33**, 609.
  LANGMUIR, I. and KINGDOM, K. H. (1925). *Proc. Roy. Soc.* **A109**, 61.

CHAPTER 3

THE ARC PLASMA

SINCE, as we have seen, it is difficult to produce a high degree of ionization by heating a gas, laboratory plasmas are most easily produced by electrical discharges. Of such plasmas, probably the best understood is the positive column of the d.c. arc, which we will now study.

When a current is passed through a low-pressure gas, electrons are produced at the cathode and shot into the gas. These electrons make collisions with the gas atoms and, under suitable conditions, ionize them to produce more electrons. At the same time, collisions between the original and secondary electrons result in an equipartion of energy, so that the electrons acquire a roughly Maxwellian distribution at some temperature T_-. At moderately low pressures and currents greater than a few milliamperes, the number of electrons is sufficiently great for the drift velocity representing the current to be much less than the thermal velocity represented by T_-. Since these electrons are neutralized by the ions produced along with the secondary electrons, the discharge vessel is largely filled with a plasma stretching up toward the cathode from the anode. This is the positive column.

1. THE DIFFUSION THEORY OF THE POSITIVE COLUMN

The structure of the positive column was first investigated by SCHOTTKY. Because of their high thermal speeds, the electrons rush out of the centre of the plasma toward the walls, giving the walls a negative charge and leaving the centre of the discharge positive. The positive ions have small thermal velocities, not only because of their greater mass, but also because their temperature is held down by collision with neutral atoms. Since the electron mass m_- is much less than the ion mass, electron–ion collisions are relatively ineffective in communicating energy to the ions, while the ions communicate their energy to the neutrals very effectively. Thus, in the discharge plasma, in contrast to the equilibrium plasma, the ions are at a very low temperature, much below the electron temperature, $T_+ \ll T_-$. However, the ions are accelerated toward the walls of the vessel in the radial electric field set up by the charge separation. Thus ions and electrons are lost from the discharge, and must be replaced by new ones produced by ionizing collisions between electrons and neutrals. The electron temperature is determined by the requirement that the ionization rate should balance the loss rate.

A simple mathematical analysis of this process was given by SCHOTTKY. The ions, electrons and neutrals are considered as interdiffusing gases and the temperatures assumed uniform. Under these circumstances, the slow, steady drift of the ions and electrons can be represented by a mobility equation

$$(n\boldsymbol{v})_- = -q_-\{kT_-\nabla n_- + n_-e\mathbf{E}\} \tag{3.1.1}$$

and

$$(n\boldsymbol{v})_+ = -q_+\{kT_+\nabla n_+ - n_+e\mathbf{E}\} \tag{3.1.2}$$

where the sum of the forces due to the partial pressure gradient, grad p = $kT\,\nabla n$, and the electric field $ne\,\mathbf{E}$ are equated to the retardation $q^{-1}(n\boldsymbol{v})$ due to friction between the charged and neutral component gases. We will now assume equal rates of production for ions and electrons which with the condition of quasi-neutrality implies

$$n_+ = n_- \quad \text{and} \quad \boldsymbol{v}_+ = \boldsymbol{v}_- \tag{3.1.3}$$

thus there is no mutual friction between ions and electrons.

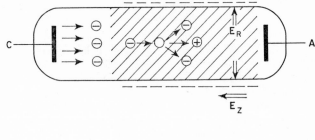

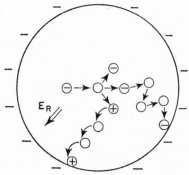

THE POSITIVE COLUMN

Fig. 3.1. Structure of the positive column. Electrons produced in column fly to walls which become negatively charged, attracting ions which diffuse through neutrals. Energy comes from axial electric field and flows radially to the walls.

With these assumptions, the electric field may be eliminated from eqs. (3.1.1.) and (3.1.2) leaving

$$nv = -k(T_+ + T_-)\frac{q_+ q_-}{q_+ + q_-}\, \nabla n \qquad (3.1.4)$$

This has the form of a diffusion equation

$$nv = -\, D_a\, \nabla n$$

where D_a is the ambipolar diffusion coefficient. Since the mobility q and the diffusion coefficient D are related by $D = qkT$ we may write

$$D_a = \frac{D_+ D_-}{T_+ D_- + T_- D_+}(T_+ + T_-)$$

Further, since $q_+ \ll q_-$ and $T_+ \ll T_-$, we have

$$D_a \simeq D_+\frac{T_-}{T_+}$$

Thus the ionized gas diffuses to the wall under the electron pressure with a mobility determined by the rate of loss of momentum from ions to neutrals.

To determine the spatial distribution of the ionized component, we observe that ions and electrons are produced in any volume at a rate proportional to electron density. This will be true in most moderate density plasmas where the production process is the ionization of the neutrals by electron impact if the ion density is low enough for the neutral density to remain uniform. Then, for a steady state, the equation of continuity for the ions becomes

$$\mathrm{div}\,(nv) = \lambda n \qquad (3.1.5)$$

where $\lambda = n_g \langle \sigma_i v \rangle$ is the ionization rate per electron.

Now assuming D_a is constant, we obtain from eqs. (3.1.4) and (3.1.5) the ambipolar diffusion equation for the distribution of the ionized gas:

$$\nabla^2 n + \frac{\lambda}{D_a}n = 0 \qquad (3.1.6)$$

The appropriate boundary conditions for eq. (3.1.6) are that the density gradient should vanish on the axis of symmetry of the containing vessel, and that the density, which must be positive, should fall to a low value at the walls, in first approximation, to zero.

The boundary conditions can be satisfied only for a particular value of λ/D_a, i.e. an eigenvalue problem is posed, and since the quantities λ and D_a depend on electron temperature, the eigenvalue determines T_- through the *plasma balance equation.*

For example, in a cylindrical tube eq. (3.1.6) becomes

$$\frac{1}{r}\frac{d}{dr}\left(r\frac{dn}{dr}\right) + \frac{\lambda}{D_a}n = 0$$

or writing

$$s^2 = r^2 \frac{\lambda}{D_a}$$

$$\frac{d^2 n}{ds^2} + \frac{1}{s}\frac{dn}{ds} + n = 0$$

which is satisfied by $n = n_0 J_0(s)$, J_0 being the zero order Bessel function. J_0 vanishes for $s = 2 \cdot 4$, hence the plasma balance equation determining the electron temperature becomes

$$\frac{\lambda}{D_a} R^2 = (2 \cdot 4)^2 = s_0{}^2$$

where R is the radius of the tube. To write this explicitly we must express λ and D_a in terms of the electron temperature. If the ionization cross section σ_i is known

$$\lambda n = n\, n_g \int f(v)\sigma_i(v)v\, dv$$

where $f(v)$ is the electron velocity distribution, i.e the fraction of the electrons having velocity v. If f is Maxwellian, as is approximately the case in the positive column,

$$\lambda(T_-) = n_g \sqrt{(2/\pi)}(m/kT_-)^{3/2} \int dv\, \sigma_i(v)v^3 \exp(-\tfrac{1}{2}mv^2/kT_-)$$

$$= 4n_g(2\pi m)^{-1/2}(kT_-)^{-3/2} \int_0^\infty dE\, E\, \sigma(E) \exp(-E/kT_-) \qquad (3.1.7)$$

The ambipolar diffusion coefficient $D_a \simeq q_+ kT_-$ may be written in terms of the mean free path l_f for ions through neutrals. q_+ is determined by equating the rate of loss of momentum by collisions to the force acting, thus

$$F = q^{-1}v = (1/\tau)Mv; \qquad q_+ = (\tau/M)$$

where the mean free time $\tau = l_f \sqrt{(M/kT_+)}$.

A more sophisticated treatment of the plasma balance equation can be given, but its application is hampered by the occurrence of more complex ionization processes, such as ionization from metastable states, for which cross sections are not known.

An alternative treatment of the positive column was given by LANGMUIR and TONKS (1929). These authors observe first that the electron drift velocity is small compared to the thermal velocities, so that the electron density is given approximately by

$$kT_- \nabla n_- + n_- e\mathbf{E} = 0$$

hence

$$n_- = n_0 \exp(eV/kT_-) \tag{3.1.8}$$

while the ion pressure gradient is small compared with the electric force, hence

$$nv_+ \simeq q_+eE \tag{3.1.9}$$

equations which lead to the Schottky results, but have the advantage of being easily generalized. A particularly important case is that of very low pressure where the ion mean-free path exceeds the tube size so that ions fall freely.

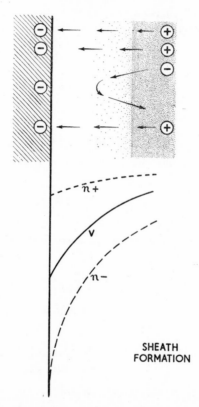

Fig. 3.2. Structure of the plasma sheath. Negative charge on walls repels electrons and attracts ions, so that near wall there is a strong field and no quasi-neutrality.

2. SHEATH FORMATION

The theory of the positive column presented here breaks down very close to a wall, where we have assumed that the density vanishes although the flux does not.

It is easily seen that very close to a wall quasi-neutrality is unlikely to hold, for the electron flux to the wall is approximately

$$f_- = n_w^- \sqrt{(2kT_-/\pi m)}$$

where n_w^- is the electron density at the wall. If ion and electron fluxes and densities are to remain equal, the ions must acquire the mean thermal speed of electrons, hence must attain energies of several keV. In fact the walls acquire a negative charge and repel the electrons while attracting ions, so that very near the wall there is a region, the sheath, in which quasi-neutrality does not hold and in which a large electric field retards electrons and accelerates ions toward the wall. We shall now give a simple treatment of the conditions for sheath formation, following BOHM (in GUTHRIE and WAKERLING, 1949), and an analysis of the sheath structure after LANGMUIR. For this analysis it is enough to consider a plane absorbing wall in contact with a semi-infinite plasma; moreover, since, as we shall show, the sheath thickness is much less than the mean free path, collisions between particles can be neglected, but we must give up the assumption of quasi-neutrality.

Since the electrons are repelled from the wall, they have an approximately Boltzmann distribution

$$n_- = n_0 \exp(eV/kT)$$

while the ions falling freely toward the wall have their density determined by the equation of continuity as

$$n_+(x)v_+(x) = n(0)v(v_0)$$

where the origin $x = 0$ is taken at a point within the plasma where quasi-neutrality holds. The ion velocity is determined by the conservation of energy

$$\tfrac{1}{2}Mv_+^2(x) + eV(x) = \tfrac{1}{2}Mv_+^2v_0$$

where the zero of potential has been taken at $x = 0$, hence $n(0) = n_0$. The ion density is now

$$n(x) = \frac{n_0 v(v_0)}{\sqrt{[v^2(v_0) - 2(eV(x)/M)]}}$$

and the potential V is determined by Poisson's equation

$$\frac{\mathrm{d}^2 V}{\mathrm{d}x^2} = 4\pi e(n_- - n_+) = 4\pi n_0 e\left\{ \exp(eV/kT_-) - \frac{1}{[1 - (2eV/Mv_0^2)]^{1/2}} \right\}$$

On introducing $\eta = -eV/kT_-$ and a unit of length λ_D such that $\xi = x/\lambda_D$ and λ_D is the Debye length

$$\lambda_D^2 = \frac{kT}{4\pi n_0 e^2} \tag{3.2.1}$$

this becomes

$$\frac{d^2\eta}{d\xi^2} = \frac{1}{\sqrt{(1+r\eta)}} - \exp(-\eta) \qquad (3.2.2)$$

where

$$r = \frac{kT}{\frac{1}{2}Mv_0^2}$$

If η is small we can expand the right-hand side, obtaining

$$\frac{d^2\eta}{d\xi^2} = 1 - \frac{1}{2}r\eta - (1-\eta) + \ldots \simeq \eta\left(1 - \frac{r}{2}\right)$$

If $r > 2$, the solutions to this oscillate with a wavelength

$$\lambda = \frac{\lambda_D}{2\pi\sqrt{(r/2-1)}}$$

while if $r < 2$, one solution increases exponentially. This gives a condition which must be satisfied if the plasma is to remain quasi-neutral; if

$$\frac{1}{2}Mv_0^2 < \frac{1}{2}kT \qquad (3.2.3)$$

a disturbance in potential will not grow; however, if that condition is violated, the potential will increase exponentially in a distance of order λ_D, a large electric field will appear, and a large charge separation will be produced.

We can now find the potential drop across the sheath from the requirement that no net current flows to the wall. This requires that the rate at which ions flow into the sheath equals the rate at which electrons reach the wall, i.e.

$$n_0\sqrt{(kT_-/M)} = n_0\sqrt{[(2/\pi)(kT_-/m)]} \exp(-\eta_0)$$

$$\eta_0 = -\frac{eV}{kT_-} = \frac{1}{2}\ln\left(\frac{2M}{\pi m}\right) = 3 \cdot 53 + \frac{1}{2}\ln\frac{M}{M_p} \qquad (3.2.4)$$

where M_p is the mass of the proton.

It is also possible to estimate the sheath thickness for if, at $x = 0$,

$$\eta = 0 \text{ and } \eta' = (1+2/r+C)^{\frac{1}{2}} \simeq \lambda_D/l_f, \text{ then}$$

$$\frac{1}{2}(\eta')^2 = (2/r)\sqrt{(1+r\eta)} + \exp(-\eta) + C$$

$$\xi_0 = \int_0^{n_0} \frac{d\eta}{[(4/r)\sqrt{(1+r\eta)} + 2\exp(-\eta) + 2C]^{\frac{1}{2}}}$$

For large η

$$\xi_0 \simeq \frac{1}{2}r^{1/4} \int_0^{n_0} d\eta/\eta^{1/4} \simeq \frac{2}{3}r^{1/4}\eta_0^{3/4} \simeq 2 \qquad (3.2.5)$$

and the sheath thickness is $\sim 2\lambda_D$. Table 3.1 gives values of λ_D in cm. Since under usual discharge conditions the ion mean free path (m.f.p.) is $\sim 0\cdot3$ cm, usually increasing at high temperatures, the assumption of a collisionless sheath is justified.

Table 3.1. The Debye Length $\lambda_D = \sqrt{(kT_-/4\pi ne^2)}cm$

T (eV) \ $c(cm^{-3})$	10^{10}	10^{12}	10^{14}	10^{16}
1	$2\cdot5\times10^{-2}$	$2\cdot5\times10^{-3}$	$2\cdot5\times10^{-4}$	$2\cdot5\times10^{-5}$
10	$8\cdot3\times10^{-2}$	$8\cdot3\times10^{-3}$	$8\cdot3\times10^{-4}$	$8\cdot3\times10^{-5}$
100	$0\cdot25$	$2\cdot5\times10^{-2}$	$2\cdot5\times10^{-3}$	$2\cdot5\times20^{-4}$

It remains to justify the approximate boundary condition $n = 0$ on the walls of the tube. This we do by showing that it agrees approximately with the sheath edge condition. Very roughly, the ordered ion velocity is given by $\frac{1}{2}Mv_+^2 \simeq eEl_f$, where l_f is the m.f.p. Further, since $n_- \simeq n_0 \exp(eV/kT')$ $= n_0J_0[s_0(r/R)]$, using the Bessel function solution

$$E = -\frac{dV}{dr} = -\frac{s_0}{R}\frac{kT_-}{e}\frac{J_0'}{J_0}$$

hence the sheath edge condition becomes

$$\tfrac{1}{2}Mv_0^2 = \tfrac{1}{2}kT_- = eEl_f = -\frac{s_0}{R}kT_-l_f\frac{J_0'}{J_0}$$

or

$$J_0 \simeq -2s_0\frac{l_f}{R}J_0'$$

Since $l_f \ll R$, this implies J_0 is small at the sheath edge, and since the sheath edge is close to the wall, $J_0(s_0)$ is small, i.e.

$$J_0(s_0) \simeq 0 + o(l_f/R)$$

3. ION LIFE

It is of interest to determine the life-time of an arc plasma. Although the plasma may persist indefinitely the ions and electrons composing it are continually lost to the walls, being replaced by new ones, and the actual life of any ion is rather short. Since the rate of production of ions is $N\lambda$ clearly this is also the loss rate, thus the mean life of an ion is $t_0 = \lambda^{-1}$. From the plasma balance relation $s_0^2 = (R^2\lambda/D_a)$, this is

$$t_0 = \frac{1}{\lambda} = \frac{R^2}{s_0^2 D_a} = \frac{1}{s_0^2}\sqrt{(T_+/T_-)}\sqrt{(M/kT_-)}R \cdot \frac{R}{l_f} = \frac{1}{2s_0^2}\sqrt{(T_+/T_-)}\frac{R}{l_f}t_1$$

$$(3.3.1)$$

where t_1 is the time needed for an ion of energy $\frac{1}{2}kT_-$ to cross the tube and l_f is the mean free path. Typically $l_f = 0 \cdot 2$ cm, $R = 10$, $\frac{1}{2}t_1 \simeq 7 \times 10^{-6}$ sec, $T_- = 10^4$, $T_+ = 400$, and $t_0 \simeq 5 \times 10^{-5}$ sec.

Before describing the experimental evidence supporting this theory, we must examine one of the more powerful devices for studying low-density plasma. This is the Langmuir probe. At a normal wall, no current is collected and the plasma is held positive with respect to the wall by sheath potential.

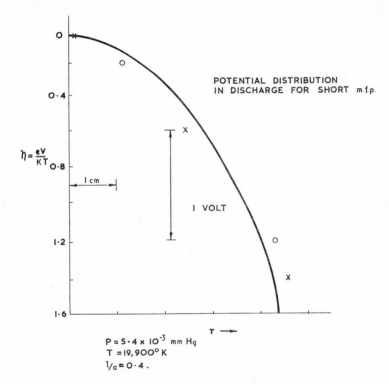

FIG. 3.3(a). Structure of the positive column. Measured and theoretical values of the potential as a function of radius for short mean free path, where ions diffuse.

If the potential of a small section of the wall is made less negative with respect to the plasma then an excess of electrons will reach the wall, while the ion current is only slightly altered. The electron current will be $\sim \sqrt{(kT)} \exp(eV/kT)$; hence by plotting the log of the current against V, the probe potential, a straight line of slope (e/kT_-) should be obtained. This curve should depart from linear for positive potentials, when the electron current reaches $\sqrt{[(2/\pi)(kT/m_e)]}n$, where n is the plasma density near the walls, since beyond that, the Maxwell distribution is altered. Experiments by LANGMUIR and TONKS (1926) have verified this probe's characteristic shape, and the plotting of probe characteristics enables the electron density and temperature to be determined. Furthermore, the local plasma potential can be determined.

TONKS and LANGMUIR (1929) in a paper which gave a treatment of the low-pressure arc in the limit of long mean free path as well as in the diffusion range, gave also some measurements in support of the theory. They present curves of the plasma potential as a function of radius in the long and short mean free path cases and find good agreement with theory.

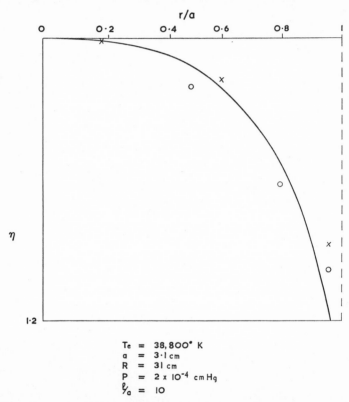

$$T_e = 38,800° \text{ K}$$
$$a = 3 \cdot 1 \text{ cm}$$
$$R = 31 \text{ cm}$$
$$P = 2 \times 10^{-4} \text{ cm Hg}$$
$$\frac{l}{a} = 10$$

FIG. 3.3(b). Structure of the positive column for long mean free path, where ions fall freely. Potential and temperature from Langmuir probe measurements. Solid lines calculated from Langmuir–Tonks theory. (Langmuir and Tonks, *Phys. Rev.* **34**, 876, 1929).

They also use the plasma balance equation to determine the specific ionization rate λ and compare this with a direct calculation of $n_g \langle \sigma v \rangle$ for ionization, using experimental values for the ionization cross section.

Current (A)	$T_e°\text{K}$	$\lambda \ (10^{-4} \text{ sec}^{-1})$	$n_g \langle \sigma v \rangle \ (10^{-4} \text{ sec}^{-1})$
0·5	27,500	7·29	1·6
1	29,000	7·48	2·1
2	26,600	7·15	1·4
8	19,500	6·3	0·21

Here the agreement is rather bad, probably a reflection of the importance of two-stage ionization processes even at low densities. These should be important for two reasons: at modest electron temperatures only the tail of the distribution contributes to the ionization process and any reduction

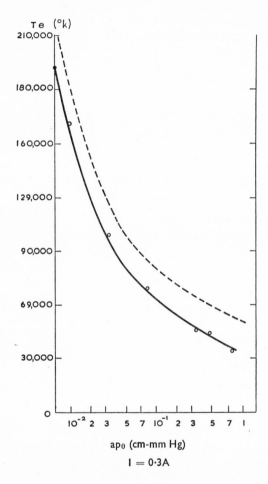

FIG. 3.4. Characteristics of the positive column of a helium discharge. Electron temperature T_e from probe measurements vs. product of gas pressure p_0 and tube radius a. Dotted curve, values calculated from Langmuir–Tonks theory (Karelina *J. P. U.S.S.R.* **6**, 218, 1942).

in the ionization potential increases the effective cross section exponentially, while at the same time the intrinsic cross sections are much higher for ionization from excited states.

In spite of these difficulties attempts have been made to calculate the approximate characteristics of the positive column, noticeably by KARFELD

(1941) and KARELINA (1942). From the plasma balance equation, the electron temperature T_- can be obtained as a function of ap_0, the product of the tube radius and gas pressure, and here the difficulty already observed in Langmuir's calculation of λ appears, measured temperatures being ~ 20 per cent below calculated ones. Given the electron temperature and an estimate of the elastic cross section, the electron mobility can be calculated, thus a relation between the number of electrons per unit length, N_-, the applied electric field E and the current, i, can be obtained. From the electron

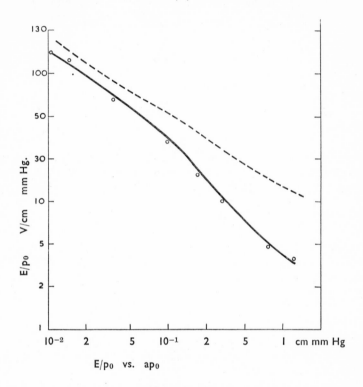

FIG. 3.5. Characteristics of the positive column of a helium discharge. Ratio of axial electric field to pressure vs. the product ap_0. Dotted curve, theoretical values (Karelina, *op. cit.*).

temperature and the ionization rate, the kinetic energy carried to the wall per ion pair can be calculated and since the ionization potential is known, an estimate of the radiation loss, which involves approximations to the inelastic cross section, permits the evaluation of the energy loss per ion pair. Since the total energy loss must be equal to the Joule heating, Ei, a second relation can be obtained between N_-, E and i. From these, i/N and E/p can be obtained as functions of ap_0. It should be observed that the current and voltage are independent, a feature which makes the discharge an interesting circuit element. Indeed, owing to the occurrence of secondary ionization processes the discharge can sometimes have negative characteristics, E decreasing as i increases. While the agreement between theory and experiment displayed by Karelina for the helium discharge is not exact, it is sufficiently close that we can consider the basis of the theory as verified.

Karelina's experiments were carried out in a long (1 m), narrow (32 mm), hot cathode helium arc, measurements being made by Langmuir probes. The pressure was low enough for the Langmuir–Tonks long mean free path theory to be applicable, instead of the formally slightly simpler diffusion theory.

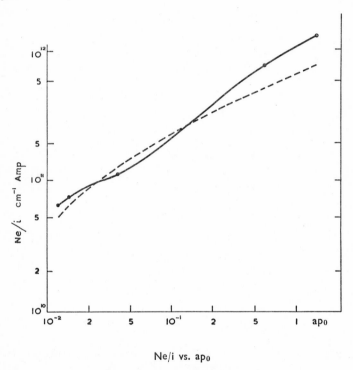

Ne/i vs. ap_0

Fig. 3.6. Characteristics of the positive column of a helium discharge. Ratio of number of electrons/unit length to current (from probe measurements) vs. product ap_0. Dotted curve, theoretical values (Karelina, *op. cit.*).

4. MAGNETIC CONFINEMENT—THE PINCH EFFECT

We will now consider a process which suggests that under some circumstances the ion life in the positive column may be increased so that the plasma tends toward equilibrium. This is the pinch effect, the confinement of a plasma by its own magnetic field, a phenomenon which occurs only at moderately high current (cf. TONKS, 1939).

To understand the effect, note that if a current is flowing, electrons are drifting along the tube with a mean velocity w, hence, in addition to the

pressure gradient and the electric field, the electron gas experiences the
Lorentz force $-n(e/c)\mathbf{w} \times \mathbf{B}$, and the mobility equation for electrons becomes

$$n\mathbf{v}_- = q_-\{-kT_-\boldsymbol{\nabla} n_- - ne\mathbf{E} - n(e/c)\mathbf{w} \times \mathbf{B}\} \tag{3.4.1}$$

Since there is no magnetic effect on the ions, the total diffusion equation
becomes, with $\mathbf{j}$ (e.m.u.) $= ne\mathbf{w}/c$

$$n\mathbf{v} = -D_a\left\{\boldsymbol{\nabla} n - \frac{\mathbf{j} \times \mathbf{B}}{k(T_+ + T_-)}\right\} \tag{3.4.2}$$

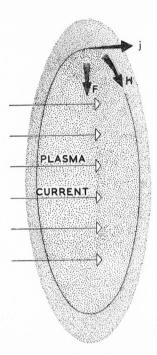

FIG. 3.7. Origin of the pinch effect. Current density $\mathbf{j}$ produces field $\mathbf{H}$ and
compressive force $\mathbf{F} = \mathbf{j} \times \mathbf{B}$.

To proceed, we must discover how $\mathbf{j}$ depends on the radius. For quite
moderate degrees of ionization it is easily shown that the current is determined by the interdiffusion of electrons and ions, which move relative to
one another in the axial, though not in the radial, direction. Since the low-
energy electron–ion cross section is much greater than the electron–neutral
cross section, electron–neutral collisions may be neglected and the axial
drift velocity determined by equating the rate at which electrons lose
momentum by collision with ions to the rate at which momentum is supplied
by the axial field, i.e.

$$\frac{mw}{\tau_{+-}} = -eE_z$$

Thus

$$= ne\frac{w}{c} = n\tau\frac{e^2}{mc}E_z \qquad (3.4.3)$$

But since

$$\tau_{\pm} = \frac{l_{\pm}}{\langle v \rangle} = \frac{1}{n_+\langle \sigma v \rangle} \qquad (3.4.4)$$

$$j = \frac{1}{\langle \sigma v \rangle}\frac{e^2}{mc}E_z \qquad (3.4.5)$$

Hence if E_z is uniform, the current density is uniform.

The magnetic field is then determined as

$$B_\phi = 2\pi r j_z$$

and

$$(j \times B)_r = -j_z B_\phi = -2\pi j_z^2 r$$

If we use this in eq. (3.4.2), take the divergence as before, introduce the ionization rate, still assuming a uniform density of neutrals, then again introduce the variable $s^2 = (\lambda/D_a)r^2$, we obtain the characteristic equation for a cylindrical system

$$\frac{d^2n}{ds^2} + \frac{1}{s}\frac{dn}{ds} + n = -\beta \qquad (3.4.6)$$

where

$$\beta = 4\pi j^2\frac{D_a}{\lambda k(T_+ + T_-)} = 4\pi j^2\frac{D_a}{\lambda kT}$$

This is satisfied by

$$n = (n_0 + \beta)J_0(s) - \beta$$

and the boundary condition demands

$$J_0(s_0) = \frac{\beta}{n_0 + \beta}$$

β, which has the dimensions of a density may be written $4\pi j^2(R^2/kTs_0^2)$ and since kT is small, while the remaining numbers are near unity, it is a large number. Unless β is comparable to n_0, $\beta/(n_0 + \beta)$ is small and s_0 must be small, so that the boundary condition becomes, approximately

$$1 - \tfrac{1}{4}s_0^2 = \frac{\beta}{n_0 + \beta} = 1 - \frac{1}{1 + \beta/n_0}$$

It proves convenient to introduce a new parameter b in place of β where

$$b = \frac{\beta}{n_0}\frac{s_0^2}{4R^2} = \pi n_0\frac{e^2}{mc^2}\frac{mw_0^2}{kT} \qquad (3.4.7)$$

so that

$$s_0^2 \simeq 4(1 - bR^2) \tag{3.4.8}$$

and

$$n(r) \simeq n_0\left(1 + 4b\frac{R^2}{s_0^2}\right)\left(1 - \tfrac{1}{4}s_0^2\frac{r^2}{R^2}\right) - n_0 4b\frac{R^2}{s_0^2}$$

$$\simeq n_0\left[1 - \left(b + \frac{s_0^2}{4R^2}\right)r^2\right]$$

As $bR^2 \to 1$, $s_0 \to 0$ and

$$n \to n_0(1 - br^2) \tag{3.4.9}$$

The increase in ion life t_0 can be seen by returning to eq. (3.3.1), and noting that as $bR^2 \to 1$, $s_0 \to 0$ and $t_0 \to \infty$. Alternatively, we can use eq. (3.4.2) to calculate the radial drift velocity.

$$nv = D_a\left\{-\frac{\mathrm{d}n}{\mathrm{d}r} - 2\pi\frac{j^2 r}{kT}\right\}$$

$$= D_a\left\{2n_0\left(b + \frac{s_0^2}{4R^2}\right)r - 2\pi n_0^2\frac{e^2 w_0^2}{c^2 kT}r\right\}$$

$$= D_a 2n_0 b\left\{\frac{s_0^2}{4bR^2}r + r\left(1 - \pi n_0\frac{e^2 w_0^2}{c^2 kTb}\right)\right\}$$

$$= D_a\frac{2n_0}{R^2}(1 - bR^2)r \quad \text{hence} \quad v \to 0 \quad \text{as} \quad bR^2 \to 1$$

using eq. (3.4.9).

If s_0 is small, we may express the axial density in terms of the total density as $n_0 = N/[\pi R^2(1 - \tfrac{1}{2}bR^2)]$ and the condition $bR^2 = 1$ becomes

$$N\frac{e^2}{mc^2}\ \frac{\tfrac{1}{2}mw_0^2}{kT} = 1 \tag{3.4.10}$$

In several problems the dimensionless quantity $N(e^2/mc^2) = Nr_0 = \nu$, occurs where N is the number of electrons per unit length and r_0 the classical electron radius. Also the ratio $R_\mathscr{E}$ of the energy drift motion $\tfrac{1}{2}mw^2$ to the temperature is frequently important, and in terms of these the condition becomes

$$\nu R_\mathscr{E} = 1$$

Alternatively, we may multiply the top and bottom of eq. (3.4.10) by N to obtain

$$N^2 e^2\frac{w_0^2}{c^2} = 2NkT \tag{3.4.11}$$

or
$$I^2 = 2NkT \qquad (3.4.12)$$

If $bR^2 > 1$, then the density vanishes at $br^2 = 1$, and the relations (3.4.11) and (3.4.12) continue to hold even though the plasma is isolated from the walls.

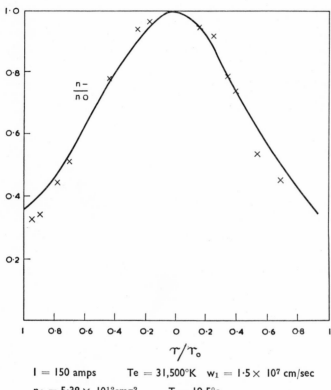

$$I = 150 \text{ amps} \qquad T_e = 31{,}500°K \quad w_1 = 1{\cdot}5 \times 10^7 \text{ cm/sec}$$
$$n_0 = 5{\cdot}38 \times 10^{12}\text{cm}^{-3} \qquad T = 19{\cdot}5°c$$

FIG. 3.8. Electron density distribution in pinched discharge. Measured values of electron density (from Langmuir probes) normalized to central density vs. distance from axis. Electron temperature Te and central density n_0 from probe measurements, axial drift w calculated from total current. Solid curve, theoretical values. (cf. Thonemann and Cowhig, *Proc. Phys. Soc.* B. **64**, 345, 1951).

This has been an exceedingly simplified discussion of the pinch effect, but it has displayed some aspects of the phenomenon. To proceed with the study of such systems, which are of great interest in plasma physics, it is necessary to use even cruder models of the plasma, but much more powerful methods of study.

An early experiment on the constriction of an arc was performed by THONEMANN and COWHIG (1951). These authors assumed that the electron

4

axial drift velocity rather than the current density was uniform across the tube, supporting this by experimental evidence, and obtained a density distribution in the form

$$\frac{n}{n_0} = (1+br^2)^{-2}$$

where $b = (\pi n_0 e^2 w^2/2kTc^2)$ was a constant that could be expressed in terms of the measurable electron temperature, current and drift velocity. Probe measurements of electron density were plotted against radius for a current of 150 A in a 10^{-3} mm pressure mercury discharge and were found in good agreement with theory.

Since it is difficult to produce fully ionized discharges, for which $2NkT < 10^6$ ergs/cm, it is difficult to obtain a confined discharge at currents much less than $\sim 10^4$ A, and at these high currents the plasma is found to be pulled away from the walls, but instead of retaining a steady cylindrically symmetric configuration, the discharge thrashes about within the tube and only by high-speed photographic techniques can its constricted nature be revealed. This is a particularly dramatic example of the instability associated with magnetically confined plasmas.

BIBLIOGRAPHY

SCHOTTKY, W. (1925). Z. f. Phys. 31, 163.

LANGMUIR, I. and TONKS, L. (1929). Phys. Rev. 34, 874.

LANGMUIR, I. and TONKS, L. (1926). Phys. Rev. 28, 104.

THONEMANN, P. C. and COWHIG, W. T. (1951). Proc. Phys. Soc. B64, 345.

KARFELD, B. (1941). J. Phys. U.S.S.R., 5, 135.

KARELINA, N. A. (1942). J. Phys. U.S.S.R., 6, 218.

TONKS, L. (1939). Phys. Rev. 56, 360 (an early but full discussion of the effect of magnetic fields on the arc).

GUTHRIE, A. and WAKERLING, R. K. (ed.) (1949). The Characteristics of Electrical Discharges in Magnetic Fields Chapter 3. p. 27. McGraw-Hill.

Treatises on gas discharges are

THOMSON, J. J. and THOMSON, G. P. (1933). Conduction of Electricity Through Gases, Cambridge. A complete and fascinating account of early knowledge.

VON ENGEL, A. (1955). Ionized Gases, Oxford.

FLUGGE, S. (1956). Handbuch der Physik Vol. XXI. Electron Emission and Gas Discharge. Vol. XXII. Gas Discharge II. Springer, Göttingen.

FRANCIS, G. (1960). Ionization Phenomena in Gases, Butterworth, London.

BROWN, S. C. (1961). Basic Data of Plasma Physics, Wiley, New York.

CHAPTER 4

MAGNETOHYDRODYNAMICS I

In the last chapter we discussed the diffusion theory of the arc and ended by describing a system in which the ionized component of the gas was completely confined by its own magnetic field. Under such circumstances the drift velocity vanishes and eq. (3.4.2) may be written as

$$\nabla p = \frac{1}{c}\mathbf{j} \times \mathbf{B}$$

where $p = n_+kT_+ + n_-kT_-$ represents the total pressure of the ionized gas. In this expression the molecular properties of the gas, ionization cross sections, mean free paths, etc., are irrelevant, the ionized component being described purely in macroscopic terms. Moreover, the neutral component is irrelevant and could be absent. Although this description of an ionized gas is greatly over-simplified, many of the essential features are preserved and the simplification permits the discussion of such complicated problems as the stability of configurations.

We shall now discuss this simplified model which represents the plasma as an electrically conducting perfect gas, thus neglecting all effects of the neutral gas, as well as the details of interaction between ions and electrons. At a later stage we will subject the fully ionized gas to a closer scrutiny and attempt to assess the limitations of this approximation.

The study of the motion of a conducting fluid interacting with electric and magnetic fields is the subject of magnetohydrodynamics, but before proceeding with that we must discuss the decay of fields in conductors in order to discover the relative importance of electric current and charge.

1. THE DECAY OF CHARGE AND CURRENT IN CONDUCTORS

To describe the decay of charges and currents in a stationary conductor we shall use Maxwell's equations together with Ohm's law relating the current to the electric field. In Gaussian units these are:

$$\frac{1}{\mu} \operatorname{curl} \mathbf{B} = \frac{4\pi}{c}\mathbf{j} + \frac{\epsilon}{c}\frac{\partial \mathbf{E}}{\partial t} \tag{4.1.1}$$

$$\operatorname{curl} \mathbf{E} = -\frac{1}{c}\frac{\partial \mathbf{B}}{\partial t} \tag{4.1.2}$$

$$\epsilon \operatorname{div} \mathbf{E} = 4\pi q \tag{4.1.3}$$

$$\operatorname{div} \mathbf{B} = 0 \tag{4.1.4}$$

$$\mathbf{j} = \sigma \mathbf{E} \tag{4.1.5}$$

To describe the decay of charge we take the divergence of eq. (4.1.1) and assuming the constants of the medium, the permeability μ, dielectric constant ϵ, and conductivity σ are uniform obtain, using eqs. (4.1.3) and (4.1.5),

$$0 = \frac{4\pi}{c}\text{div}\,\mathbf{j} + \frac{\epsilon}{c}\frac{\partial}{\partial t}\text{div}\,\mathbf{E} = \frac{1}{c}\left(4\pi\sigma\,\text{div}\,\mathbf{E} + \epsilon\frac{\partial}{\partial t}\text{div}\,\mathbf{E}\right) = \frac{4\pi}{c}\left(\frac{4\pi\sigma}{\epsilon}q + \frac{\partial q}{\partial t}\right)$$

(4.1.6.)

This is the continuity equation for the charge since

$$\frac{\partial q}{\partial t} + \text{div}\,\mathbf{j} = \frac{\partial q}{\partial t} + \sigma\,\text{div}\,\mathbf{E} = \frac{\partial q}{\partial t} + \frac{4\pi\sigma}{\epsilon}q = 0$$

and shows that a free charge q will decay exponentially as $q = q_0\exp(-t/\tau_q)$ where

$$\tau_q = \frac{\epsilon}{4\pi\sigma} \tag{4.1.7}$$

To discuss the decay of current it is convenient although not necessary to neglect the displacement current $(\epsilon/c)(\partial\mathbf{E}/\partial t)$, thus reverting to the pre-Maxwell electrical equations. Then by taking the curl of eq. (4.1.1), and eliminating $\mathbf{j}$ and $\mathbf{E}$ by (4.1.5) and (4.1.2), we obtain

$$\text{curl curl}\,\mathbf{B} = -\nabla^2\mathbf{B} = -\frac{4\pi\mu\sigma}{c^2}\frac{\partial\mathbf{B}}{\partial t} \tag{4.1.8}$$

To estimate the decay time of the field, observe that the L.H.S. is roughly B/L^2 where L is a measure of the distance over which $\mathbf{B}$ changes significantly, hence, the decay time is

$$\tau_j = \frac{4\pi\mu\sigma L^2}{c^2} \tag{4.1.9}$$

For example, if a field is confined to a conducting slab infinite in area, but of thickness D, the appropriate fundamental solutions to eq. (4.1.8) are

$$B_n = B_n{}^0\sin\left\{n\left(\frac{2\pi x}{D}\right)\right\}\exp(-\gamma_n t)$$

where

$$\gamma_n^{-1} = \frac{1}{n^2}\frac{4\pi\mu\sigma}{c^2}\left(\frac{D}{2\pi}\right)^2$$

and the decay time $\tau_j \simeq (4\pi\mu\sigma/c^2)(D/2\pi)^2$.

For numerical estimates we need the Gaussian conductivity

$$\sigma(\text{sec}^{-1}) = 9\times10^{11}\sigma(\text{mho cm}^{-1})$$

In copper

$$\sigma = 5\times10^5 \text{ mho cm}^{-1} = 4\cdot5\times10^{17} \text{ sec}^{-1}$$

and $\tau_q \simeq 2 \times 10^{-19}$ sec while $\tau_j \simeq 0 \cdot 6^2 L^2$ sec. It is the slow penetration of magnetic fields that enables relatively thin metal sheets to act as screens against rapidly alternating fields. At the other extreme, the enormous volume of conducting material in astronomical bodies can maintain currents for very long times. The earth, for example, has a core of a conductivity probably $\sim 10^{15}$ sec^{-1} and a radius ~ 5000 km so that the characteristic decay time for a magnetic field is $\sim 2 \cdot 5 \times 10^{12}$ sec $\simeq 10^5$ years. Also, from the extremely small value of τ_q it is clear that a conductor resembles a plasma in remaining quasi-neutral. Because of this, the effect of electric fields on free charges can be neglected in the dynamical equations of motion, although electric fields still may appear as a result of changes in magnetic flux.

2. THE EQUATIONS OF MAGNETOHYDRODYNAMICS

The motion of a normal fluid is described by the familiar equations of hydrodynamics which represent the conservation laws of mechanics. The conservation of matter is described by the equation of continuity

$$\frac{\partial \rho}{\partial t} + \mathbf{v} . \boldsymbol{\nabla} \rho + \rho \operatorname{div} \mathbf{v} = 0 \qquad (4.2.1)$$

where ρ is the density of the fluid and $\mathbf{v}$ the velocity. This equation equates the rate of increase of matter in an element of fluid $(\partial \rho / \partial t) + \mathbf{v} . \boldsymbol{\nabla} \rho = (D\rho/Dt)$ to the net rate at which matter flows into that element, $-\rho \operatorname{div} \mathbf{v}$. Conservation of momentum is described by

$$\rho \left(\frac{\partial \mathbf{v}}{\partial t} + \mathbf{v} . \boldsymbol{\nabla} \mathbf{v} \right) = -\boldsymbol{\nabla} p + \mathbf{F} \qquad (4.2.2)$$

which equates the rate of gain of momentum in a fluid element to the forces which act upon it. Here $\mathbf{F}$ represents an arbitrary volume force, and p the pressure, or more generally, the stress tensor. This equation acquires content only when some expression is given for the pressure or the stress tensor, and it is only at this stage that the physical properties of the fluid are required. The necessary relation between pressure and the remaining flow parameters is usually determined by experiment, but in the absence of experimental data, recourse may sometimes be had to an underlying theory of fluid structure such as the kinetic theory of gases. For most problems, the simplest possible representation of p is required, and usually an attempt is made to represent the physics of the fluid by one of a number of simple models. If compressibility and viscosity can be neglected, the constancy of density implies

$$\operatorname{div} \mathbf{v} = 0 \qquad (4.2.3)$$

a relation, in addition to eqs. (4.2.1) and (4.2.2), which may be used to eliminate the pressure. If the fluid is viscous there occur, besides the hydrostatic pressure, additional terms in the stress tensor

$$p_{ij} = \mu\left(\frac{\partial v_i}{\partial x_j} + \frac{\partial v_j}{\partial x_i}\right) - \frac{2}{3}\mu \operatorname{div} \mathbf{v}\, \delta_{ij} \tag{4.2.4}$$

where μ is the coefficient of viscosity. If the fluid is compressible, it is usually possible to assume local thermodynamic equilibrium and calculate the pressure from the equation of state, $\phi(p, \rho, T) = 0$, e.g. $p - R\rho T = 0$ for a perfect gas. Often conditions are such that some thermodynamic variable,

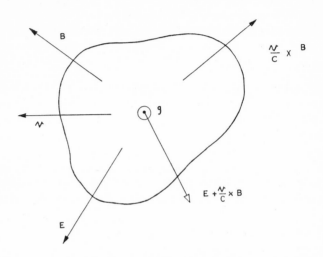

FIG. 4.1. The Lorentz force and the effective electric field. Force exerted on a charge g sharing velocity $\mathbf{v}$ of the fluid
$$g\,\mathbf{E}^* = g\,[\mathbf{E} + (\mathbf{v}/c)\,\times\mathbf{B}]$$

temperature or more frequently entropy, is constant and a reduced equation of state directly relating pressure and density may be used. An example of this is the equation of state for adiabatic flow of a perfect gas

$$\frac{D}{Dt}(p\rho^{-\gamma}) = 0 \tag{4.2.5}$$

where $\gamma(>1)$ is the polytropic index, or the ratio of specific heats.

If no such reduction is possible, the full equation of state must be used and the hydrodynamic equations supplemented by an expression determining the transport of internal energy, such as

$$C_v\frac{DT}{Dt} + p \operatorname{div} \mathbf{v} + K\nabla^2 T = 0$$

the energy transport equation for a perfect gas, where C_v is the volume specific heat, and K the thermal conductivity.

The transition to magnetohydrodynamics is made by including in $\mathbf{F}$ the magnetic stress $(1/c)\mathbf{j} \times \mathbf{B}$, then using Maxwell's equations to determine the fields. At this stage a further "equation of state" is needed to relate the current density to the fields and the fluid motion. Many such relations have been suggested, but the simplest and most used is an obvious generalization of Ohm's law in which the electric field is taken as that seen by an observer moving with the fluid, i.e. the force on a unit charge moving with the fluid velocity $\mathbf{v}$, which is the sum of the electric field $\mathbf{E}$ and the Lorentz force, $(\mathbf{v}/c) \times \mathbf{B}$,

$$\mathbf{E}^* = \left(\mathbf{E} + \frac{\mathbf{v}}{c} \times \mathbf{B} \right)$$

thus

$$\mathbf{j} = \sigma \left(\mathbf{E} + \frac{\mathbf{v}}{c} \times \mathbf{B} \right) \tag{4.2.6}$$

A useful variant on this is the assumption of perfect conductivity

$$\mathbf{E} + \frac{\mathbf{v}}{c} \times \mathbf{B} = 0 \tag{4.2.7}$$

For convenience, we will now assemble the equations of magnetohydrodynamics in the first form, at the same time making the assumption which is valid for all slow motions, that the displacement current can be neglected. We have the hydrodynamic equations $[D/Dt = (\partial/\partial t) + \mathbf{v} \cdot \mathbf{\nabla}$, is the substantial time derivative]

$$\frac{D}{Dt}\rho + \rho \operatorname{div} \mathbf{v} = 0 \qquad\qquad \mathbf{I}'$$

$$\rho\frac{D\mathbf{v}}{Dt} = -\mathbf{\nabla}p + \frac{1}{c}\mathbf{j} \times \mathbf{B} \qquad\qquad \mathbf{II}'$$

Maxwell's equations

$$\frac{1}{\mu}\operatorname{curl} \mathbf{B} = \frac{4\pi}{c}\mathbf{j} \qquad\qquad \mathbf{III}'$$

$$\operatorname{curl} \mathbf{E} = -\frac{1}{c}\frac{\partial \mathbf{B}}{\partial t} \qquad\qquad \mathbf{IV}'$$

$$\operatorname{div} \mathbf{B} = 0 \qquad\qquad \mathbf{V}'$$

$$\operatorname{div} \mathbf{E} = \frac{4\pi q}{\epsilon} \qquad\qquad \mathbf{VI}'$$

and the two "equations of state"

$$\frac{D}{Dt}(p\rho^{-\gamma}) = 0 \quad \text{or} \quad \operatorname{div} \mathbf{v} = 0 \qquad\qquad \mathbf{VII}'$$

and

$$\mathbf{j} = \sigma \left(\mathbf{E} + \frac{\mathbf{v}}{c} \times \mathbf{B} \right) \quad \text{or} \quad \mathbf{E} + \frac{\mathbf{v}}{c} \times \mathbf{B} = 0 \qquad\qquad \mathbf{VIII}'$$

It is possible to transform these equations and effect a very significant compression by eliminating $\mathbf{E}$ and $\mathbf{j}$, leaving ρ, $\mathbf{v}$, p and $\mathbf{B}$ as variables. To do this first use III′ to eliminate the current from II′, so that the Maxwell stress gradient

$$(1/c)\mathbf{j} \times \mathbf{B} = (1/4\pi\mu)(\text{curl}\,\mathbf{B}) \times \mathbf{B} = -(1/8\pi\mu)\nabla B^2 + (1/4\pi\mu)\mathbf{B}\,.\nabla\mathbf{B}$$

Next take the curl of III′, use VIII′ for the current $\mathbf{j}$, and IV′ to eliminate curl $\mathbf{E}$: thus,

$$\text{curl}\,[(4\pi/c)\mathbf{j}] = (4\pi\sigma/c^2)[c\,\text{curl}\,\mathbf{E} + \text{curl}(\mathbf{v}\times\mathbf{B})] =$$

$$-(4\pi\sigma/c^2)[(\partial\mathbf{B}/\partial t) + (\mathbf{v}\,.\,\nabla)\mathbf{B} + \mathbf{B}\,\text{div}\,\mathbf{v} - (\mathbf{B}\,.\,\nabla)\mathbf{v}]$$

Then the second form of the magnetohydrodynamic equations becomes:

$$\frac{D\rho}{Dt} + \rho\,\text{div}\,\mathbf{v} = 0 \qquad\qquad\text{I}$$

$$\rho\frac{D\mathbf{v}}{Dt} = -\nabla p - \frac{1}{8\pi\mu}\nabla B^2 + \frac{1}{4\pi\mu}(\mathbf{B}\,.\,\nabla)\mathbf{B} \qquad\qquad\text{II}$$

$$\frac{D\mathbf{B}}{Dt} + \mathbf{B}\,\text{div}\,\mathbf{v} - (\mathbf{B}\,.\,\nabla)\mathbf{v} = \frac{c^2}{4\pi\mu\sigma}\nabla^2\mathbf{B} \quad\text{or}\quad = 0 \qquad\qquad\text{III}$$

$$\text{div}\,\mathbf{B} = 0 \qquad\qquad\text{IV}$$

and

$$\frac{D}{Dt}(p\rho^{-\gamma}) = 0 \quad\text{or}\quad \text{div}\,\mathbf{v} = 0 \qquad\qquad\text{V}$$

3. IMMEDIATE CONSEQUENCES OF THE MAGNETOHYDRODYNAMIC EQUATIONS

(a) *Magnetic Pressure*

A complete understanding of this complex set of equations has not yet been obtained, but some immediate consequences are fairly obvious. For example, consider II for motion at right angles to a unidirectional magnetic field. Then the magnetic contribution to the stress reduces to $(1/8\pi\mu)\nabla B^2$, the gradient of the magnetic pressure. The magnitude of this term can be estimated by noting that a field of 5000 gauss produces a pressure

$$\frac{1}{8\pi}(5000)^2 \simeq 10^6 \text{ dynes/cm}^2 \simeq 1 \text{ atm.}$$

In more general geometries, the Maxwell stress tensor is more complex, but by introducing the unit vector $\mathbf{b}$ in the direction of $\mathbf{B}$ its contribution may be seen to reduce to $-[\nabla - \mathbf{b}(\mathbf{b}\,.\,\nabla)](B^2/8\pi) + (\mathbf{n}/R)(B^2/4\pi)$, thus no force is exerted in the direction of the line of force, while in the direction $\mathbf{n}$ of the principal normal, the gradient of $(B^2/8\pi)$ is reduced by $(B^2/4\pi R)$ where R is the radius of curvature of the field line.

(b) *Flux Trapping—The Frozen-in Field*

In the case of perfect conductivity, III implies that flux is trapped in the fluid, i.e. that the flux threading a closed curve moving with the fluid is constant. This is most easily proved by noting the formal equivalence between III and the equation for transport of vorticity in an inviscid fluid,

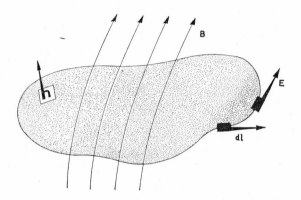

FIG. 4.2. Conservation of flux.

$$\oint \mathbf{E}^* \cdot d\mathbf{l} = (d/dt)\int \mathbf{B} \cdot \mathbf{n} \; dA = d(d\phi)/dt; \text{ and if } \mathbf{E}^* = 0, \; d(d\phi)/dt = 0$$

and invoking Kelvin's circulation theorem. It is easily shown directly, however, for consider the flux crossing an element dA, and introduce a cartesian coordinate system with axis parallel to $\mathbf{B}$. Then the flux crossing dA is

$$d\phi = \mathbf{B} \cdot \mathbf{n} \; dA = B\Delta x \Delta y$$

Since the surface shares the motion of the fluid

$$\frac{d}{dt}(\Delta x) = \frac{d}{dt}(x + \Delta x - x) = V_x(x + \Delta x) - V_x(x) = \frac{\partial V_x}{\partial x}\Delta x$$

and

$$\frac{d}{dt}(\Delta x \, \Delta y) = \left(\frac{\partial V_x}{\partial x} + \frac{\partial V_y}{\partial y}\right)\Delta x \Delta y$$

Hence the rate of change of the element of flux is

$$\frac{D}{Dt}(d\phi) = \frac{DB}{Dt}\Delta x \Delta y + B\left(\frac{\partial V_x}{\partial x} + \frac{\partial V_y}{\partial y}\right)\Delta x \Delta y$$

$$= \left[\frac{DB}{Dt} + \mathbf{B} \operatorname{div} \mathbf{v} - (\mathbf{B} \cdot \nabla)\mathbf{v}\right]_z \Delta x \Delta y = 0 \quad \text{by} \quad \text{III}$$

The physical reason for flux trapping is also clear. Since the fluid is a perfect conductor, all electric fields in the fluid must vanish when measured by an observer sharing the fluid motion. In particular, the e.m.f. around any closed curve moving with the fluid must vanish, thus there can be no change of the magnetic flux threading such a loop.

The effects of flux trapping even in a highly dissipative system have been dramatically demonstrated in experiments with mercury flowing between the poles of a magnet. ALPHER *et al.* (1960), for example, allowed mercury to flow through a shallow non-conducting channel placed between the poles of a large magnet, a process accompanied by no spectacular phenomena. If, however, electrodes were placed on either side of the channel and shorted, an hydraulic discontinuity appeared between them. Even more striking was the effect of fixing a small copper plate in contact with the mercury on the bottom of the channel; when the magnetic field was switched on this interrupted the flow almost as would a solid object. The cause of these effects is the alteration in the induced current pattern when an insulating boundary is replaced by a conductor. In particular, for the second experiment, when the magnetic lines ran from the mercury into copper their identity was preserved, and trapped in the copper, they retarded the mercury, while in the insulating layer the field lines could freely break and rejoin.

(c) *Conditions for Magnetohydrodynamic Behaviour*

For typical magnetohydrodynamic behaviour, the fluid velocity and the magnetic field should interact as strongly as possible, thus in II the magnetic terms should be comparable to the acceleration, which will then be determined by the fields. At the same time in III the right side, which represents normal diffusion of the field, should be negligible in comparison with the convective terms on the left, which represent the rate at which flux is transported by fluid motions. For steady flow the first of these conditions demands

$$\tfrac{1}{2}\rho \frac{V^2}{L} \simeq \frac{B^2}{8\pi L} \quad \text{or} \quad v \simeq V_A = \sqrt{(B^2/4\pi\rho)} \qquad (4.3.1)$$

where V_A is the Alfvén speed, an important speed in magnetohydrodynamics. The second condition, flux convection rather than diffusion, demands

$$v\frac{B}{L} \gg \frac{c^2}{4\pi\mu\sigma}\frac{B}{L^2}$$

i.e.

$$v \gg \frac{c^2}{4\pi\mu\sigma L} \qquad (4.3.2)$$

These conditions may be combined to give the condition for typical magnetohydrodynamic behaviour

$$M = \frac{\mu\sigma}{c^2}LB\sqrt{(4\pi/\rho)} \gg 1 \qquad (4.3.3)$$

This condition was derived by LUNDQUIST (1952) who called M the magnetic Reynold's number. It is tabulated in Table 4.1 for a number of astrophysical and laboratory systems. This table shows that because of their great size, most astrophysical conductors should display magneto-hydrodynamic behaviour, while on the other hand such behaviour is produced in the laboratory only with difficulty. The value of M is large for gaseous plasmas, but the Alfvén velocity is large ($\sim 10^7$ cm sec^{-1}) and the magnetic field diffusion time is short ($\sim 10^{-3}$ sec), thus magnetohydrodynamic phenomena require high velocity, are of short duration, and can be observed only by refined techniques.

Table 4.1. The Magnetic Reynold's Number

System	Scale	Field (gauss)	Density (g cm^{-3})	Conductivity (σ sec^{-1})	M
Astrophysical					
Earth's core	10^3 km	1	12	10^{15}	10^2
Ionosphere	10^2 km	0·2	10^{-8}	11^{11}	10
Solar atmosphere	10^4 km	10^2	10^{-9}	10^{13}	10^8
Solar corona	10^6 km	10^{-5}	10^{-20}	10^{16}	10^{11}
Hot gaseous nebula	0·1 light yr	10^{-5}	10^{-22}	10^{13}	10^{14}
Hot interstellar gas	1·0 light yr	10^{-6}	10^{-24}	10^{13}	10^{15}
Laboratory	10 cm	1000			
Mercury			13·5	10^{17}	1·0
Liquid Sodium			0·93	10^{18}	40·0
Normal arc plasma			10^{-8}	10^{15}	10^3
Hot confined plasma			10^{-9}	10^{15}	10^4
$n = 10^{15}$ cm^{-3}, $T = 10^6$ °K			10^{-9}	10^{15}	10^4

A good many experiments have been carried out to demonstrate the conditions under which typically magnetohydrodynamic behaviour should appear. In liquids dissipative processes usually dominate, and the transition to typical magnetohydrodynamic behaviour is most easily observed in the ionizing shock tube. An example of such an experiment is that of DOLDER (1958). He used an argon shock tube driven by an oxygen–hydrogen explosion, as did PETSCHEK, and produced ionizing shocks. Around the tube there was a coil producing a magnetic field through which the gas flowed. If magnetohydrodynamic behaviour occurred, the gas was accelerated toward the centre of the tube as it went through the field region, and beyond that would execute radial oscillations. These oscillations showed up as characteristic patterns of light beyond the interaction region. The theory of PETSCHEK was used to calculate both the density ρ and conductivity σ behind the shock, as well as the time τ needed to reach thermal equilibrium. Since the length of the ionized column was short, only if $\tau < 10^{-5}$ sec could an interaction be expected. From the calculated values of ρ and σ and the known values of the magnetic field and tube radius, the magnetic Reynold's number M could be calculated. It was found that interactions occurred only in the expected region. Subsequent experiments on the distortion of the magnetic field verified the calculated value of σ.

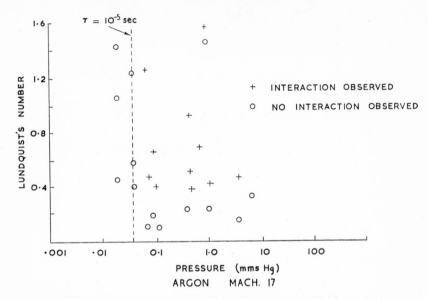

FIG. 4.3. Lundquist's number as a criterion for magneto-hydrodynamic behaviour. Observations on the occurence of magnetic-fluid interactions in a shock tube, showing that if Lundquist's number $M = (\mu\sigma/c^2)\ LB\sqrt{4\pi/\rho} > 0.4$, and if ionization time $<$ duration of flow i.e. to right of line $\tau = 10^{-5}$ sec, interaction is present (Dolder and Hide, *Nature*, **118**, 1116, 1958).

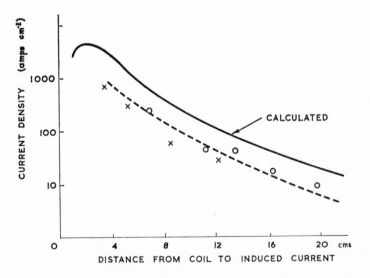

FIG. 4.4. Magnitude of magnetohydrodynamic interaction. By measuring distortion in magnetic field, current distribution in plasma may be determined as a function of distance from inducing coil. Measured values are shown, with theoretical curve for a fully ionized gas. (Dolder, *op. cit.*).

4. MAGNETOHYDROSTATICS

Magnetohydrodynamic equilibrium of stationary fluid requires (j,e.m.u.)

$$\nabla p = \mathbf{j} \times \mathbf{B} \tag{4.4.1}$$

If the pressure is a scalar, there are severe restrictions on the magnetic field. Since clearly $\mathbf{B} \cdot \nabla p = 0$ and $\mathbf{j} \cdot \nabla p = 0$, the magnetic field lines and the currents must lie in surfaces of constant pressure and the magnetic field must form a set of magnetic surfaces. An analytic constraint was given by FERRARO

$$0 = \operatorname{curl}(\nabla p) = -\operatorname{curl}\left[\frac{1}{8\pi}\nabla\,B^2 - \frac{1}{4\pi}(\mathbf{B} \cdot \nabla)\mathbf{B}\right] = \frac{1}{4\pi}\operatorname{curl}(\mathbf{B} \cdot \nabla)\mathbf{B}$$

The complete properties of the solutions to this complex non-linear partial differential equation are not known, however some simple systems have been studied. If field lines are straight then equilibrium requires $p + (B^2/8\pi)$ = constant, and in particular there exist equilibria in which a fluid is confined to a cylindrical region by a magnetic field parallel to the axis and azimuthal currents about the axis. Similarly a cylindrical flux tube could be held in equilibrium by a conducting fluid. We have already displayed an example of a gas confined by a uniform axial current, and it is clear that arbitrary axial currents can maintain systems in equilibrium. An interesting relation holds for any such system. If we write $B_\phi = 2I/r$ the equilibrium may be written

$$\frac{\partial}{\partial r}p = -2jI/r$$

This may be integrated to

$$p(r) - p(R) = 2\int_r^R I(s)\frac{j(s)}{s}\,\mathrm{d}s$$

a relationship which on being multiplied by $2\pi r\,\mathrm{d}r$ and integrated from 0 to R yields

$$2\pi\int_0^R p(r)r\,\mathrm{d}r - p(R)\;\pi R^2 = 4\pi\int_0^R r\mathrm{d}r\int^R \frac{j(s)}{s}I(s)\,\mathrm{d}s$$

$$= 2\pi\int_0^R \mathrm{d}r r j(r)I(r) = \tfrac{1}{2}I^2(R)$$

Hence if $p(R) = 0$, the following relation holds for a confined cylinder of isothermal perfect gas:

$$NkT = \tfrac{1}{2}I^2 \tag{4.4.2}$$

There is an important class of cylindrical equilibria in which the gas pressure is balanced by helical field lines. In these, the pressure due to the axial magnetic field is simply added to the gas pressure and relationships similar to eq. (4.4.2) are easily derived.

5. MAGNETIC ISOLATION OF PLASMA

The cylindrical equilibria described so far have been two-dimensional and it is of interest to demonstrate the existence of a three-dimensional equilibrium in which a conducting fluid is held in place by a magnetic fluid.

It is not difficult to show that in the simplest confining geometry, where the field lines and currents lie on closed surfaces of constant pressure, and in which the magnetic field and current density are solenoidal, the magnetic surfaces form a set of nested toroids.

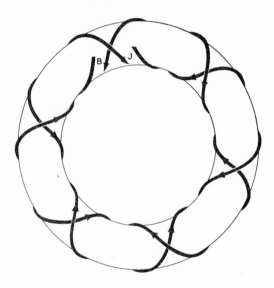

A MAGNETIC SURFACE

FIG. 4.5. Magnetohydrostatic equilibrium, a closed magnetic surface, i.e. a surface of uniform pressure containing the magnetic field **B** and the current density **j**.

In this geometry there exists an analogue of the confinement of fluid in a cylinder by an axial current, but no analogue of confinement by an axial field. For, if the cylinder is bent into a torus of radius R, the field lines acquire a radius of curvature R, and Ferraro's condition (4.4.1) cannot be satisfied since curl $(\mathbf{B} \cdot \nabla \mathbf{B}) = -(\partial/\partial z)(B^2/R)$, where z measures displacement out of the plane of the major circle of the torus, and only for the two-dimensional case is confinement possible.

It is possible to search for these equilibria by exploring an analogy between the *steady flow* of an incompressible fluid, and the static equilibrium of a magnetohydrodynamic fluid (GRAD and RUBIN) for the incompressible hydrodynamic equations may be written

$$\rho\left[\frac{\partial \mathbf{v}}{\partial t} + (\mathrm{curl}\,\mathbf{v})\times \mathbf{v}\right] = -\boldsymbol{\nabla}(p + \tfrac{1}{2}\rho v^2)$$

or, for a steady state

$$(\mathrm{curl}\,\mathbf{v})\times \mathbf{v} = -\boldsymbol{\nabla}\left(\frac{p}{\rho} + \tfrac{1}{2}v^2\right) = -\boldsymbol{\nabla}p^* \qquad (4.5.1)$$

which is formally equivalent to eq. 4.4.1 with $\mathbf{v} \to \mathbf{B}$, $p^* \to 4\pi p$. Boundary conditions for the magnetohydrostatic problem require that the plasma surface be a magnetic surface, or that the field be parallel to perfectly conducting walls; thus the corresponding hydrodynamic problem is that of the free jet, or of rigid boundaries with free slip.

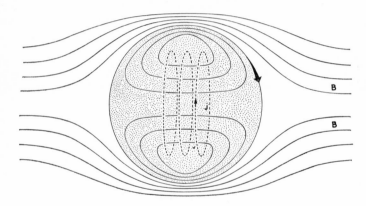

FIG. 4.6. Magnetohydrostatic analogue of Hill's spherical vortex.

An analogy of the confined plasma is then provided by a vortex ring, a particular example being Hill's spherical vortex, where the surfaces of constant pressure are, in cylindrical coordinates, r, z

$$\psi = \begin{cases} -\tfrac{3}{4}B_0(r^2/a^2)[a^2 - (r^2 + z^2)] = \text{const.} & r^2 + z^2 < a^2 \\[2mm] \tfrac{1}{2}B_0 r^2\left[1 - \dfrac{a^3}{(r^2 + z^2)^{3/2}}\right] = \text{const.} & r^2 + z^2 > a^2 \end{cases}$$

It is fairly easy to describe an extensive, though still highly specialized, class of axially symmetric equilibria. This is most easily described in a cylindrical polar system centred on the axis of symmetry, (r, θ, z).

The condition div $B = 0$ is satisfied by introducing a stream function $\psi(r, z)$ such that

$$rB_r = -\frac{\partial \psi}{\partial z}, \qquad rB_z = \frac{\partial \psi}{\partial r}, \qquad B_\theta = B_\theta(r, z) \qquad (4.5.2)$$

The components of $\mathbf{j} \times \mathbf{B} = \boldsymbol{\nabla} p$ then become

$$\frac{\partial p}{\partial r} + B_\theta \frac{1}{r} \frac{\partial}{\partial r} r B_\theta + \frac{1}{r^2} \frac{\partial \psi}{\partial r} \Delta^2 \psi = 0 \qquad (4.5.3)$$

$$\frac{1}{r^2} \frac{\partial \psi}{\partial r} \frac{\partial}{\partial z} r B_\theta - \frac{1}{r^2} \frac{\partial \psi}{\partial z} \frac{\partial}{\partial r} (r B_\theta) = 0 \qquad (4.5.4)$$

$$\frac{\partial p}{\partial z} + B_\theta \frac{\partial}{\partial z} B_\theta + \frac{1}{r^2} \frac{\partial \psi}{\partial z} \Delta^2 \psi = 0 \qquad (4.5.5)$$

where

$$\Delta^2 \psi = \frac{\partial^2 \psi}{\partial z^2} + \frac{\partial^2 \psi}{\partial r^2} - \frac{1}{r} \frac{\partial \psi}{\partial r}$$

The second of these, (4.5.4), which states that the Jacobian

$$J\left(\frac{\psi, r B_\theta}{r, \ z}\right) = 0,$$

implies that $r B_\theta$ is a function of ψ alone;

$$r B_\theta = f(\psi) \qquad (4.5.6)$$

The remaining two equations (4.5.3) and (4.5.5) may be written

$$\frac{\partial p}{\partial r} + \frac{\partial \psi}{\partial r} \left[\frac{1}{r^2} \Delta^2 \psi + \frac{1}{r^2} f f' \right] = 0$$

$$\frac{\partial p}{\partial z} + \frac{\partial \psi}{\partial z} \left[\frac{1}{r^2} \Delta^2 \psi + \frac{1}{r^2} f f' \right] = 0$$

and eliminating the square bracket between these gives

$$\frac{\partial p}{\partial r} \frac{\partial \psi}{\partial z} - \frac{\partial p}{\partial z} \frac{\partial \psi}{\partial r} = 0$$

Thus p also is a function of ψ alone

$$p = g(\psi) \qquad (4.5.7)$$

The surfaces $\psi = $ constant can then be identified with the magnetic surfaces, and the basic equation of the equilibrium becomes

$$\Delta^2 \psi + f f'(\psi) + r^2 g'(\psi) = 0 \qquad (4.5.8)$$

where the (') indicates differentiation with respect to ψ, and f and g are arbitrary functions of ψ. To proceed it is necessary to choose the arbitrary functions f and g, and reasonably simple solutions are obtained if f and g are chosen so that eq. (4.5.8) is linear, i.e. $g = a\psi$ or $a\psi^2$, $f = b\psi$. Of the two possible choices for pressure, the first leads to slightly simpler results, although it does make eq. (4.5.8) inhomogeneous, (4.5.8) reducing to

$$\frac{\partial^2\psi}{\partial z^2} + \frac{\partial^2\psi}{\partial r^2} - \frac{1}{r}\frac{\partial\psi}{\partial r} + b^2\psi = r^2 a \tag{4.5.9}$$

with solutions

$$\psi = \frac{a}{b^2}r^2 + \sum_k A(k)r B_1[\sqrt{(b^2-k^2)}\ r]\exp(ikz) \tag{4.5.10}$$

where B_1 is an arbitrary first-order Bessel function and the A are arbitrary constants. If the second choice is made for p, the term on the right of eq. (4.5.9) becomes $ar^2\psi$ and simple basic solutions are not easily obtained, although solutions for small a may be obtained by an expansion procedure. This set of solutions is great enough to satisfy arbitrary boundary conditions, and, in particular, solutions have been found which satisfy boundary conditions on a torus of circular cross section (LAING et al., cf. LÜST and SCHLÜTER).

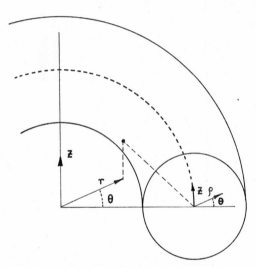

FIG. 4.7. Coordinates used for describing equilibria in a toroidal tube.

It has also been shown that solutions fitting into a torus of circular cross section can be obtained by expanding in inverse powers of the aspect ratio (WHITEMAN). The first approximation then becomes

$$\psi = J_0[\sqrt{(a+b^2)}\rho] \tag{4.5.11}$$

where ρ is the distance from the centre of the minor circle in the torus.

Several other particular solutions have been found. GRAD has stressed the equivalence between magnetohydrostatic equilibria and the steady flow of an incompressible fluid, and has used this analogy to discuss the data needed to specify a configuration. KRUSKAL and KULSRUD have considered the general topological properties of the toroidal configuration.

5

6. REALIZATION OF MAGNETIC CONFINEMENT

The possibility of producing a magnetohydrodynamically confined plasma has stimulated an enormous research effort in plasma physics. The ultimate target of most of this research has been the controlled release of the nuclear energy obtainable by fusing light nuclei. It is known that many exothermic nuclear reactions with high intrinsic cross sections are inhibited at low

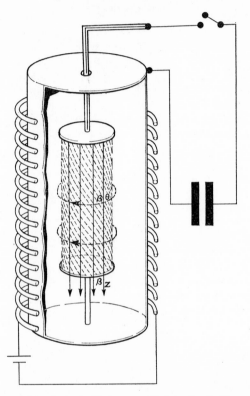

Fig. 4.8. The straight pinched discharge. External windings supply axial stabilizing field B_z. Voltage from capacitor bank applied between electrodes produces axial current I_z and azimuthal collapsing field B_θ.

energies by the Coulomb repulsion between the like charges on the nuclei, and at low energies the reaction cross sections have the form

$$\sigma(w) = (A/w)\exp\{-B/\sqrt{w}\}$$

where w is the energy in the centre of mass system.

The most promising reactions are those between the isotopes of hydrogen:

$$D+D \begin{array}{l} \nearrow \text{He}^3+\text{n}+3\cdot27 \text{ MeV} \\ \\ \searrow \text{T}+\text{H}+4\cdot03 \text{ MeV} \end{array}$$

and

$$D+T \rightarrow He^4 + n + 17 \cdot 6 \text{ MeV}$$

For the first reaction, the branching ratio $\simeq \frac{1}{2}$, and the constants A, B are

$$A_{DD} = 182 \text{ barns–keV} = 182 \times 10^{-24} \text{ cms–keV.}$$
$$B_{DD} = 44 \cdot 24 \text{ (keV)}^{1/2};$$

while

$$A_{DT} = 2 \cdot 2 \times 10^4 \text{ barns–keV,}$$
$$B_{DT} = 44 \cdot 24 \text{ (keV)}^{1/2}$$

With these cross sections, the reaction rates in a hot gas, $\frac{1}{2}n_D^2 \langle \sigma v(T) \rangle_{DD}$, $n_D n_T \langle \sigma v \rangle_{DT}$ may be calculated by integrating over a Maxwell distribution, thus

$$\langle \sigma v \rangle_{DD} \simeq 2 \cdot 33 \times 10^{-14} T^{-2/3} \exp - (18 \cdot 8 T^{-1/3}) \text{ cm}^3 \text{ sec}^{-1}$$

$$\langle \sigma v \rangle_{DT} \simeq 3 \cdot 7 \times 10^{-12} T^{-2/3} \exp - (19 \cdot 9 T^{-1/3}) \text{ cm}^3 \text{ sec}^{-1}$$

T being in keV. The power released by thermonuclear reactions at any temperature is then easily calculated, and is easily seen to be negligible until $T \sim$ a few keV. To obtain a net energy release, the power released by nuclear reactions must exceed the essential energy losses of the system. The most certain of these is bremsstrahlung, the radiation produced as an electron is accelerated in the presence of an ion, and is

$$P_r \simeq 5 \cdot 35 \times 10^{-31} n^2 \sqrt{T} \quad W \text{ cm}^{-3}$$

n being the electron (or ion) density.

It is easily shown that $P_n > P_{\text{rad}}$ requires for $D-D$, $T \geqslant 40 \text{ keV}$, and for $D-T$, $T > 4 \text{ keV}$.

It is, however, not enough to reach these temperatures; the gas must be held there until enough energy has been produced to replace that used in heating it, i.e. until ~ 1 per cent burn-up has occurred. This puts a condition on the product of number density n and confinement time τ, since the total energy produced per unit volume $= (P_n - P_{\text{rad}})\tau = f_1(T)n^2\tau$, while the thermal energy $Q = 3nkT$, hence the condition becomes $n\tau > 3kT/f_1(T)$ $\simeq 10^{16} \text{ cm}^{-3} \text{ sec for DD}$, $10^{14} \text{ cm}^{-3} \text{ sec for DT}$. So far, magnetic containment seems to be the most promising method of realizing these rather improbable conditions at modest pressure and controllable rates of energy release, and a great deal of ingenuity has gone into inventing magnetic containing configurations. Most of these, however, have been bedevilled by instabilities of some sort, and little evidence has yet been obtained for successful containment.

The simplest configuration is probably the linear pinch, a high current gas discharge produced by discharging a condenser bank between two electrodes at either end of a cylindrical vessel. While such a device does not *contain* the plasma, it compresses it axially. If the current rises rapidly the collapse is dominated by plasma inertia and is a dynamic process, while if the rise is slow, the compression may be *adiabatic*, the inertia may be negligible and the plasma passes through a series of equilibrium configurations.

An example of such a sequence of configurations is seen in the work of BURKHARDT and LOVBERG, in which the plasma initially contained an axial magnetic field B_z, and was compressed by a rapidly rising current. The discharge current of 250 kA was produced in deuterium at a pressure of 60 μ, in a tube of diameter 13 cm, length 61 cm, the time to peak current being 6 μ sec. The magnetic field was measured by a set of magnetic probes, and the pressure deduced from the assumption of magnetohydrostatic equilibrium. The results displayed in Fig. 6.14 at least show a positive

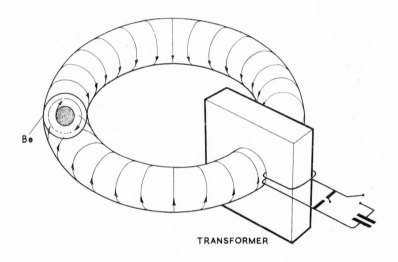

FIG. 4.9. The toroidal pinch. External windings supply stabilizing field B_z along torus. Capacitor bank discharged through pulsed transformer to produce current j_z and collapsing field B_θ.

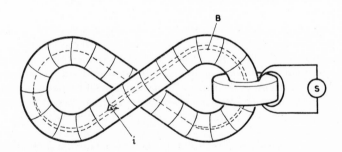

FIG. 4.10. The stellarator. D.C. confining field produced by external windings on tube, which to satisfy equilibrium requirements must be deformed into a figure of eight. The magnetic axis and one other field line demonstrate the rotational transform, ι. Transformer produces an axial current for heating plasma.

pressure. This is peaked in the current layer at intermediate periods where the plasma is locally heated by the current.

The *toroidal* pinch is a confining configuration in which the discharge is produced by induction, the gas forming the secondary of a pulse transformer. Experiments have been performed in this geometry of much longer duration than those involving electrodes, an example being the ZETA experiment (BUTT). This was a large toroidal vessel (bore 1 m, mean circumference

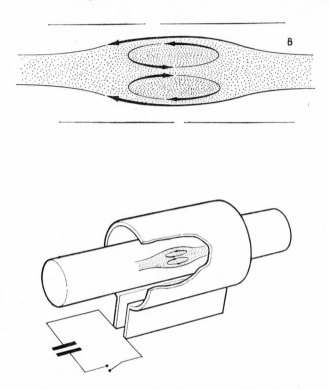

FIG. 4.11. Fast collapsing plasma, the θ pinch. Ringing condenser bank in primary induces B_z pointing to right in centre of plasma on first half cycle, and collapses with B pointing left on second half cycle.

10 m), containing $\frac{1}{8}\,\mu$ deuterium in which a current of 180 kA was induced, rising to its maximum in ~ 1 msec and persisting for ~ 3 msec. The magnetic profiles were again measured by magnetic probes and the results compared with simple magnetohydrodynamic equilibrium configurations (Fig. 4.12) (LEES and RUSBRIDGE).

Although the discharge persisted for a considerable time, the electron temperature remained modest, 25 eV, as determined from the excitation of highly ionized impurity atoms OV and NV, and knowing the energy content and the rate of energy input, the energy containment time is found at $100\,\mu$ sec. A similar containment time for impurity ions is suggested by a study of the dynamics of the excitation present. At the same time, the Doppler width of impurity lines has been measured, and when interpreted as a thermal broadening demands temperatures of 500 eV. This is consistent with the presence of violent turbulent motions within the plasma, and casts doubt on the interpretation of magnetic probe data.

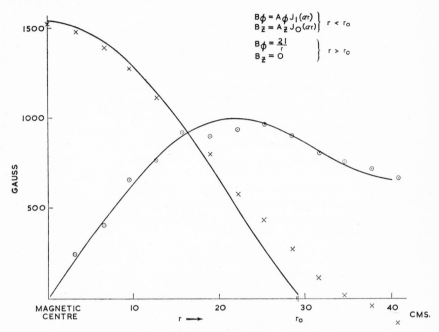

FIG. 4.12. Magnetic fields in a slow toroidal pinch. Axial field B_z and azimuthal field B as measured in $ZETA$. Solid curves show simple theoretical equilibrium. (Lees and Rusbridge, *Proc. 4th Int. Conf. on Ion. Phen. in Gases*, 1960).

A more sophisticated device is the stellarator (SPITZER) in which the magnetic fields are produced by currents in external conductors. Unlike the pinch, the stellarator may be operated with approximately vacuum fields. A simple toroidal solenoid will not, as we have seen, produce a confining field; however, if such a solenoid is twisted into a figure-eight, the magnetic field lines do not close on themselves and a confining configuration is produced. Such configurations have been described by the rotational transform, i.e. the angular displacement of the intersection of the field line with a fixed surface normal to the torus-axis on going once around the major axis (Fig. 4.10). For irrational transforms, any magnetic line traces out a magnetic surface. Detailed experiments were performed in the B.1 stellarator (COOR). This was a figure-eight tube, 480 cm in length, and 5 cm in diameter, in which fields of 30 kg were produced for 30 millisec. Ionization was produced first by a pulse of h.f. and subsequently by a transformer induced current of less than 2000 A in low pressure of $0.5\,\mu$ hydrogen, deuterium or helium.

The electron density was measured by the phase shift of 8·6 cm μwaves, and the temperature from spectral lines. It was found that the electron density dropped in 2 msec from 5×10^{13} (complete ionization) to 10^{12}, and then after 1–30 msec, depending on the confining field, vanished rather suddenly. This indicates the action of some cooperative loss process, since simple diffusion through the magnetic field would have resulted in a plasma life of ~ 1 sec so that no loss of plasma should have been expected until the field disappeared. On the other hand, if the ohmic current attained such a value that the rotational transform was eliminated a sudden drop in current and plasma density occurred. This suggests that the basic confining process had been correctly described.

More apparent success has been obtained with dynamic devices, in which a rapid compression of the plasma has suddenly heated it (KOLB; BOYER et al.). Much interest has been shown in the axial compression devices, or thetatron, in which a cylindrical plasma is compressed by a rapidly rising axial field, the plasma being allowed to escape out of the ends, which may be extremely narrow. It appears that the alternating nature of the applied field may result in a reversed axial field being produced at the centre, the resulting configuration being a collapsing torus—like the Hill vortex (KOLB; OSOVETS). In this device the plasma loss seems not to exceed the expected end losses—which may be large—and all the symptoms of an extremely hot gas appear, although the same hopes were raised by early work with the simple pinch, only to be proved false when more detailed knowledge was available.

BIBLIOGRAPHY

Introductions to Magnetohydrodynamics are
1. ALFVÉN H. (1950). *Cosmical Electrodynamics* Oxford University Press, London.
2. COWLING, T. G. (1957). *Magnetohydrodynamics* Interscience, New York.
Less accessible, but more detailed are
3. SYROVATSKII, C. J. (1957). *Usp. Fisz. Nauk.* **62**, 247.
4. GRAD, H. and colleagues.
   N.Y.O. 6486. Notes on Magnetohydrodynamics. Inst. of Math. Sci.
   N.Y.U. I–VIII (1956–58).
A selection of research papers with a strong magnetohydrodynamic flavour is
   FRENKIEL F. N. and SEARS, W. R. (1960). *Rev. Mod. Phys.* **32**, 695 *et seq.*
Particular references are
   ALPHER, R. A., HURWITZ, H., JOHNSON, R. H., and WHITE, D. R. (1960). *Rev. Mod. Phys.* **32**.
   LUNDQUIST, S. (1952). *Ark. f. Fys.* **5**, 297.
   DOLDER, K. and HIDE, R. (1958). *Nature* (Lond.) **181**, 1116; (1960). *Rev. Mod. Phys.* **32**, 770.
   FERRARO, V. C. A. (1954) *Astrophys. J.* **119**, 407.
   GRAD, H. and RUBIN, H. (1959). *Proc. 2nd Geneva Conf.* Vol. **31**, 190.
   LAING, E. W., ROBERTS, S. J., and WHIPPLE, R. T. P. (1959). *J. Nucl. Energ.* C. Plasma Physics. Acc. and Therm. Research. **1**, 49.
   LÜST, R. and SCHLÜTER, A. (1957). *Z. Naturforsch.* **12**, 850.
   WHITEMAN, K. (1960) A.E.R.E. *Report* R.3135, Atomic Energy Research Establishment, Harwell. H.M. Stationery Office.
   KRUSKAL, M. D. and KULRSUD, R. M. (1958). *Phys. Fluids* **1**, 265.
   TUCK, J. L. *Proc. 2nd Geneva Conf.* P.1860; *Progress in Nuclear Energy*, Vol. 1, 66, Pergamon Press, London.

BURKHARDT, L. C. and LOVBERG, R. H. *Proc. 2nd Geneva Conf. Prog. Nuc. En.* XI. **1**, 405.

BUTT, E. P., CARRUTHERS, R., MITCHELL, J., PEASE, R. S., THONEMANN, P. C., BIRD, M. A., BLEARS, J., and HARTELL, E. R. (1959) *Proc. 2nd Geneva Conf.* P1519.—*Prog. Nuc. En.* XI.

LEES, D. J. and RUSBRIDGE, M. G. (1960). *Proc. 4th Int. Conf. on Ionization Phenomena on Gases*, p.954 North Holland.

SPITZER, L. (1958). *Phys. Fluids* **1**, 253.

COOR, T., ELLIS, R. A., HEALD, M. A., KRANZ, K. A., and CUNNINGHAM, S. P. (1959) *Proc. 2nd Geneva Conf. Prog. Nuc. En.* XI. **1**, 125.

KOLB, A. (1960) *Rev. Mod. Phys.* **32**, 748. *Proc. 2nd Geneva Conf.* P/345.

BOYER, K., ELMORE, W. C., LITTLE, E. M. and QUINN, W. E. *Proc. 2nd Geneva Conf.* P/356.

OSOVETZ, S. M., NASEDKIN, Y. F., PAVLOV, E. I., PETROV, Y. F., and SCHEDRIN, N. I. *Proc. 2nd Geneva Conf.* P/225.

CHAPTER 5

MAGNETOHYDRODYNAMICS II

ONLY a few of the possible magnetohydrodynamic equilibria have been investigated, and even less is known about the magnetohydrodynamics even of ideal fluids; however some of the general properties of the system and a few important solutions are known, including the generalization of the theory of sound.

1. GENERAL PROPERTIES

If the magnetic field retains such a form that it can preserve equilibrium, i.e. if $\mathbf{j} \times \mathbf{B}$ is derivable from a potential, most of the results of normal hydrodynamics hold. This is not generally true, and many of the standard hydrodynamical theories fail, e.g.

(a) *Bernoulli's Theorem for Steady Flow*

The equations of motion may be written

$$\rho\left\{\frac{\partial \mathbf{v}}{\partial t} + \boldsymbol{\psi} \times \mathbf{v} + \boldsymbol{\nabla}(\tfrac{1}{2}v^2)\right\} = -\boldsymbol{\nabla}\left(p + \frac{B^2}{8\pi}\right) + \frac{1}{4\pi}(\mathbf{B} \cdot \boldsymbol{\nabla})\mathbf{B} \qquad (5.1.1)$$

where $\boldsymbol{\psi} = \text{curl } \mathbf{v}$ is the vorticity. The last term may be written

$$\frac{1}{4\pi}(\mathbf{B} \cdot \boldsymbol{\nabla})\mathbf{B} = (B^2/4\pi R)\mathbf{n} + \mathbf{b}(\mathbf{b} \cdot \boldsymbol{\nabla})(B^2/8\pi)$$

where $\mathbf{b}$ and $\mathbf{n}$ are the unit tangent and principal normal to the field line, and R its radius of curvature. For steady flow of a uniform incompressible fluid the scalar product of eq. (5.1.1) with $\mathbf{v}$ may be written

$$\mathbf{v} \cdot \boldsymbol{\nabla}\left(p + \frac{B^2}{8\pi} + \tfrac{1}{2}\rho v^2\right) = \mathbf{v} \cdot \mathbf{n}\frac{B^2}{4\pi R} + \mathbf{v} \cdot \mathbf{b}\mathbf{b} \cdot \boldsymbol{\nabla}\left(\frac{B^2}{8\pi}\right) \qquad (5.1.2)$$

and only if the R.H.S. vanishes does Bernoulli's theorem hold.

(b) *Kelvin's Circulation Theorem*

Again, for uniform incompressible fluid, the curl of (5.1.1) yields

$$\begin{aligned}
\rho\,\text{curl}\left(\frac{\partial \mathbf{v}}{\partial t} + (\mathbf{v} \cdot \boldsymbol{\nabla})\mathbf{v}\right) &= \rho\left\{\frac{D\boldsymbol{\psi}}{Dt} + \boldsymbol{\psi}\,\text{div}\,\mathbf{v} - (\boldsymbol{\psi} \cdot \boldsymbol{\nabla})\mathbf{v}\right\} \\
&= \frac{1}{4\pi}\text{curl}\,(\mathbf{B} \cdot \boldsymbol{\nabla})\mathbf{B} = \frac{1}{c}(\mathbf{B} \cdot \boldsymbol{\nabla})\mathbf{j} - (\mathbf{j} \cdot \boldsymbol{\nabla})\mathbf{B}
\end{aligned} \qquad (5.1.3)$$

Only if the R.H.S. vanishes is the flux of vorticity across a surface, or the line integral of the flow around a closed loop, a constant. The failure of this conservation theorem is most important. As we shall see, it permits shear waves to be transmitted through the fluid.

Although electric charges do not play an important role in magnetohydrodynamics, a polarization can occur and the motion can produce a charge separation.

From current continuity in steady conditions, Ohm's law implies

$$0 = \operatorname{div}\mathbf{j} = \sigma\left[\operatorname{div}\mathbf{E} + \operatorname{div}\left(\frac{\mathbf{v}}{c}\times\mathbf{B}\right)\right] = \sigma\left[4\pi q + \frac{\mathbf{v}}{c}.\operatorname{curl}\mathbf{B} - \frac{\mathbf{B}}{c}.\operatorname{curl}\mathbf{v}\right]$$

(5.1.4)

hence

$$q + \frac{1}{c^2}\mathbf{v}.\mathbf{j} = \frac{1}{4\pi c}\mathbf{B}.\boldsymbol{\psi}$$

2. INCOMPRESSIBLE FLOW—PARTICULAR SOLUTIONS

(a) *Parallel Stationary Flow*

A particular steady solution for the motion of an incompressible uniform fluid is

$$\mathbf{v} = \frac{\mathbf{B}}{\sqrt{4\pi\rho}}$$

(5.2.1)

the pressure satisfying

$$p + \tfrac{1}{2}\rho v^2 = \text{constant}$$

(5.2.2)

for eq. (5.1.1) implies

$$(\operatorname{curl}\mathbf{v})\times\mathbf{v} = -\frac{1}{\rho}\boldsymbol{\nabla}(p + \tfrac{1}{2}\rho v^2) + \frac{1}{4\pi\rho}(\operatorname{curl}\mathbf{B})\times\mathbf{B}$$

while the magnetic field is unaltered by velocities parallel to itself.

(b) *Hartmann Flow—The Electromagnetic gauge and the Electromagnetic Pump*

If a conducting fluid flows with a velocity $\mathbf{v}$ across a magnetic field, while an electric field is applied at right angles to the magnetic field and the flow, then, in general, a current $\mathbf{j} = \sigma(\mathbf{E} + \mathbf{v}\times\mathbf{B}/c)$ will flow and a force $\mathbf{j}\times\mathbf{B}$ act on the fluid. This force may be used to drive the fluid against a pressure gradient. It is so used in the electromagnetic pump, a device developed to drive liquid metals and applied in the liquid sodium cooling circuits of advanced nuclear reactors. Conversely, if no current flows, an electric field $\mathbf{E} = -(\mathbf{v}/c)\times\mathbf{B}$ must appear across the fluid and a voltage must appear across the tube proportional to the flow of fluid through the tube. This effect is now used in the electromagnetic flowmeter, which is used to measure both the flow of liquid metals and the flow of blood through capillaries. It was first used by Faraday in an unsuccessful attempt to measure the flow in the Thames. Since he used the earth's field as his magnetic field, the expected potential difference was $< 0\cdot1$ V, hence it is not surprising that the attempt failed.

This flow, which was first studied by HARTMANN in liquid mercury, is of sufficient interest to be analysed in slightly more detail. Consider first Hartmann's problem; a viscous incompressible fluid of finite conductivity flows in the OX direction in a flat tube effectively infinite in the OZ direction, along which there is a magnetic field B. Between the walls, separated by a distance $2L$, there is an electric field E. For steady flow we have (j Gaussian)

$$-\frac{\partial p}{\partial x} + \mu \frac{\partial^2 v}{\partial y^2} = -\frac{1}{c}Bj = -\frac{\sigma B}{c}\left(E - \frac{vB}{c}\right)$$

where σ is the conductivity and μ the viscosity. This may be written, introducing $v_0 = Ec/B$,

$$\frac{\partial^2 v}{\partial y^2} = \frac{\sigma B^2}{\mu c^2}\left[v(y) - v_0 + \frac{c^2}{\sigma B^2}\frac{\partial p}{\partial x}\right] \qquad (5.2.3)$$

which is satisfied by

$$v = \left(v_0 - \frac{c^2}{\sigma B^2}\frac{\partial p}{\partial x}\right)\left(1 - \frac{\cosh Ny/L}{\cosh N}\right) \qquad (5.2.4)$$

where $N^2 = (\sigma B^2/\mu c^2)L^2$. When B, and with it N, vanishes, this reduces to

$$v = \frac{L^2}{2\mu}\left(-\frac{\partial p}{\partial x}\right)\left(1 - \frac{y^2}{L^2}\right)$$

plane Poiseuille flow. If we introduce $v_p = (L^2/\mu)(-\partial p/\partial x)$, eq. (5.2.4) may be written

$$v = \left(v_0 + \frac{v_p}{N^2}\right)\left(1 - \frac{\cosh Ny/L}{\cosh N}\right)$$

and the total flow through the tube

$$\bar{v}A = \frac{A}{2L}\int_{-L}^{L} v\,dy = \frac{A}{2}\cdot\int_{-1}^{1} v\frac{dy}{L}$$

becomes

$$\bar{v}A = (v_0 + v_p/N^2)\left(1 - \frac{\tanh N}{N}\right)\cdot A \qquad (5.2.5)$$

If we consider a numerical example here, some of the difficulties of magnetic pumping are obvious. Consider, for example, the problem of driving a column of mercury through a tube $\sim 0\cdot 2$ cm in width and 1 cm long against a pressure head of 1 atm. Since for mercury $\sigma \simeq 10^{18}$, $\mu \simeq 0\cdot 01$, the Poiseuille velocity $v_p \simeq (0\cdot 01/0\cdot 01)$. $10^6 \simeq 10^6$. In a magnetic field of ~ 5000 g, $N^2 \simeq 250$ and $N \simeq 16$, the electric field needed to produce a positive flow is $E = (B/c)(v_p/N^2) \simeq 0\cdot 2$ V/cm and the potential across the tube is ~ 0.04 V. If the potential is increased by 10 per cent, the mean flow velocity becomes $\sim 4 \times 10^3$ cm/sec, the current density ~ 2000 A/cm^2. The power used is ~ 80 W/cm^2 and the internal efficiency ~ 10 per cent. The internal efficiency $\sim (v/v_0)$ can be improved by increasing the electric field, but this increases the velocity. However, even at this low field, the Reynold's number is $\sim 10^5$ and the flow is turbulent. The difficulty with this device

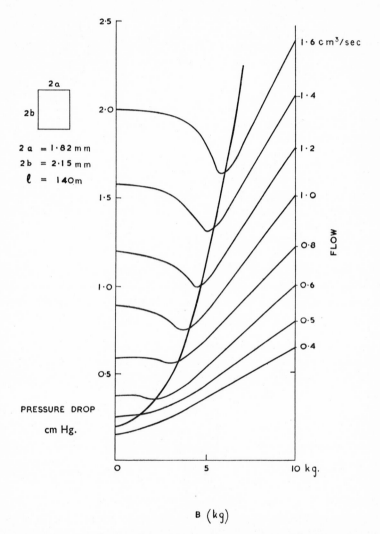

FIG. 5.1. Flow of mercury across a magnetic field. Curves showing pressure as a function of magnetic field strength at fixed rate of flow through a tube of dimensions shown. Flow is turbulent to left of parabolic curve, which demonstrates inhibition of turbulence by a magnetic field (Hartmann and Lazarus, *Kgl. Dansk. Vid. Sel. Mat-fys. Med.* **15**, 7, 1937).

lies in its low impedance. High d.c. power is required at an extremely low voltage and it is difficult to realize an efficient power source.

Although there are serious difficulties in realizing an efficient electromagnetic pump, HARTMANN showed that the basic physical processes had been correctly described. This he did by pumping mercury at a measured rate through a tube crossing a magnetic field and measuring the pressure gradient along the tube as a function of the flow speed and the magnetic field strength.

Since his tubes had insulating walls, he could not make use of eq. (5.2.5) directly; instead, since no net current could flow through the plasma, an electric field had to appear across the tube. This modified the pressure gradient to

$$-\frac{\partial p}{\partial x} = vA \; \frac{\mu}{L^2} \; \frac{N^2 \tanh N}{N - \tanh N}$$

a function which $\sim N^2$ for small N; $\sim N$ for large N. He found good agreement between theory and experiment for high fields and small flow, but at high flow speeds, the pressure gradient became too high, a phenomenon which he associated with the onset of turbulence (cf. Fig. 5.1); thus as a by-product of his experiment he learned that a magnetic field can inhibit the onset of turbulence in a conducting fluid.

3. ALFVÉN WAVES

An incompressible fluid will not propagate oscillations, since longitudinal waves require compression, and transverse waves which require the transmission of vorticity through the fluid are excluded by Kelvin's theorem. In magnetohydrodynamic flow, however, Kelvin's theorem does not hold, and transverse waves can propagate. These are the oscillations discovered by Alfvén, one of the first characteristic magnetohydrodynamic phenomena to be understood. Alfvén waves may be analysed as follows. Consider a uniform, incompressible, perfectly conducting fluid at rest in a uniform magnetic field $\mathbf{B}$, and let this be perturbed by the introduction of a small velocity $\mathbf{v}$ and a small disturbance of the magnetic field $\mathbf{B}'$. The linearized equations of motion become

$$\rho \frac{\partial \mathbf{v}}{\partial t} = -\nabla p + \frac{1}{4\pi}(\text{curl } \mathbf{B}') \times \mathbf{B} \tag{5.3.1}$$

and

$$\frac{\partial \mathbf{B}'}{\partial t} - (\mathbf{B} \cdot \nabla)\mathbf{v} = 0 \tag{5.3.2}$$

The magnetic field perturbation can be eliminated leaving

$$\rho \frac{\partial^2 \mathbf{v}}{\partial t^2} = -\nabla\left(\frac{\partial p}{\partial t}\right) + \frac{1}{4\pi}(\text{curl}(\mathbf{B} \cdot \nabla \mathbf{v})) \times \mathbf{B}$$

and the pressure eliminated by taking the curl, leaving

$$\frac{\partial^2 \psi}{\partial t^2} = \frac{1}{4\pi\rho}(\mathbf{B}.\boldsymbol{\nabla})^2\psi \tag{5.3.3}$$

If we substitute a plane wave $\psi \sim \exp(i\omega t - i\,\mathbf{k}.\mathbf{r})$ into eq. (5.3.3), the phase velocity $V = \omega/k = C_A \cos\theta$, where $\cos\theta$ is the angle between $\mathbf{k}$ and $\mathbf{B}$, and $C_A = (B^2/4\pi\rho)^{1/2}$ is the Alfvén speed. The waves actually propagate only along the magnetic field, and may be envisaged as elastic oscillations of the frozen-in field, the magnetic field providing the elasticity and the fluid the inertia.

4. COMPRESSIBLE HARTMANN FLOW, AND SOME APPLICATIONS

Although realistic representations of the flow of a compressible conducting fluid are scarce, a few solutions are known. A particularly simple and important flow is the Hartmann flow of a compressible fluid, a flow which is not

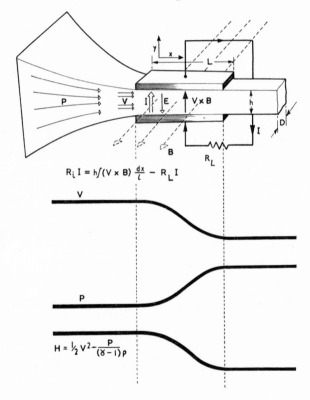

DIRECT CONVERSION

Fig. 5.2. Direct conversion of kinetic to electrical energy. Flow of conducting fluid across field $\mathbf{B}$ induces Lorentz force $(\boldsymbol{v}) \times \mathbf{B}$ on charges and current I in load resistor R_L. Pressure increases, but total energy of fluid decreases.

merely fairly tractable but has important possible applications in the direct conversion of thermal energy into electricity, and in the use of plasma as a propulsive element. We shall now analyse these processes.

(a) *Direct Conversion*

One of the more interesting possible applications of magnetohydrodynamics lies in the direct conversion of the thermal energy in a gas into electric energy. In this, the voltage which is used as a measure of flow in the electromagnetic flowmeter is used to drive a current through an external circuit, thus releasing useful electric energy directly. Hot rapidly moving gas, e.g. from a jet engine, may be made electrically conducting by "seeding", i.e. the addition of small amounts of readily ionized material such as sodium (for example, a partial pressure of 1 mm of sodium in a gas at $\sim 2000°$K and normal density gives a resistivity of about 3 Ω-cm). If the conducting gas is then passed through a non-conducting tube immersed in a transverse magnetic field, there is no effect on the flow, since no currents can flow transverse to the field. However, if conducting plates are let into the wall, and connected through an external resistor, a current will flow, the gas will do work against the field, its speed will be reduced, and energy will be extracted appearing in the external circuit.

The energy in the external circuit $R_2 I^2$ is simply related to the flow velocity, the magnetic field strength and the resistivity of the fluid. The external current is given by

$$R_2 I = V = ED$$

where D is the separation between the electrodes. The current through the gas is given by

$$I = \int j \, dA = H . \int j \, dx = A_1 \frac{1}{L} \int j \, dx = \frac{A_1}{\eta} . \left[E + \frac{1}{L} \int \frac{u}{c} \times B \, dx \right]$$

$$= \frac{A_1}{\eta . D} . \left[ED + \frac{D}{L} \int \left(\frac{u}{c} \times B \right) dx \right] = \frac{1}{R_1} \left[-V + \frac{D}{L} \int \left(\frac{u}{c} \times B \right) dx \right]$$

where R_1 is the resistance of the conducting gas between the electrodes. Hence

$$(R_1 + R_2) I = \frac{D}{L} \int_0^L \left(\frac{u}{c} \times B \right) dx = D \left\langle \frac{u}{c} \times B \right\rangle$$

where L is the length of the electrode in the flow direction. Thus, the gas acts as a generator with internal resistance $R_1 = \eta D / A$ producing a voltage $V_1 = D \langle (u/c) \times B \rangle 300$ volts.

This voltage can be considerable; for example $V \simeq 900$ volts for a flow velocity of 6×10^5 [Mach 2 for a gas of mass number 30, typical of combustion products and a temperature of $2000°$], in a field of 15,000 gauss and in a 10 cm tube.

If any considerable current flows through the seeded gas, breakdown will occur, and we must expect an arc to form, in which the electron temperature is determined by ionization processes at $\sim 1\text{--}2$ eV, and the electrical resistivity becomes a function of electron temperature alone, $\eta \simeq \cdot 07 T^{3/2}$ Ω-cm (T in eV) $\simeq \cdot 07$ Ω-cm and for 10 cm square electrodes $R_1 \simeq 0 \cdot 07$. Into a matched load, we could then get a current of $\sim 6{,}500$ A, and a power of $11 \cdot 7$ MW. If the density of the incoming gas is $\sim 10^{-4}$ g/cm^3, this is an efficiency of ~ 50 per cent.

To examine the process in more detail let us consider a compressible gas, with initial density, velocity and pressure, ρ_0, u_0, p_0, and a resistivity, η, flowing in a magnetic field between electrodes extending from $x = 0$ to $x = L$, and let us further assume that the current flowing between the electrodes is not great enough seriously to alter the applied magnetic field B_0. The flow, which for present purposes is assumed laminar, steady and one-dimensional, is determined by the following relations: (j and E in e.m.u.)

$$\left.\begin{array}{l} \rho u = f = \text{const} \quad \text{(continuity of mass)} \\[2mm] \dfrac{\mathrm{d}}{\mathrm{d}x}(fu) + \dfrac{\mathrm{d}p}{\mathrm{d}x} + Bj(x) = 0 \quad \text{(momentum)} \\[2mm] \dfrac{\gamma}{\gamma-1}p\dfrac{\mathrm{d}u}{\mathrm{d}x} + \dfrac{1}{\gamma-1}u\dfrac{\mathrm{d}p}{\mathrm{d}x} = \eta j^2 \quad \text{(energy)} \\[4mm] \text{and} \\[1mm] \eta j = [E+uB] \quad \text{(Ohm's law)} \end{array}\right\} \tag{5.4.1}$$

If we now introduce as dependent variable $I = H \int j \, \mathrm{d}x$, the current, and as independent variable u, the velocity, then the pressure and the dependent variable x may be eliminated, for from (5.4.1)

$$fu + p + \frac{B \cdot I}{H} = (fu_0 + p_0)$$

and

$$\frac{\gamma}{\gamma-1}p + \frac{u}{\gamma-1}\frac{\mathrm{d}p}{\mathrm{d}u} = (E+uB_0)\frac{1}{H}\frac{\mathrm{d}I}{\mathrm{d}u}$$

Hence

$$\frac{\mathrm{d}}{\mathrm{d}u}\left(\left[E + \frac{\gamma}{\gamma-1}uB_0\right]\frac{I}{H}\right) = \frac{\gamma}{\gamma-1}(fu_0 + p_0) - \frac{\gamma+1}{\gamma-1}fu$$

and

$$\left[E + \frac{\gamma}{\gamma-1}uB_0\right]\frac{I}{H} = \frac{\gamma}{\gamma-1}(fu_0 + p_0)(u - u_0) - \frac{1}{2}\frac{\gamma+1}{\gamma-1}f(u^2 - u_0^2)$$

or on introducing the initial Mach number,

$$M^2 = \frac{\rho u_0{}^2}{\gamma p_0} = \frac{f u_0}{\gamma p_0}$$

$$\left[E + \frac{\gamma}{\gamma-1} u B_0\right]\frac{I}{H} = \frac{\gamma+1}{2(\gamma-1)} f u_0{}^2 \left[\frac{2}{\gamma+1}\frac{M^2-1}{M^2} - \left(1 - \frac{u}{u_0}\right)\right]\left(1 - \frac{u}{u_0}\right)$$

$$(5.4.2)$$

Since I and $E + [\gamma/(\gamma-1)]u.B_0 > E + u.B_0 > 0$, and $u < u_0$; $M^2 > 1$, hence, the incoming flow must be supersonic; further, the electrode must end before the velocity has dropped below u_{min}.

$$u_0 - u_{min} = \frac{2}{\gamma+1}\frac{M^2-1}{M^2}$$

and I drops to zero. For some value of u/u_0, the current has its maximum value. This can be discovered by differentiating eq. (5.4.2). Before doing so, however, we must eliminate E, which is determined by the current, external resistance R_2, and electrode separation D by $E = -I(R_2/D)$, thus obtaining a quadratic relation for I

$$\left[\frac{\gamma}{\gamma-1} u B_0 - \frac{R_2 H}{D}\frac{I}{H}\right]\cdot\frac{I}{H} = \frac{\gamma+1}{2(\gamma-1)} f u_0{}^2 \left[\frac{2}{\gamma+1}\frac{M^2-1}{M^2} - \left(1 - \frac{u}{u_0}\right)\right]\left(1 - \frac{u}{u_0}\right)$$

Introducing a change of notation,

$$Z = \frac{2\gamma}{\gamma+1}\frac{B_0{}^2}{f u_0}\frac{I}{B_0 H} = \frac{2\gamma}{\gamma+1}\frac{I}{I_0}$$

$$w = 1 - \frac{u}{u_0}, \quad \alpha = R_2\frac{\gamma^2-1}{2\gamma^2}\frac{H}{D}\frac{f}{B_0{}^2} = \frac{1}{4}\frac{R_2}{R_0}, \quad \text{and} \quad \beta = \frac{2}{\gamma+1}\frac{M^2-1}{M^2} \quad (5.4.3)$$

$$(1 - w - \alpha Z)Z = (\beta - w)w \qquad (5.4.4)$$

At its maximum Z_M; $w = \frac{1}{2}(\beta + Z_M)$, and

$$Z_M = \frac{2-\beta}{1+4\alpha}\left[1 - \left\{1 - \beta^2\frac{(1+4\alpha)}{(\beta-2)^2}\right\}^{\frac{1}{2}}\right]$$

where the sign of the root is determined by the condition that $Z = 0$ at $\beta = 0$, or $w = 0$,

$$I_M = I_0\frac{\gamma M^2+1}{\gamma M^2}\frac{1 - \sqrt{\left[1 - \left(\frac{M^2-1}{\gamma M^2+1}\right)^2\left(1 + \frac{R_2}{R_0}\right)\right]}}{1 + \frac{R_2}{R_0}}$$

We may now attempt to determine R_2 so that the extracted power is a maximum; so that

6

$$P = R_2 I^2 = R_0 I_0^2 \left(\frac{\gamma M^2 + 1}{\gamma M^2}\right)^2 \frac{R_2/R_0}{(1 + R_2/R_0)^2} \left\{1 - \sqrt{\left[1 - \left(\frac{M^2 - 1}{\gamma M^2 + 1}\right)^2 \left(1 + \frac{R_2}{R_0}\right)\right]}\right\}^2$$

is a maximum.

If we replace R_2/R_0 by

$$y = \sqrt{\left[1 - \left(\frac{M^2 - 1}{\gamma M^2 + 1}\right)^2 \left(1 + \frac{R_2}{R_0}\right)\right]}$$

$$\frac{R_2}{R_0} = \left\{\left(\frac{\gamma M^2 + 1}{M^2 - 1}\right)^2 (1 - y^2) - 1\right\}$$

and

$$P(y) = R_0 I_0^2 \left(\frac{M^2 - 1}{\gamma M^2}\right)^2 \left\{1 - \left(\frac{M^2 - 1}{\gamma M^2 + 1}\right)^2 - y^2\right\} \frac{1}{(1 + y)^2}$$

is a decreasing function of y, having its maximum at $y = 0$, where

$$P_M = R_0 I_0^2 \frac{\gamma + 1}{\gamma^2} \left(\frac{M^2 - 1}{\gamma M^2 + 1}\right)^2 \frac{(\gamma - 1)M^2 + 2}{M^2} \tag{5.4.5}$$

$$R_2/R_0 = \frac{(\gamma + 1)M^2\{(\gamma - 1)M^2 + 2\}}{(M^2 - 1)^2} \tag{5.4.6}$$

$$I/I_0 = \frac{(M^2 - 1)^2}{\gamma M^2 (\gamma M^2 + 1)} \tag{5.4.7}$$

P_M is a steadily increasing function of M, and has as its maximum

$$P = \frac{\gamma^2 - 1}{\gamma^4} R_0 I_0^2 = \frac{\gamma^2 - 1}{\gamma^4} \cdot \frac{1}{2}\left(\frac{\gamma^2}{\gamma^2 - 1}\right) \cdot \frac{D}{H} \cdot \frac{B_0^2}{f u_0} \cdot u_0 \cdot \left(\frac{f u_0}{B_0}\right)^2 \cdot {}_0{}^2 H^2$$

$$= \frac{\gamma^2 - 1}{\gamma^4} \left\{\left[\frac{\gamma^2}{\gamma^2 - 1}\right] \cdot \tfrac{1}{2} f u_0^2 \cdot D \cdot H\right\}$$

$$= \frac{1}{\gamma^2} \cdot \tfrac{1}{2} f u_0^2 D \cdot H \tag{5.4.8}$$

The efficiency at this point is

$$\frac{P}{\left[\dfrac{f u_0^2}{2} + \dfrac{p}{\gamma - 1}\right] D \cdot H} = \frac{P}{\tfrac{1}{2} f u_0^2 \cdot D \cdot H \left[1 + \dfrac{2}{\gamma(\gamma - 1)^2} \dfrac{1}{M^2}\right]}$$

$$\rightarrow \frac{1}{\gamma^2} (= 0 \cdot 36 \quad \text{for} \quad \gamma = 5/3) \tag{5.4.9}$$

The greatest difficulty in utilizing this device lies in the low value of the resistance. To realize maximum efficiency, the external resistance must be

$R_2 = (\gamma^2 - 1) R_0 = (\gamma^2/2) \cdot D/H(B_0^2/fu_0) \cdot u_0 \cdot 10^{-9} \, \Omega$. For example, if $u_0 \simeq 10^6$ cm/sec, $B_0^2/fu_0 = 1$ and $D/H = 10$, $R_2 = \frac{25}{18} \cdot 10^{-2} \, \Omega$. If we consider a magnetic field of 10,000 gauss (implying a density $\rho = 10^{-4}$ g/cm^3) and an electrode width (H) of 1 cm, then the current $I = (1/\gamma^2)I_0 = (1/\gamma^2) \times (fu_0/B_0^2) \cdot BH = 0 \cdot 36 \, I_0 = 3 \cdot 6 \times 10^4$ A and the extracted power $\simeq 18$ MW, which is $0 \cdot 36$ of the 50 MW passing through the tube. The requirement that the current density remain positive, $E + uB > 0$, puts a restriction on for $\gamma < 2$ which prevents the attaining of this ideal efficiency.

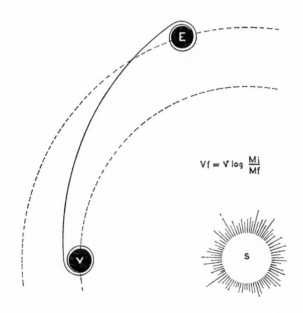

FIG. 5.3. Possible path of low thrust high specific impulse interplanetary vehicle.

There are many practical difficulties in realizing a device of this kind. A major one lies in providing electrodes through which the enormous currents can flow and in handling the extremely hot gas. The analysis presented here is highly idealized, but it does suggest that moderate extraction efficiency can be reached, even with a single electrode, whereas any practical device would use many electrodes.

An experiment on the extraction of power from a moving plasma has been performed (PAIN, 1961), in which an argon plasma produced by a shock was allowed to pass at a flow Mach number of ~ 3 between electrodes in a transverse magnetic field. The electrodes were connected by a small resistor over which the voltage was measured, and hence the current and power output deduced. As might be expected, the power varied with this resistance and reached a maximum when the external resistance was equal to the internal resistance of the plasma. In order to relate the resistance to the resistivity of the plasma, the tube was filled with a solution of known conductivity and the inter-electrode resistance measured. The extracted power was large, $\sim 0 \cdot 3$ MW, representing ~ 30 per cent of the kinetic energy in the gas. While this is consistent with eq. (5.4.9) detailed comparison is obscured by the ionization processes in the gas (20 per cent ionization).

Plasma Propulsion

A further important future application of magnetohydrodynamics may be in the propulsion of rockets through interplanetary space, where the low inertia and high velocities attainable with plasma may be of great importance (MOECKEL, 1959). An important parameter in specifying the performance of a rocket is the speed with which the propellent is ejected, since this is critical in determining the final velocity that can be reached. Since plasma can be accelerated by electromagnetic means to very high velocities, it may be profitable to depart from usual rocket techniques, in which the energy source and the propellent gas are combined, and to use a separate energy supply and electric acceleration methods. To understand these effects, let us first consider the motion of a rocket in field free space. A rocket is propelled by hurling matter away from itself with velocity v; whereupon conservation of momentum yields

$$\frac{d}{dt}(Mu) + \dot{M}(v-u) = M\dot{u} + u\dot{M} + \dot{M}(v-u) = 0$$

$$\dot{u} + v\frac{\dot{M}}{M} = 0$$

and hence

$$u - u_0 = v \log\frac{M_0}{M} \tag{5.4.11}$$

Thus, the final velocity of the rocket is proportional to the velocity with which the propellent is ejected, and varies only logarithmically with the ratio of final to initial masses. It is this logarithmic dependence on mass which demands enormous rockets to deliver small pay loads. When conservation of energy is considered the situation is somewhat altered. If the power production is a constant fraction of the final mass, i.e. $W = M_f/\alpha$, and the rocket runs for a time t_0, then

$$M_0 = M_f - \dot{M}t_0 \quad \text{and} \quad \frac{1}{2}\dot{M}v^2 = W = \frac{M_f}{\alpha}$$

and

$$M_0 = M_f\left(1 + \frac{2t_0}{\alpha v^2}\right)$$

and

$$u - u_0 = v \log\left(1 + \frac{2t_0}{\alpha v^2}\right) \tag{5.4.12}$$

Hence u depends on v and on a second characteristic velocity $V = \sqrt{(2t_0/\alpha)}$, a function of the time of burning and the mass to power ratio of the system. If V is fixed the optimum value of v is determined as $v \simeq 1\cdot97\ V$ for which $\Delta u \simeq 1\cdot6v$, and $M_f/M_0 \simeq 1/5$. If $\alpha \approx 5$ g/W, a moderately optimistic figure and $t_0 \simeq 100$ days, a reasonable figure for interplanetary flight, $v \simeq 8 \times 10^6$ cm/sec, which is sufficient to take a rocket from Earth to Mars. Such a machine has an extremely low acceleration, for $a = \simeq v/t_0 \simeq 0\cdot8$ cm/sec^2 $\simeq 10^{-3}\,g$, and cannot ascend from the earth's surface, but would need to be either placed or assembled in orbit by high-thrust rockets. If, however, chemical rockets are used for which $v = 10^5$ cm/sec, then the mass transported $\simeq 10^{-4}$ of the initial mass; and if large loads are ever to be transported between the planets, high-velocity low-thrust drive is needed.

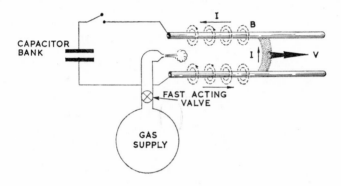

Fig. 5.4. Principle of the rail gun. Burst of gas released by fast acting valve is ionized by condenser discharge and driven down rail by self field.

One method of accelerating plasma is to reverse the direct conversion system discussed in the last section, applying a voltage to the plasma and driving it across a magnetic field. A variant on this uses the field produced by the current itself as the driving field, a particular example being the rail gun. This device, which operates *in vacuo*, consists of two parallel rails connected to the terminals of a charged condenser bank. A rapidly acting valve at the end of the rails emits a puff of gas between them, which breaks down in the electric field and carries a high current. The current interacting with its own field then yields a force which accelerates the puff of gas down the rails.

This system may most easily be analysed using a somewhat modified magnetohydrodynamic language. The magnetic field is proportional to the current, hence the total force on the gas is proportional to I^2 (for two thin wires of radius r_0 separated by a distance $2R$, $F = \beta I^2 \simeq 8 \log(2R/r_0)I^2$). The current, however, is determined by the applied voltage, and for low resistance and fast rising currents by the varying inductance of the circuit, through

$$V(t) = \frac{\mathrm{d}}{\mathrm{d}t}(LI) \qquad (5.4.13)$$

or

$$I = \frac{1}{L(t)} \int V \, \mathrm{d}t$$

The motion is particularly simple if the voltage is applied impulsively, for example, by using the first quarter cycle of a ringing condenser. If this is shorted at zero voltage, its energy is trapped in the current system, and $\int V \mathrm{d}t$ becomes a constant for the remainder of the motion.

The inductance in turn depends on the distance, x, travelled by the gas, $L = L_0 + L'x$ (for two thin wires $L' = 8 \log[2R/r_0]$). If the mass of the accelerated gas is m, and if gas loss processes are negligible, an approximate equation of motion is

$$m\ddot{x} = \beta I^2 = \beta \frac{(\int V \, \mathrm{d}t)^2}{(L(x))^2} = \frac{\beta(\int V \, \mathrm{d}t)^2}{[L_0 + L'x]^2} \qquad (5.4.14)$$

or, introducing τ such that

$$\frac{\mathrm{d}\tau}{\mathrm{d}t} = \sqrt{\left(\frac{\beta}{m}\right)} \int V \, \mathrm{d}t = \text{constant}$$

$$\frac{\mathrm{d}^2 x}{\mathrm{d}\tau^2} = \frac{1}{(L_0 + L'x)^2}$$

Hence, if $\dot{x} = 0$ at $x = 0$

$$\frac{1}{2}\left(\frac{\mathrm{d}x}{\mathrm{d}\tau}\right)^2 = \frac{x}{L_0(L_0 + L'x)}$$

From this

$$\frac{1}{2}mv^2 = \frac{\beta}{L'}\left(\frac{1}{L_0} - \frac{1}{L_0 + L'x}\right)\left[\int V \mathrm{d}t\right]^2$$

but since $\beta = L'$, the rate of doing work on a moving conductor being

$$I^2 v \frac{\partial L}{\partial x} = v\beta I^2,$$

this is simply

$$\frac{1}{2}mv^2 = \left[\int V \mathrm{d}t\right]^2 \left(\frac{1}{L_0} - \frac{1}{L_0 + L'x}\right)$$

and the kinetic energy with which the pulse leaves the rails is

$$E_{mech} = \frac{1}{2}mv^2{}_f = \left[\int V \mathrm{d}t\right]^2 \left[\frac{1}{L_0} - \frac{1}{L_f}\right]$$

where L_f is the final value of the inductance. Moreover, the magnetic energy at this stage is

$$E_{mag} = \tfrac{1}{2}L I_f{}^2 = \tfrac{1}{2}\left[\int V\mathrm{d}t\right]^2 \Big/ L_f$$

and the efficiency

$$
\begin{aligned}
\mathscr{E}_{ff} &= E_{mech}/(E_{mech}+E_{mag}) \\
&= \frac{L_f I_f{}^2[(L_f/L_0)-1]}{L_f I_f{}^2[(L_f/L_0)-1+\tfrac{1}{2}]} = \frac{L_f-L_0}{L_f-\tfrac{1}{2}L_0}
\end{aligned}
\tag{5.4.15}
$$

and as long as dissipative effects are negligible, quite high efficiencies should be possible.

As a numerical example, suppose that the pulse contains 10^{18} hydrogen atoms, $m \simeq 10^{-6}\,g$ and $I_0 \simeq 10^4$ A, while $L_f/L_0 \simeq 50$, and $\beta \simeq 2$ and $t = 10^{-5}$ sec, then $V \simeq 10^6$ cm/sec, and the length of the rail $\simeq 100$ cm. The thrust of a device of this kind is modest; if running steadily, one pulse per 10^{-5} sec, $nmv = 10^5$ dynes $\simeq 100$ g, at which the power consumption is ~ 10 kW. While the thrust is small, it is not without use as a propulsion device, and could give a 1000 kg mass an acceleration of $10^{-4}\, g_0$ where $g_0 \simeq$ acceleration due to gravity at the earth's surface. If the initial current is raised to 3×10^4, the acceleration on 1000 kg reaches $10^{-3}\, g_0$ which is ample for interplanetary flight (e.g. time to Mars at $10^{-3}\, g_0$ is only slightly greater than with an impulsive acceleration).

Rapid propulsion of a plasma has been achieved in a somewhat similar manner by BOSTICK (1956). Instead of long rails, he used short stubs of titanium electrodes loaded with deuterium at a separation of 0·005 in. and discharged brief (0·1–0·5 μsec) high currents (1000–10,000 A) through them. He discovered that at low pressures the spark produced was blown away by the magnetic forces with velocities of $\sim 2 \times 10^7$ cm/sec becoming detached and proceeding as an isolated current-bearing loop whose subsequent dynamical behaviour was unexpected and amusing. Since his device was driven by a condenser discharge, it was a single-shot machine and the thrust was unmeasurable, however the high specific impulse is there, and much interest has been shown in possible developments of this device (BLACKMANN, 1959).

5. MAGNETOSONIC WAVES

The Alfvén wave represents one of the possible oscillations of the compressible fluid, as well as of the incompressible fluid, but compressive waves are also modified by magnetic fields. Let us attempt to describe the propagation of plane waves through a uniform, perfectly conducting, isentropic, compressible gas in a uniform magnetic field. The relevant linearized equations of motion are Gaussian units

$$\frac{\partial \rho}{\partial t} + \rho_0 \operatorname{div} \mathbf{v} = 0 \tag{5.5.1}$$

$$\rho_0 \frac{\partial \mathbf{v}}{\partial t} = -\nabla p + \frac{1}{4\pi}(\text{curl}\,\mathbf{B}) \times \mathbf{B}_0 \qquad (5.5.2)$$

$$\frac{\partial p}{\partial t} - \frac{\gamma p_0}{\rho_0}\frac{\partial \rho}{\partial t} = 0 \qquad (5.5.3)$$

$$\mathbf{E} + \frac{\mathbf{v}}{c} \times \mathbf{B}_0 = 0 \qquad (5.5.4)$$

$$\frac{1}{c}\frac{\partial \mathbf{B}}{\partial t} = -\,\text{curl}\,\mathbf{E} \qquad (5.5.5)$$

where the quantities with the subscript 0 refer to the undisturbed state. It is possible to proceed with the equations in this form; however, it is more convenient to make use of the fact that in the theory of sound not only the velocities $\mathbf{v}$ but the displacements $\boldsymbol{\xi}(r, t)$ are small, and that in the linear approximation $\partial\boldsymbol{\xi}/\partial t = \mathbf{v}$. If we assume that the displacements vanish at some time $t = 0$, several of the equations may be integrated, i.e. (5.5.1) becomes

$$\rho + \rho_0\,\text{div}\,\boldsymbol{\xi} = 0$$

(5.5.3) becomes

$$p + \frac{\gamma p_0}{\rho_0}\rho = 0 \quad \text{or} \quad p = -\gamma p_0\,\text{div}\,\boldsymbol{\xi}$$

while eqs. (5.5.4) and (5.5.5) become

$$\frac{\partial \mathbf{B}}{\partial t} = -c(\text{curl}\,\mathbf{E}) = \text{curl}\left(\frac{\partial \boldsymbol{\xi}}{\partial t} \times \mathbf{B}_0\right)$$

so that the magnetic field perturbation is

$$\mathbf{B} = \text{curl}(\,\boldsymbol{\xi} \times \mathbf{B}_0) \qquad (5.5.6)$$

In eq. (5.5.2) we need $(1/4\pi)(\text{curl}\,\mathbf{B}) \times \mathbf{B}_0$, which may be expressed as

$$\frac{1}{4\pi}\Big\{\nabla[B_0{}^2\nabla\cdot\boldsymbol{\xi} - (\mathbf{B}_0\cdot\nabla)(\mathbf{B}_0\cdot\boldsymbol{\xi})] + (\mathbf{B}_0\cdot\nabla)^2\boldsymbol{\xi} - \mathbf{B}_0[\mathbf{B}_0\cdot\nabla(\nabla\cdot\boldsymbol{\xi})]\Big\}$$

and the fundamental equation for magnetosonic waves becomes

$$\rho_0\ddot{\boldsymbol{\xi}} - \gamma p_0\nabla(\nabla\cdot\boldsymbol{\xi}) - \frac{1}{4\pi}\nabla(B_0{}^2\nabla\cdot\boldsymbol{\xi} - \mathbf{B}_0\cdot\nabla\mathbf{B}_0\cdot\boldsymbol{\xi}) - \frac{1}{4\pi}(\mathbf{B}_0\cdot\nabla)^2\boldsymbol{\xi} +$$

$$+ \frac{1}{4\pi}[\mathbf{B}_0(\mathbf{B}_0\cdot\nabla)\nabla\cdot\boldsymbol{\xi}] = 0$$

or

$$\ddot{\boldsymbol{\xi}} - \frac{\gamma p_0}{\rho_0}\nabla(\nabla\cdot\boldsymbol{\xi}) - \frac{1}{4\pi}(\text{curl}\,\mathbf{B}) \times \mathbf{B}_0 = 0 \qquad (5.5.7)$$

If we introduce the Alfvén speed $C_A{}^2 = B_0{}^2/4\pi\rho_0$, the sound speed $C_S{}^2$ $= \gamma p_0/\rho_0$, their ratio $\alpha = C_S{}^2/C_A{}^2 = (\gamma/2)\beta$ where $\beta = 8\pi(p/B^2)$, and a unit vector $\mathbf{b}$ in the direction $\mathbf{B}_0$, eq. (5.5.7) becomes

$$(\ddot{\boldsymbol{\xi}}/C_A{}^2) - \boldsymbol{\nabla}[(\alpha+1)\boldsymbol{\nabla}\cdot\boldsymbol{\xi} - (\mathbf{b}\cdot\boldsymbol{\nabla})(\mathbf{b}\cdot\boldsymbol{\xi})] - (\mathbf{b}\cdot\boldsymbol{\nabla})^2\boldsymbol{\xi} + (\mathbf{b}\cdot\boldsymbol{\nabla})(\boldsymbol{\nabla}\cdot\boldsymbol{\xi})\mathbf{b} = 0$$

$$(5.5.8)$$

Since the acceleration is not in the direction of the displacements, the waves described by this equation are not, in general, longitudinal; indeed since the Alfvén waves are among them, we have already displayed a possible transverse solution. If now we introduce a plane wave solution, $\boldsymbol{\xi}(\mathbf{r}, t)$ $= \boldsymbol{\xi}_0 \exp[i(2\pi/\lambda)(\mathbf{k}\cdot\mathbf{r} - Vt)$, eq. (5.5.8), is reduced to three algebraic equations for the components $\xi_i = (\xi_x, \xi_y, \xi_z)$ of the wave amplitude $\boldsymbol{\xi}_0$,

$$\frac{V^2}{C_A{}^2}\xi_i + A_{ij}\xi_j = 0 \qquad (5.5.9)$$

where A_{ij} is a function of $\mathbf{b}$, $\mathbf{k}$ and α.

This set of homogeneous equations has a non-trivial solution only if the determinant of the coefficients ξ_i vanishes; hence, a cubic equation is obtained which must be satisfied by the square of the phase velocity V. The roots are most easily obtained by forming the scalar products of eq. (5.5.9) with $\mathbf{k}$, $\mathbf{b}$, and cross product with $\mathbf{k}$ followed by the scalar product with $\mathbf{b}$, so that instead of ξ_i, the three scalars $\mathbf{k}\cdot\boldsymbol{\xi}$, $\mathbf{b}\cdot\boldsymbol{\xi}$ and $\mathbf{b}\cdot\mathbf{k}\times\boldsymbol{\xi}$ appear as independent variables. These equations are

$$\left[\frac{V^2}{C_A{}^2} - (1+\alpha)\right]\mathbf{k}\cdot\boldsymbol{\xi} + (\mathbf{b}\cdot\mathbf{k})\mathbf{k}\cdot\boldsymbol{\xi} = 0 \qquad (5.5.10)$$

$$\frac{V^2}{C_A{}^2}\mathbf{b}\cdot\boldsymbol{\xi} - \alpha(\mathbf{b}\cdot\mathbf{k})\mathbf{k}\cdot\boldsymbol{\xi} = 0 \qquad (5.5.11)$$

and

$$\left[\frac{V^2}{C_A{}^2} - (\mathbf{b}\cdot\mathbf{k})^2\right]\mathbf{b}\cdot\mathbf{k}\times\boldsymbol{\xi} = 0 \qquad (5.5.12)$$

thus one root is the Alfvén wave velocity $V^2 = C_A{}^2 \cos^2\theta$, and the other two are roots of the quadratic $V^4 - (1+\alpha)V^2 + \alpha\cos^2\theta = 0$, where $\cos\theta$ $= \mathbf{b}\cdot\mathbf{k}$, whence

$$V_{\pm}{}^2 = \tfrac{1}{2}\{(C_A{}^2 + C_s{}^2) \pm \sqrt{[(C_A{}^2 + C_s{}^2)^2 - 4C_s{}^2C_A{}^2 \cos^2\theta]}\} \qquad (5.5.13)$$

Thus, in addition to the purely transverse waves, there are two classes of magnetosonic waves, fast and slow, corresponding to the $+$ and $-$ signs in eq. (5.5.13). Equation (5.5.12) implies that although these waves are not necessarily longitudinal, the vectors $\boldsymbol{\xi}$, $\mathbf{k}$ and $\mathbf{b}$ are co-planar. In the direction of the magnetic field, $\theta = 0$,

$$V_+ = \left\{ \frac{C_A{}^2 + C_s{}^2 + |C_A - C_s{}^2|}{2} \right\}^{\frac{1}{2}} = \max(C_A, C_s)$$

$$V_- = \frac{\{C_A{}^2 + C_s{}^2 - |C_A{}^2 - C_s{}^2|\}^{\frac{1}{2}}}{2} = \min(C_A, C_s)$$

while normal to the field $V_+ = \sqrt{(C_A{}^2 + C_s{}^2)}$ and $V_- = 0$. The kinematic difference between these waves can be seen by examining the relative signs of $\mathbf{k}_\perp \cdot \boldsymbol{\xi}_\perp$ and $\mathbf{k}_\parallel \xi_\parallel$. From eq. (5.5.10)

$$\mathbf{k}_\perp \cdot \boldsymbol{\xi}_\perp = - \frac{[(V^2/C_A{}^2) - \alpha]}{[(V^2/C_A) - (1 + \alpha)]} \mathbf{k}_\parallel \, \xi_\parallel$$

and using eq. (5.5.13), the coefficient on the right may be written

$$\frac{(1 - \alpha) \pm \sqrt{[(1 + \alpha)^2 - 4\alpha \cos^2 \theta]}}{(1 + \alpha) \pm \sqrt{[(1 + \alpha)^2 - 4\alpha \cos^2 \theta]}}$$

which is positive for the upper and negative for the lower signs; thus, for the fast wave the parallel and perpendicular components of the displacement $\boldsymbol{\xi}$ are in phase, while for the slow wave they are 180° out of phase. The dynamical difference is also easily recognized: for the fast wave the magnetic and gas pressure perturbations are in phase, while for the slow wave they are 180° out of phase.

The increase in the gas pressure is

$$\delta p_G = -\gamma p_0 \, \mathrm{div} \, \boldsymbol{\xi} = C_s{}^2 \, \delta \rho \qquad (5.5.14)$$

while, using eq. (5.5.6), the increase in magnetic pressure is

$$\delta p_B = \frac{1}{4\pi} \mathbf{B}_0 \cdot \mathbf{B}' = i \frac{2\pi}{\lambda} \frac{B_0{}^2}{4\pi} [(\mathbf{b} \cdot \mathbf{k})(\mathbf{b} \cdot \boldsymbol{\xi}) - \mathbf{k} \cdot \boldsymbol{\xi}]$$

$$= i \frac{2\pi}{\lambda} \frac{B_0{}^2}{4\pi} [(-V^2/C_A{}^2) + 1 + \alpha - 1] \mathbf{k} \cdot \boldsymbol{\xi}$$

$$\hspace{6cm} (5.5.15)$$

$$= (V^2 - C_s{}^2) \, \delta \rho, \text{ using eq. (5.5.10)}$$

and $V_+{}^2 - C_s{}^2 > 0$,

while $\quad V_-{}^2 - C_s{}^2 = \frac{1}{2}\{C_A{}^2 - C_s{}^2 - \sqrt{[(C_A{}^2 + C_s{}^2)^2 - 4C_A{}^2 C_s{}^2 \cos^2 \theta]}\} < 0$

In terms of the density increment $\delta \rho / \rho$, the displacement is

$$\boldsymbol{\xi} = - \frac{1}{V^2 - C_A{}^2 \cos^2 \theta} [(C_A{}^2 + C_s{}^2 - (C_s{}^2 C_A{}^2 / V^2) \cos^2 \theta) \mathbf{k} - C_A{}^2 \cos \theta \, \mathbf{b}] \frac{i\lambda}{2\pi} \frac{\delta \rho}{\rho}$$

$$\hspace{8cm} (5.5.16)$$

For propagation in the direction of the field, the entire density increment occurs on the wave which moves with the sound speed. If we consider longitudinal oscillations in any other direction, e.g. waves induced by the normal oscillations of a smooth non-conducting plane whose normal makes an angle θ with the field, the relative amplitudes $\delta\rho_+$ and $\delta\rho_-$ are determined by the condition

$$\mathbf{k} \times \boldsymbol{\xi} = -\frac{i\lambda}{2\pi} \frac{C_A^2}{\rho_0} \cos\theta \, \mathbf{k} \times \mathbf{b} \left[\frac{\delta\rho_+}{V_+^2 - C_A^2 \cos^2\theta} + \frac{\delta\rho_-}{V_-^2 - C_A^2 \cos^2\theta} \right] = 0 \tag{5.5.17}$$

hence

$$\frac{\delta\rho_-}{\delta\rho_+} = \frac{C_A^2 \cos^2\theta - V_-^2}{V_+^2 - C_A^2 \cos^2\theta}$$

which goes to zero for propagation normal to the field lines, and for propagation almost along them becomes $\sim [(1-\alpha)^2/(1+\alpha) \sin^2\theta]$ for $\alpha < 1$.

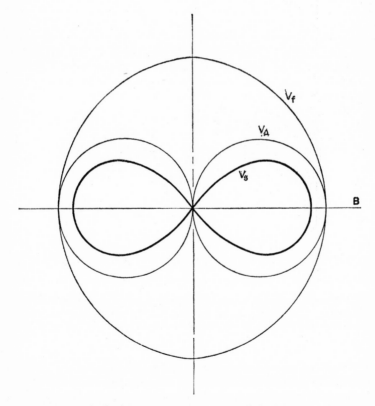

FIG. 5.5. Magnetohydrodynamic sound waves. Unit interval after passing through origin plane waves normal to radius vector from origin intersects curve. V_f fast wave, V_S slow wave, V_A Alfvén wave.

There is remarkably little evidence for the propagation of magnetosonic waves through a plasma. Most easily produced plasmas are highly dissipative, noisy and of short duration; however, some experiments on the propagation of Alfvén waves have been performed. One such experiment was that of HARDCASTLE and JEPHCOTT, who used as a plasma a transformer-induced

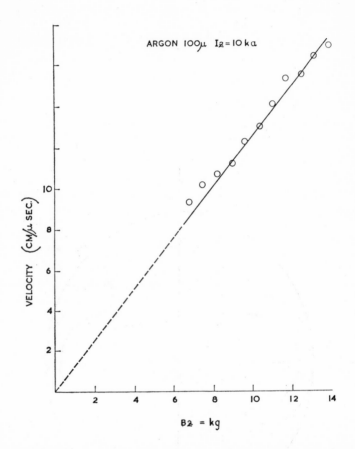

FIG. 5.6. Velocity of Alfvén waves. Measured speed of magnetically produced Alfvén wave in a low pressure argon discharge in a strong magnetic field. Straight line is theoretical value. (Hardcastle and Jephcott, A.E.R.E. report R 3 109).

ring discharge in a strong axial magnetic field $\sim$ (6–14 kGauss) in argon, neon and helium, and at peak current sent an oscillating discharge through a coil placed near the torus in such a way as to produce a perturbed magnetic field normal to the initial one. The disturbance then propagated around the tube and was picked up by search coils. The velocity was shown to be proportional to the magnetic field strength (Fig. 5.6) and was used to deduce the plasma density $\sim 7 \times 10^{14}$, which was in fair agreement with that measured by Langmuir probes $\sim 10^{15}$.

6. PROPAGATION FROM A POINT SOURCE

The consequences of an anisotropic phase velocity are not completely obvious. The plot of phase velocity vs. direction of the wave vector does not, for example, represent the wave front produced by an isotropic pulse at the origin. To find this it is necessary to recall that the length of the vector from the origin to a point on the curve represents the distance

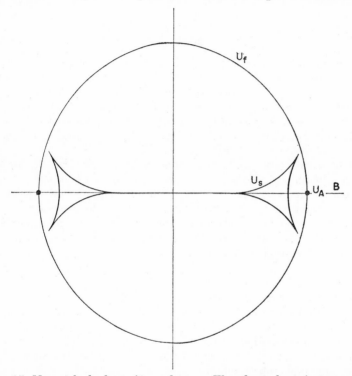

Fig. 5.7. Magnetohydrodynamic sound waves. Wave fronts due to instantaneous point source at the origin after unit time. Alfvén wave produces two points on the field line. U_f, fast wave, U_S, slow wave, U_A Alfvén wave.

travelled by the plane phase surface normal to that vector, and the wave front due to an isotropic pulse can be obtained by finding the constant phase surface, the envelope of the normal planes. For an isotropic velocity the phase velocity curve $v(\theta)$ is a circle centred on the origin, and the envelope of normal planes is the same circle. For the Alfvén wave, $v(\theta)$ is a circle passing through the origin, and the normal planes pass through the opposite end of the diameter; thus for the Alfvén wave, a point signal is transmitted along the field lines as two points moving in opposite directions. The properties of the fast and slow waves are less obvious, but the coordinates

(X, Y) can be given parametrically in terms of the phase velocity $v(\theta)$ and the angle between the wave vector and the magnetic field by

$$X = v \cos \theta - \frac{\mathrm{d}v}{\mathrm{d}\theta} \sin \theta \qquad (5.6.1)$$

$$Y = v \sin \theta + \frac{\mathrm{d}v}{\mathrm{d}\theta} \cos \theta$$

The slope $\mathrm{d}X/\mathrm{d}Y$ is $-\tan \theta$ and the curvature is

$$\frac{\mathrm{d}^2 Y}{\mathrm{d}X^2} = \frac{1}{\sin^3\theta} \left(\frac{1}{v + (\mathrm{d}^2 v/\mathrm{d}\theta^2)} \right) \qquad (5.6.2)$$

The denominator here is proportional to the curvature of $1/v(\theta)$, hence when the wave vector $k(\omega, \theta)$ has a point of inflection, the wave front from a pulse has a cusp. The wave front for the fast wave has no surprising properties, but for the slow wave the wave front is displaced along the field lines and is a very small cusped object. This implies, that if $C_s < C_A$, it is possible for a pressure pulse to travel down the field lines with very slight lateral dispersion (cf. Fig. 5.7).

This pressure pulse has been invoked by LIGHTHILL to explain certain anomalies in the radar echo from rockets passing through the ionosphere; the apparent size varies enormously. Lighthill suggests that a compressive wave from the rocket increases the local plasma frequency until reflection occurs from the gas behind the wave. Since it travels only along the Earth's magnetic field, the strength of the reflection depends on the orientation of the beam with respect to that field.

7. SHOCKS

A further development of the theory of sound may be effected; the dispersion relation eqs. (5.5.13) and (5.5.12) give not merely the velocity of linearized sound waves, but the velocities of the characteristic surfaces for the true non-linear motions of the fluid. To understand this remark, consider the problem of unsteady one-dimensional flow, for which the magnetohydrodynamic equations take the form

$$\frac{\partial Y_i}{\partial t} = A_{ij} \frac{\partial Y_j}{\partial x} \qquad (5.7.1)$$

where A_{ij} may be functions of the dependent variables Y_j, and the functions Y_i satisfying (5.7.1) may be written as $Y(x, t) = Y(x + \int V \, \mathrm{d}t)$ for some V depending on the A_{ij}, for substituting this in eq. (5.7.1), reduces it to

$$-V \frac{\partial Y_i}{\partial x} = A_{ij} \frac{\partial Y_j}{\partial x}$$

a set of algebraic relations between the derivatives of Y, which can be satisfied only if the velocities V satisfy the characteristic equation

$$|A_{ij} + V\delta_{ij}| = 0 \qquad (5.7.2)$$

This relation could be obtained in another way. If we consider the propagation of a small short wave disturbance through a plasma, not necessarily at rest, the equation of motion for the disturbance does not generally have the form of eq. (5.7.1), since it involves in addition derivatives of unperturbed quantities. However, if the disturbance is steep, its derivatives are large, the magnitude of the disturbance can be neglected when compared with its derivative, and the equation for sound propagation reduced to the form (5.7.1). More precisely, it has the form (5.5.1)–(5.5.5) with $\partial/\partial t + \mathbf{U} \cdot \nabla$, where $\mathbf{U}$ is the velocity in the undisturbed system. In this linearized form however, the coefficients A_{ij} are given functions of the independent variable, x, t, since they depend only on the unperturbed quantities, $\mathbf{U}$, p_0, $\mathbf{B}_0$, which are supposed known.

For the non-linear problem, if the values of the dynamical variables v, ρ, p, $\mathbf{B}$ are given on $X = 0$ as a function of time, the initial values will propagate through space remaining constant on the characteristic surfaces $X(t)$ which move with velocities V.

There are seven possible velocities:

U, the fluid velocity; $U \pm V_A$, where V_A is the speed of the Alfvén wave; $V_A = C_A \cos \theta$, θ being the angle between the direction of propagation and the magnetic field direction, as in the theory of sound; $U \pm V_\pm$, where $V_\pm$ are the fast and slow sound speeds

$$V_\pm = 2^{-\frac{1}{2}}\{C_A^2 + C_s^2 \pm \sqrt{[(C_A^2 + C_s^2)^2 - 4C_A^2 C_s^2 \cos^2\theta]}\}^{\frac{1}{2}}$$

In these expressions it must be observed that the Alfvén speeds and the sound speeds depend on the local values of the magnetic field, pressure and density, hence are functions of the solutions to the problem.

In the similar treatment of the flow of a compressible non-conducting fluid, there are only three characteristics: U, and $U \pm C_s$, where C_s is the sound speed and for these a somewhat paradoxical phenomenon occurs. Consider a characteristic surface, moving relative to the fluid with a velocity $C_s = \sqrt{\gamma p/\rho}$ and over which an increase in density $\delta\rho$ occurs. Behind this surface, the characteristic speed increases since

$$2C_s\delta C_s = \gamma\frac{\delta p}{\rho} - \frac{p}{\rho^2}\delta\rho = C_s^2\left(\frac{\delta p}{p} - \frac{\delta\rho}{\rho}\right)$$

but for adiabatic flow $p \sim \rho^\gamma$, hence $\delta p/p = \gamma(\delta\rho/\rho)$, and

$$\delta C_s = \frac{\gamma - 1}{2}\frac{\delta\rho}{\rho}C_s$$

This means that provided $\gamma > 1$ any characteristic behind the first will eventually overtake it, until finally a discontinuity in density occurs. At this point the adiabatic flow equations break down and a shock wave is produced—a narrow region in which rapid changes in density, pressure and velocity occur, and dissipative effects, negligible elsewhere, result in an increase in the entropy of the fluid.

If the characteristic speeds $V_\pm$ increase on compression, a similar phenomenon might be expected in magnetohydrodynamics. The increment in V on the passage of a characteristic surface will be suitably determined if $\delta C_A{}^2$, $\delta C_s{}^2$ and $\delta(\cos^2\theta)$ are expressed in terms of $\delta\rho$. We may use eqs. (5.5.4)–(5.5.15), and on observing from eq. (5.5.6) that $\mathbf{k}\cdot\delta\mathbf{B} = 0$

$$\delta(\cos^2\theta) = \delta\left(\frac{\mathbf{k}\cdot\mathbf{B}}{B}\right)^2 = \frac{2(\mathbf{k}\cdot\mathbf{B})\mathbf{k}\cdot\delta\mathbf{B}}{B^2} - \frac{(\mathbf{k}\cdot\mathbf{B})^2}{B^2}\frac{\delta(B^2)}{B^2}$$

$$= -2\cos^2\theta\frac{(V^2-C_s{}^2)}{C_A{}^2}\delta\rho/\rho$$

Differentiating eq. (5.5.13):

$$\delta V^2[2V^2-(C_s{}^2+C_A{}^2)] - V^2(\delta C_s{}^2+\delta C_A{}^2) + \delta C_s{}^2 C_A{}^2\cos^2\theta +$$

$$+ \delta C_A{}^2 C_s{}^2\cos^2\theta + C_A{}^2 C_s{}^2\delta(\cos^2\theta) = \delta V^2[2V^2-(C_s{}^2+C_A{}^2)] -$$

$$- \{V^2[2V^2-(C_s{}^2+C_A{}^2)+(\gamma-2)C_s{}^2] - (\gamma-2)C_s{}^2 C_A{}^2\cos^2\theta\}\frac{\delta\rho}{\rho} = 0$$

or

$$\frac{\delta V^2}{V^2} = \frac{\delta\rho}{\rho}\left\{1 + \frac{\gamma-2}{2}\frac{C_s{}^2\ [V^2-C_A{}^2\cos^2\theta]}{V^2[V^2-\frac{1}{2}(C_s{}^2+C_A{}^2)]}\right\} \qquad (5.7.3)$$

Since $-1 < \gamma-2 < 1$, δV^2 will have the sign of $\delta\rho$ provided that

$$|\mathbf{F}| = \left|\frac{C_s{}^2\ [V^2-C_A{}^2\cos^2\theta]}{2V^2[V^2-\frac{1}{2}(C_s{}^2+C_A{}^2)]}\right| < 1$$

Introducing as new variables

$$x = \frac{\alpha}{1+\alpha}, \qquad z = \sqrt{\left[1 - \frac{4\alpha}{(1+\alpha)^2}\cos^2\theta\right]}$$

where $\alpha = C_s{}^2/C_A{}^2$, this condition may be written, since

$$2V^2 = (C_s{}^2+C_A{}^2)[1\pm z]$$

and

$$\pm F = \frac{x}{1\pm z}\cdot\frac{1}{z}\left[1\pm z - \frac{(1-z^2)}{2x}\right] = \frac{x}{z} - \frac{(1\pm z)}{2z} = \frac{x-\frac{1}{2}}{z}\pm\frac{1}{2}$$

as

$$|F| = \left|\frac{x-\frac{1}{2}}{z}\pm\frac{1}{2}\right| < 1$$

The minimum value of z at $\cos^2\theta = 1$ is $(1-\alpha')/1+\alpha')$, for which

$$\frac{x-\frac{1}{2}}{z} = \frac{\alpha/(1+\alpha)-\frac{1}{2}}{(1-\alpha)/(1+\alpha)} = -\frac{1}{2}\frac{(1-\alpha)}{1+\alpha}\cdot\frac{1+\alpha}{1-\alpha} = \frac{1}{2}$$

Hence $|F(x, t)| < 1$. It is easily seen that only when the magnetosonic wave degenerates to the Alfvén wave does δV^2 vanish. Thus in spite of the increased complexity of magnetohydrodynamics, the passage of a compressive wave leads to an increase in the characteristic speed, and to a steepening of any compressive wave front just as in normal hydrodynamics.

The immediate consequence of this steepening process is that the increase of density in a compressive one-dimensional flow occurs as a discontinuity. Of course, this discontinuity is a mathematical artifact, the actual physical flow is continuous; however, the flow can develop extremely abrupt transitions for which the adiabatic description is inadequate. Usually the details of the flow in these transition regions are not of great interest and serve merely to link the flow ahead with that behind the transition; hence it is of great importance that conditions on either side of the transition are linked by certain purely algebraic relations, the Rankine–Hugoniot relations. We shall now derive these relations for the simplest case of one-dimensional flow normal to the magnetic field. Since the adiabatic description is inadequate, we must use the equations for dissipative flow, introducing the viscosity μ and the electrical resistivity η. These are for steady flow

$$\frac{\partial}{\partial x}(\rho u) = 0 \tag{5.7.4}$$

$$\rho u\frac{\partial u}{\partial x} + \frac{\partial}{\partial x}\left(p + \frac{B^2}{8\pi}\right) = \mu\frac{\partial^2 u}{\partial x^2} \tag{5.7.5}$$

$$u\frac{\partial B}{\partial x} + \frac{B\partial u}{\partial x} = \eta\frac{\partial^2 B}{\partial x^2} \tag{5.7.6}$$

We now integrate these equations between two regions of uniform flow characterized by constants ρ_1, p_1, u_1, B_1 and ρ_2, p_2, u_2, B_2, obtaining

$$\rho_1 u_1 - \rho_2 u_2 = 0 \tag{5.7.7}$$

$$\left(\rho_1 u_1^2 + p_1 + \frac{B_1^2}{8\pi}\right) - \left(\rho_2 u_2^2 + p_2 + \frac{B_2^2}{8\pi}\right) = \mu\frac{\partial u}{\partial x}\Big|_2^1 = 0 \tag{5.7.8}$$

$$u_1 B_1 - u_2 B_2 = \eta\frac{\partial B}{\partial x}\Big|_2^1 = 0 \tag{5.7.9}$$

the right-hand sides vanishing since the limits of integration are in regions of uniform flow.

Since there are four variables in each region, one further relation would be enough to characterize those in region 2 completely as functions in region 1. The necessary relation is obtained by studying the energy balance. If we multiply eq. (5.7.5) by u before integrating, we obtain

$$\rho u^2\frac{\partial}{\partial x}u + u\frac{\partial}{\partial x}\left(p + \frac{B^2}{8\pi}\right) = \mu u\frac{\partial^2 u}{\partial x^2} \tag{5.7.10}$$

which may then be integrated

$$\int_2^1 \rho u^2 \frac{\partial u}{\partial x}\,dx + \int_2^1 \left[u\frac{\partial}{\partial x}\left(p+\frac{B^2}{8\pi}\right) - \mu u\frac{\partial^2 u}{\partial x^2}\right] dx = 0 \qquad (5.7.11)$$

$$\rho u \tfrac{1}{2}u^2 \Big|_2^1 + up\Big|_2^1 - \int_2^1 p\frac{\partial u}{\partial x}\,dx - \mu u\frac{\partial u}{\partial x}\Big|_2^1 + \mu\int_2^1\left(\frac{\partial u}{\partial x}\right)^2 dx + \int_2^1 \frac{uB}{4\pi}\frac{\partial B}{\partial x}\,dx = 0$$

The last integral becomes

$$\int \frac{uB}{4\pi}\frac{\partial B}{\partial x}\,dx = \frac{uB^2}{4\pi}\Big|_2^1 - \left\{ \int_2^1 \frac{1}{4\pi}\,B\frac{\partial}{\partial x}(uB) = \int_2^1 \frac{1}{4\pi}\eta B\frac{\partial^2 B}{\partial x^2} = -\int_2^1 \frac{\eta}{4\pi}\left(\frac{\partial B}{\partial x}\right)^2 dx\right\}$$

hence eq. (5.7.11) becomes

$$\rho u\left[\tfrac{1}{2}u^2 + \frac{p}{\rho} + \frac{B^2}{4\pi\rho}\right]_2^1 + \mu\int_2^1\left(\frac{du}{dx}\right)^2 dx + \frac{\eta}{4\pi}\int_2^1\left(\frac{dB}{dx}\right)^2 dx - \int_2^1 p\frac{\partial}{\partial x}\left(\frac{1}{\rho}\right)\rho u\,dx = 0$$

The last three integrals represent the rate at which heat is deposited in the fluid by viscous dissipation, by resistive dissipation, and the rate at which the gas is doing work. However, we may use the first law of thermodynamics to write

$$dU = dQ - p\,dv = C_v\delta T$$

Hence, if no change of state occurs, the last three integrals become

$$C_v(T_1 - T_2)$$

but since $p = \rho RT$

$$C_p = C_v + R, \qquad C_v T = \frac{C_v p}{R\rho} = \frac{C_v}{C_p - C_v}\frac{p}{\rho},$$

and further $\gamma = C_p/C_v$, the increase in internal energy is

$$[1/(\gamma - 1)](p/\rho)\Big|_2^1$$

The increase in enthalpy then is

$$\frac{p}{\rho} + \frac{1}{\gamma-1}\frac{p}{\rho} = \frac{\gamma}{\gamma-1}\frac{p}{\rho}$$

and the fourth Rankine–Hugoniot relation becomes

$$\left[\tfrac{1}{2}u^2 + \frac{\gamma}{\gamma-1}\frac{p}{\rho} + \frac{B^2}{4\pi\rho}\right]_2^1 = 0 \qquad (5.7.12)$$

Equations (5.7.7), (5.7.8), (5.7.9) and (5.7.12) are the Rankine–Hugoniot relations across a normal magnetohydrodynamic shock, first given by DE HOFFMAN and TELLER, and are statements of the conservation laws. If the magnetic field vanishes, these reduce to the Rankine–Hugoniot relations of normal hydrodynamics.

$$[\rho u] = 0 \qquad (5.7.13)$$

$$[\rho u^2 + p] = 0$$

$$\left[\tfrac{1}{2}u^2 + \frac{\gamma}{\gamma-1}\frac{p}{\rho}\right] = 0$$

Note that the variables ρ_2, p_2, u_2 B_2 are now given as functions of ρ_1, p_1, u_1, B_1. These relations may be used, for example, to get the flux $\rho_1 v_1$ ahead of the shock in terms of the change in pressure, or density across it. By using a frame of reference in which the fluid ahead of the shock is at rest, this becomes the shock speed

$$v_s^2 = \frac{2}{\gamma+1}\frac{C_s^2 + C_A{}^2[1 + (1-\gamma/2)(\rho_2/\rho_1 - 1)]}{(\rho_1/\rho_2) - [(\gamma-1)/(\gamma+1)]}$$

where C_s and C_A are the sound and Alfvén speeds ahead of the shock. In normal hydrodynamic flow it is usual to express this as a Mach number, i.e. the ratio, v_s/C_s, of the speed to the sound speed. In the magnetohydrodynamic case, there are three possible parametrizing velocities C_s, C_A and the magnetosonic speed $C_T = \sqrt{(C_A{}^2 + C_s{}^2)}$. In terms of the latter

$$M_T{}^2 = \frac{v_s^2}{C_T{}^2} = \frac{2}{\gamma+1}\frac{1 + (C_A/C_T)^2[1 - (\gamma/2)][(\rho_2/\rho_1) - 1]}{[(\rho_1/\rho_2) - (\gamma-1)/(\gamma+1)]} \qquad (5.7.14)$$

Note that this becomes infinite for $\rho_1/\rho_2 = (\gamma-1)/(\gamma+1)$, hence as in normal magnetohydrodynamics the maximum compression is $(\gamma+1)/(\gamma-1)$.

Furthermore, if $\gamma = 2$, the field and the fluid behave in the same way and

$$M_T{}^2 = \frac{2}{\gamma+1}\frac{1}{(\rho_1/\rho_2) - (\gamma-1)/(\gamma+1)}$$

the normal hydrodynamic result. It is also easily shown from eq. (5.7.8) that

$$(p_2 - p_1) = \rho_1 u_1^2 - \rho_2 u_2^2 + \frac{B_1^2}{8\pi} - \frac{B_2^2}{8\pi}$$

$$= \rho_1 u_1^2 \left(1 - \frac{\rho_1}{\rho_2}\right) + \frac{B_1^2}{8\pi}\left(1 - \frac{\rho_2^2}{\rho_1^2}\right) \qquad (5.7.15)$$

and for extremely high shock speeds

$$p_2 - p_1 = \left[\frac{2}{\gamma+1} \rho_1 v_s^2 + \frac{B_1^2}{8\pi}\frac{4\gamma}{\gamma-1}\right] \qquad (5.7.16)$$

hence $p_2 \sim [2/(\gamma+1)]\rho_1 v_s^2$, thus the thermal energy behind the shock

$$\frac{\gamma}{\gamma-1}\frac{p_2}{\rho_2} \to \frac{4\gamma}{(\gamma+1)^2}\cdot\tfrac{1}{2}v_i^2$$

is proportional to the kinetic energy ahead.

In contrast to normal hydrodynamics where an oblique shock is physically similar to a normal shock since the component of velocity parallel to the shock is unchanged by its passage, there exist physically distinct magneto-hydrodynamic shocks.

The conservation equations are

$$[f] = [\rho u] = 0 \qquad (5.7.17)$$

$$[p_x] = \left[\rho u^2 + p + \frac{1}{8\pi}(B_y^2 + B_z^2)\right] = 0 \qquad (5.7.18)$$

$$[p_y] = \left[\rho uv - \frac{1}{4\pi}B_x B_y\right] = 0 \qquad (5.7.19)$$

$$[p_z] = \left[\rho uw - \frac{1}{4\pi}B_x B_z\right] = 0 \qquad (5.7.20)$$

$$[B_x] = 0 \qquad (5.7.21)$$

$$[\phi_y] = [uB_y - B_x v] = 0 \qquad (5.7.22)$$

$$[\phi_z] = [uB_z - B_x w] = 0 \qquad (5.7.23)$$

$$[U] = \left[\tfrac{1}{2}(u^2 + v^2 + w^2) + \frac{\gamma}{\gamma-1}\frac{p}{\rho} + \frac{u(B_y^2 + B_z^2) - B_x(B_y v + B_z w)}{4\pi\rho u}\right] = 0 \qquad (5.7.24)$$

There are several interesting special cases of the general oblique shock. Note first that a frame of reference may always be selected so that ahead of the shock, the velocity components v, $w \sim B_y$, B_z. If then, the jump in the transverse components of the magnetic field satisfy $B_y \Delta B_y = -B_z \Delta B_z$, then from eq. (5.7.19): $\Delta v = (1/4\pi)(B_x/f) \Delta B_y$; $\Delta w = (1/4\pi)(B_x/f) \Delta B_z$, hence $(B_y^2 + B_z^2) = (v^2 + w^2) = 0$. Furthermore, from eq. (5.7.22), $u_1 B_{y1} -$

$B_x v_1 = K B_{y1}$ and from eq. (5.7.23) $u_1 B_{z1} - B_x w_1 = K B_{z1}$, are constant and the last term in eq. (5.7.24) becomes $(K/f)(B_z^2 + B_y^2)$; hence there may exist a solution for which the normal components of velocity, density and pressure are unchanged in crossing a discontinuity. From eq. (5.7.22) and (5.7.19), $u \Delta B_y = B_x \Delta v = (1/4\pi)(B_x^2/\rho u) \Delta B_y$, hence $u^2 = (B_x^2/4\pi\rho) = C_A^2 \cos^2\theta$; and this corresponds to a large-amplitude Alfvén wave.

In general the equations may be normalized. If a coordinate system is selected in which the transverse velocities v, w vanish ahead of the shock, and the total magnetic field ahead of the shock, $B_1^2 = (B_x^2 + B_y^2 + B_z^2) = B^2(\cos^2\theta + \sin^2\theta \cos^2\phi + \sin^2\theta \sin^2\phi)$ (defining the field direction, θ, ϕ), we may introduce the Alfvén Mach speed $M = \sqrt{(4\pi\rho_1 u_1^2/B_1^2)}$, the ratio $\beta = C_s^2/C_A^2 = 4\pi\gamma\rho_1/B^2_1$ and for the modifications produced by the shock $r = \rho_2/\rho_1$, $p = p_2/p_1$, $v = v_2/u_1$, $w = w_2/u_1$, $Y = B_{y2}/B_{y1}$, $Z = B_{z2}/B_{z1}$.

We may write

$$-\frac{M^2}{r}(r-1) + \frac{\beta}{\gamma}(p-1) + \tfrac{1}{2}\sin^2\theta[\cos^2\phi(Y^2-1) + \sin^2\phi(Z^2-1)] = 0 \tag{5.7.25}$$

$$M^2 v = (Y-1)\sin\theta\cos\theta\cos\phi \tag{5.7.26}$$

$$M^2 w = (Z-1)\sin\theta\cos\theta\sin\phi \tag{5.7.27}$$

$$v = \left(\frac{Y}{r} - 1\right)\tan\theta\cos\phi \tag{5.7.28}$$

$$w = \left(\frac{Z}{r} - 1\right)\tan\theta\sin\phi \tag{5.7.29}$$

$$-\frac{1}{2}\frac{M^2}{r^2}[(r^2-1) - r^2(v^2+w^2)] + \frac{\beta}{\gamma-1}\left(\frac{p}{r} - 1\right) +$$
$$+ \sin^2\theta[(Y-1)\cos^2\phi + (Z-1)\sin^2\phi] = 0 \tag{5.7.30}$$

An important special case occurs if $\sin\theta = 0$, although $Y^2 \sin^2\theta = b^2 \neq 0$, i.e. where a transverse field is developed behind the shock. For this eqs. (5.7.26) and (5.7.28) reduce to $M^2 v = b$, $rv = b$; hence either $v = b = 0$, corresponding to a normal hydrodynamic shock, or $M^2 = r$, i.e. the shock velocity $u_1 = \sqrt{(B_x^2/4\pi\rho_2)}$ = the speed of an Alfvén wave behind the shock. In the second case, the switch-on shock, the set of equations (5.7.25)–(5.7.30) reduces to

$$\frac{\beta}{\gamma}(p-1) + \tfrac{1}{2}b^2 - (r-1) = 0$$

$$\frac{\beta}{\gamma-1}\left(\frac{p}{r} - 1\right) - \frac{1}{2r}(r^2-1-b^2) = 0$$

By eliminating p we obtain

$$\tfrac{1}{2}b^2 = (r-1)\left[\frac{\gamma+1-(\gamma-1)r}{2} - \beta\right] \tag{5.7.31}$$

but since $r-1 > 0$, $\tfrac{1}{2}[\gamma+1-(\gamma-1)r] \leqslant 1$, a solution can only be found if $\beta < 1$, i.e. if ahead of the shock, the Alfvén speed exceeds the speed of sound.

In general, we may eliminate v and w from eqs. (5.7.26), (5.7.27), (5.7.28) and (5.7.29), obtaining

$$Y = \frac{rM^2 - \cos^2\theta}{M^2 - r\cos^2\theta}; \quad v = \frac{(r-1)\cos\theta\sin\theta\cos\phi}{M^2 - r\cos^2\theta}; \quad w = \frac{(r-1)\cos\theta\sin\theta\sin\phi}{M^2 - r\cos^2\theta}$$

$$(5.7.32)$$

With these substitutions, ϕ disappears from eqs. (5.7.40) and (5.7.45), and the pressure ratio p may be eliminated, leaving a cubic equation for the Mach number M as a function of the density ratio r.

$$\left(\frac{M^2}{r}\frac{(\gamma+1)-(\gamma-1)r}{2} - \beta\right)\left(\frac{M^2}{r} - \cos^2\theta\right)^2 -$$

$$\frac{M^2}{r}\sin^2\theta\left[\frac{M^2}{r}\left(\frac{\gamma+1-(\gamma-1)r}{2} - \frac{1-r}{2}\right) - \cos^2\theta\frac{\gamma+1-(\gamma-1)r}{2}\right] = 0$$

or, introducing new variables $X = M^2/r$, $h = \tfrac{1}{2}[\gamma+1-(\gamma-1)r]$,

$$\left(X - \frac{\beta}{h}\right)(X - \cos^2\theta)^2 - X\sin^2\theta\left[X\left(1 + \frac{(r-1)}{2h}\right) - \cos^2\theta\right] = 0$$

$$(5.7.33)$$

As $X \to +\infty$ this cubic $\to +\infty$, and at $X = 0$, it equals $-(\beta/h)\cos^4\theta < 0$, hence there are either one or three real roots. By examining the first and second derivative of eq. (5.7.33), it is readily seen that these roots are positive for positive h, and negative otherwise; hence, since $X > 0$, the maximum density increase of a magnetohydrodynamic shock is given by $h = 0$, i.e. $(\rho_2/\rho_1) < (\gamma+1)/(\gamma-1)$, just as in a sonic shock. To the three roots of eq. (5.7.33) correspond three distinct shocks, whose interpretation may be obtained by examining the limiting form of eq. (5.7.33) for $r = 1$, i.e.

$$(X-\beta)(X-\cos^2\theta)^2 - X\sin^2\theta[X-\cos^2\theta] = 0$$

which has as its roots $X = \cos^2\theta$

$$X = \frac{1+\beta\pm\sqrt{[(1+\beta)^2 - 4\beta\cos^2\theta]}}{2}$$

and recalling that $X = V^2/C_A^2$, $\beta = C_s^2/C_A^2$, these are seen to be the speed of the Alfvén wave, and the fast and slow magnetosonic speeds of eq. (5.5.13); thus the three possible shocks are the large amplitude analogues of the sound waves. It is interesting to observe that, regardless of how small the ratio of sound speed to Alfvén speed is ahead of the shock, the gas pressure becomes important at high compressions, since eq. (5.7.31) depends on β/h, which $\to \infty$ as $h \to 0$.

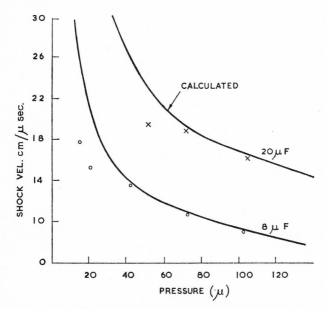

FIG. 5.8. Magnetohydrodynamic shock speed. Measured speed of strong shock produced by condenser discharge into a magnetized plasma. Shock speed vs. initial pressure. Solid curves are theoretical prediction. (Patrick, *Phys. Fluids*, **2**, 589, 1959).

The theory of magnetohydrodynamic shocks has received some verification from the experiment of PATRICK. In this experiment an annular shock tube was used with current coils so placed to produce a magnetic field with components in the direction of propagation and transverse to it. The shock was produced in low-pressure (20–120 μ) hydrogen by driving partially ionized gas by a pulsed magnetic field. In analysing the subsequent flow the gas was considered as an ideal conductor, an assumption which was acceptable since the conductivity rose rapidly on the shock front. The flow was analysed theoretically and a comparison given between the measured and experimental speeds. Other physical parameters, such as light emission, were also calculated and compared reasonably satisfactorily with experiment (Fig. 5.8).

BIBLIOGRAPHY

COWLING, T. G. (1957). *Magnetohydrodynamics*, Interscience.
SYROVATSKII, C. J. (1957). *Usp. Fiz. Nauk*. **62**, 247.
GRAD, H. and colleagues NYO 6486 *Notes on Magnetohydrodynamics* Inst. Math. Sci. N.Y. University, New York, 1956–58.

HARTMANN, J. (1937). *Kgl. Danske Videnskab. Selskab. Mat-fys. Medd.* **15**, 6.

HARTMANN, J. and LAZARUS, F. (1937). *ibid.* **15**, 7.

LEHNERT, B. (ed.) (1958). Int. Ast. Un. Sym. 6, *Electromagnetic Phenomena in Cosmical Physics* p. 50 Cambridge University Press, Cambridge.

ALFVÉN, H. (1951). *Cosmical Electrodynamics*, Oxford University Press.

CLAUSER, F. (ed.) (1960). *Plasma Dynamics*, Addison-Welsey, Reading, Mass.

Ch. 6 LIEPMAN, H. and COLE, S. D. (ed.).

Ch. 7 KANTROWITZ, A. (ed.).

PAIN, H. W. and SMY, P. R. (1961). *J. Fluid. Mec.*, **10**, 51.

BOSTICK, W. (1956). *Phys. Rev.* **104**, 292.

VON KARMAN (ed.) (1959). *Advances in Aeronautical Sciences II*, Pergamon, London.

MOECKEL, W. 1078.

BLACKMAN, V. 1111.

HARDCASTLE, R. A. and JEPHCOTT, D. F. (1960). *Proc. 4th Int. Conf. on Ionization Phenomena in Gases* Vol. II, 786.

SAWYER, G. A., SCOTT, P. L. and STRATTON, T. F. (1959). *Phys. Fluids* **2**, 47.

LÜST, R. (1959). *Fortsch. der Phys.* **7**, 503.

LIGHTHILL, M. J. (1960). *Phil. Trans.* **A252**, 317.

FRIEDRICHS, K. O. and KRANZER, H. (1958). N.Y.O. 6486 *Notes on Magnetohydrodynamics* VIII. Inst. Math. Sci. N.Y.U., New York.

DE HOFFMAN, F. and TELLER, E. (1950). *Phys. Rev.* **80**, 692.

PATRICK, R. M. (1959). *Phys. Fluids* **2**, 589.

FARADAY, M., *Faraday's Diary* 1820–1862, I pp. 407 et seq. (T. Martin, ed.), G. Bell & Sons, London.

CHAPTER 6

MAGNETOHYDRODYNAMIC STABILITY

THE study of the stability of plasma configurations has been intensively pursued, chiefly in the search for stable confining configurations which can be used as magnetic bottles for isolating masses of hot plasma. Finding such configurations appears the essential problem of controlled thermonuclear fusion research but it is of great importance to the entire study of plasmas. Except in special cases, a hot plasma cannot exist in contact with solid materials, hence, only in a magnetically confined plasma do the ions and electrons have long lives. Moreover many of the most interesting properties of a plasma are exhibited only under conditions of high temperature and low density, conditions that require magnetic confinement. Similarly, among astrophysical objects, only those configurations which are stable can be expected to be permanent.

A further stimulus to stability studies has been their relative tractability, since the problems are linear in the dependent variables. Even with this advantage, problems can become difficult.

1. THE CONCEPT OF STABILITY

The basic methods used for studying plasma stability are illustrated by the one-dimensional problem of a particle moving in a potential well; e.g. a particle sliding on a smooth surface under gravity. Equilibrium demands that the force on the particle vanish, hence that the particle sits on a flat point $dV/dz = 0$. This can happen at the bottom of a well or the top of a hill. To investigate its stability, we note that on being displaced slightly from the equilibrium point z_0, the particle experiences a force $F(z_0 + \delta z)$ $= -(d/dz)V(z_0 + \delta z) = -(d^2V/dz^2)\,\delta z$ and if $d^2V/dz^2 > 0$, F is antiparallel to δz and the particle is forced back to z_0, the equilibrium position, i.e. the bottom of a well is stable while at the top of the hill $d^2V/dz^2 < 0$, F is parallel to δz and forces the particle away from the equilibrium position. This simple example suggests three possible methods of studying stability:

(a) we may discover the sign of d^2V/dz^2, if negative, the system is unstable;

(b) if V depends on some continuous variable β, and is known to be stable (or unstable) for some range of β, it may be possible to find some critical β_0 which divides the stable from the unstable region and at which $d^2V/dz^2 = 0$;

(c) we may form the linearized equations of motion, which for this problem have the form $m(d^2\delta z/dt^2) = -(\partial^2 V/\partial z^2)\,\delta z$, and seek a solution with time dependence $\sim \exp(\Omega t)$. If the real part of $\Omega > 0$ the system is unstable. Again, if Ω is a function of β we may seek a β_0 for which $\mathscr{R}(\Omega) = 0$, the point of marginal stability.

Of these methods the last has most generality, being applicable even to dissipative systems for which no potential exists. If there is a potential, the dynamic problem is reduced to a static one at marginal stability, but either of the first two methods may be applied. Often the first method is most convenient, since no equation of motion need be solved. All three

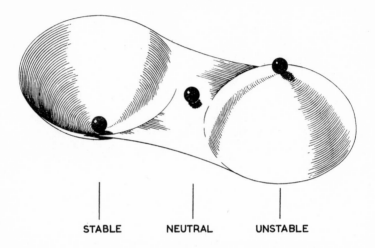

STABLE   NEUTRAL   UNSTABLE

FIG. 6.1. Principles of stability analysis. Illustrating dependence of stability on second derivative of potential. Equilibrium is stable at the bottom of a well $(\partial^2 V/\partial x^2) > 0$, unstable at the top of a hill $(\partial^2 V/\partial x^2) < 0$, neutral at half-point $(\partial^2 V/\partial x^2) = 0$.

methods are limited by linearization and are unable to distinguish between an extended flat area and a local point of inflection which is unstable. Furthermore, the theory considers only the local behaviour of the potential and describes stability against infinitesimal perturbations; for instance, a small shallow well on top of a large hill is described as stable, while a small hillock in the centre of a deep well is described as unstable, although for finite disturbances the situation is reversed.

If a mechanical system has many degrees of freedom, these arguments become a little more complicated. The motion of a disturbance in any co-ordinate δq_i involves all the displacements, thus

$$m\frac{\mathrm{d}^2}{\mathrm{d}t^2}\delta q_i = -\sum_j \frac{\partial^2 V}{\partial q_i\,\partial q_j}\delta q_j = \sum_j a_{ij}\delta q_j \qquad (6.1.1)$$

To solve systems of this kind, it is possible to introduce a linear combination of the δq_i, i.e. $\delta Q_i = b_{ij}\,\delta q_j$, which may be chosen so that the matrix on the right, $b_{ij}a_{jk}b_{kl}^{-1}$ is diagonal, so that

$$m\frac{\mathrm{d}^2}{\mathrm{d}t^2}\delta Q_i = A_i\delta Q_i \tag{6.1.2}$$

Thus the normal coordinates, Q_i, behave as independent, and have exponential time dependence. On the other hand, if we form the scalar product of eq. (6.1.1) with δq_i and integrate with respect to time,

$$\tfrac{1}{2}m\sum_i (\delta\dot{q}_i{}^2(t)) = \sum_{ij} \int \mathrm{d}t\, a_{ij}\delta q_j\delta\dot{q}_i$$

$$= \sum_{ij} \int \mathrm{d}t\frac{a_{ij}+a_{ji}}{2}(\delta q_j\delta\dot{q}_i+\delta\dot{q}_j\delta q_i)$$

$$+ \frac{a_{ij}-a_{ji}}{2}(\delta q_j\delta\dot{q}_i-\delta\dot{q}_j\delta q_i)$$

$$= \sum_{ij} \left(\frac{a_{ij}+a_{ji}}{2}\right)\delta q_i\delta q_j = \sum_{ij} a_{ij}\delta q_i\delta q_j \tag{6.1.3}$$

the a_{ij} being symmetric, since

$$a_{ij}-a_{ji} = \frac{\partial^2 V}{\partial q_i\partial q_j} - \frac{\partial^2 V}{\partial q_j\partial q_i} = 0$$

The kinetic energy will then increase if there exists any displacement $\delta\mathbf{q}$, for which $\Sigma a_{ij}\,\delta q_i\,\delta q_j > 0$, and the system is unstable. However, this is just $-[V(\mathbf{q}_0+\delta\mathbf{q})-V(\mathbf{q})] = -\delta V$, the negative of the increment in potential energy calculated to second order in $\delta\mathbf{q}$; hence the system is stable if $\delta V > 0$ for all possible displacements $\delta\mathbf{q}$.

For a continuous system such as a plasma, the vector displacement $\delta q_i(t)$, a function of time alone, must be replaced by a vector displacement $\boldsymbol{\xi}(\mathbf{x}, t)$, a function of space and time, and the set of eqs. (6.1.1) replaced by a set of partial differential equations, together with associated boundary conditions. As in eq. (6.1.2), the time dependence of $\boldsymbol{\xi}$ may be taken as exponential, and the frequency determined as eigenvalues of this partial differential system, the normal modes of the system corresponding to the δQ_i.

2. CONVECTIVE INSTABILITIES

Before discussing the formulation of the general problem of magnetohydrodynamic stability we will examine a particular mode of instability, the interchange mode. Interchange instabilities are similar to the instability of a layer of fluid heated from below, and are possible in plasmas where over some region the unperturbed magnetic field has no shear so that adjacent lines of force may be topologically equivalent. It is then possible to consider instabilities which interchange adjacent tubes of magnetic flux. Since an element of magnetic flux $\delta\phi = |B|\delta A$, where δA is an element of area normal to the lines of force, the volume of the flux tube is

$$\delta v = \delta\phi \int \frac{dl}{|B|}$$

(6.2.1)

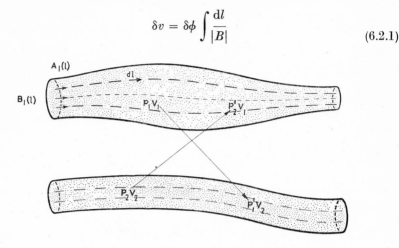

FIG. 6.2. Interchange of two flux tubes.

the integral being carried along the entire length of the flux tube. The thermal energy in the tube is $p\delta v/(\gamma-1)$, and the magnetic energy is

$$\frac{\langle B^2\rangle \delta v}{8\pi} = \frac{\delta\phi}{8\pi}\int |B|\,dl$$

(6.2.2)

On interchanging flux tubes either of the quantities may be changed and a change in total energy may occur.

One possible type of interchange is the convective in which no change of magnetic energy occurs, two tubes of equal flux being interchanged. Since $\delta W_M \sim \delta\phi \int B\,dl = \delta\phi^2 \int dl/A$ depends only on the geometry of the flux tube, it will vanish if on interchange

$$\int_1 \frac{dl}{A_1} = \int_2 \frac{dl}{A_2}$$

The change in thermal energy can be calculated as follows: if the interchange is performed adiabatically so that $p_1 \to p'_1 = p_1(v_1/v_2)^\gamma$, the difference between initial and final thermal energies is

$$-\delta W = (p_2-p_1')\frac{v_2}{\gamma-1} + (p_1-p_2')\frac{v_1}{\gamma-1} = \frac{v_2}{\gamma-1}\left[p_2-p_1\left(\frac{v_1}{v_2}\right)^\gamma\right] +$$

$$+ \frac{v_1}{\gamma-1}\left[p_1-p_2\left(\frac{v_2}{v_1}\right)^\gamma\right] = -\delta v\left[\delta p + \frac{\gamma p}{v}\delta v\right] = -\frac{\delta v}{v^\gamma}\delta(pv^\gamma)$$

(6.2.3)

and we may write as a necessary condition for stability

$$\delta v \delta(p v^\gamma) > 0$$

The usual criterion for stability against thermal convection may be obtained from this by using the temperature and pressure as variables in the second term. From $pv = RT$,

$$\frac{\delta p}{p} + \frac{\delta v}{v} = \frac{\delta T}{T}; \quad \text{and} \quad \delta p + \frac{\gamma p}{v}\delta v = p\left[\frac{\delta p}{p} + \gamma\left(\frac{\delta T}{T} - \frac{\delta p}{p}\right)\right]$$

$$= \gamma p \left[\frac{1-\gamma}{\gamma}\frac{\delta p}{p} + \frac{\delta T}{T}\right]$$

but since $T \sim p^{[(\gamma-1)/\gamma]}$ on an adiabatic change, we obtain the stability condition $\gamma \delta v(\delta T - \delta T_{\text{ad}}) > 0$, i.e. if $\partial v/\partial z > 0$ and $\partial T/\partial z < 0$, $-(\partial T/\partial z)$ $-([\partial T_{\text{ad}}/\partial z) > 0$ for stability, i.e. the temperature must decrease with height less rapidly than adiabatically for stability. As an example of the applications of eq. (6.2.3) consider a simple constricted discharge where $B = B_\theta(r)$. Then

$$v(r) = \oint \frac{dl}{B} = \frac{2\pi r}{B_\theta(r)} = \frac{\pi r^2}{I(r)} = \frac{A(r)}{I(r)} = \frac{1}{\langle j(r) \rangle}$$

Thus the gradient of v at r is opposite in sign to the gradient of the mean current density within r. For the constant current case $j(r) = \text{const}$, $\delta v = 0$ for all interchanges, and the system is marginally stable. If the current is proportional to the density, $j \sim n$, so that the Bennet distribution is produced, i.e.

$$p = \frac{p_0}{[1+(r/r_0)^2]^2}, \qquad B_\theta = \frac{B_0(r/r_0)}{[1+(r^2/r_0^2)]}, \qquad v = 2\pi(r_0/\dot{B}_0)(1+r^2/r_0^2),$$

eq. (6.2.3) becomes

$$p\delta v \cdot \left[\frac{\delta p}{p} + \gamma\frac{\delta v}{v}\right] = \frac{2\pi p_0 r_0}{B_0}\frac{\gamma-2}{[1+(r^2/r_0^2)]^3} \cdot \left[\delta\left(\frac{r^2}{r_0^2}\right)\right]^2$$

and the distribution is unstable for $\gamma < 2$.

Interest has been shown in the possibility of containing plasma in a shell about a toroidal conductor. Some idea of the stability of this configuration may be obtained by examining the stability of a low-density plasma in a dipole field. If p vanishes at the edge of the plasma, the change in thermal energy $\simeq (\delta v/\delta\phi)[(\delta p/\delta\phi) + (\gamma p/v)(\delta v/\delta\phi)] \simeq (\delta v/\delta\phi)(\delta p/\delta\phi)$. Near the edge of the plasma $p = 0$ and $\delta p/\delta\phi < 0$ if ϕ increases toward the edge of the plasma, and the stability is determined by the sign of $\delta v/\delta\phi$, which must be positive for instability. Thus if $\int(1/B)\, dl$ increases toward the edge of the plasma the system is unstable. For a dipole field $B_\theta = \mu \sin\theta/r^3$, $B_r = 2\mu(\cos\theta/r^3)$ and the field line is given by $r/r_0 = (\sin\theta)^2$, where r_0 is the distance from the origin to the point at which the field line crosses the median plane. Then

$$\oint \frac{\mathrm{d}l}{B} = \int \frac{r\,\mathrm{d}\theta\sqrt{(1+B_r^2/B_\theta^2)}}{\sqrt{(B_r^2+B_\theta^2)}} = \int \frac{r\,\mathrm{d}\theta}{|B_\theta|} = \frac{2r_0^4}{\mu}\cdot\int_0^{\pi/2} \frac{\sin^8\theta}{\sin\theta}\,\mathrm{d}\theta = \frac{32}{35}\frac{r_0^4}{\mu} > 0$$

thus

$$\frac{\mathrm{d}v}{\mathrm{d}r_0} \sim \frac{\delta v}{\delta\phi} > 0$$

the system is unstable.

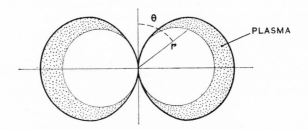

Fig. 6.3. Plasma on a dipole field.

A somewhat more elaborate analysis may be given for cylindrical shear-free systems in which $B_z(r, z)$ and $B_r(r, z) \neq 0$, but $B_\theta = 0$. Here the z flux for example, $\phi = \int B_z r\,\mathrm{d}r$, may be used to identify magnetic surfaces, on which it has been shown $\int(\mathrm{d}l/B) = $ const. Near the edge of the discharge $\delta p/\delta\phi < 0$ and again since $p \to 0$, while v remains bounded and continuous, $\delta p/\delta\phi + p\delta v/\delta\phi \simeq \delta p/\delta\phi < 0$, hence from eq. (6.2.3) the system is unstable if $\delta v/\delta\phi > 0$. To find the sign of δv let us introduce a coordinate system x, y in the plane containing B, then

$$v = \int \frac{\mathrm{d}l}{B} = \int \frac{\mathrm{d}x(1+B_y^2/B_x^2)^{\frac{1}{2}}}{(B_x^2+B_y^2)^{\frac{1}{2}}} = \int \frac{\mathrm{d}x}{B_x}$$

and

$$\frac{\delta v}{\delta\phi} = \int \frac{\delta n}{\delta\phi} \frac{\partial}{\partial n} \frac{\mathrm{d}x}{B_x}$$

where n is the normal to the field line $\mathrm{d}x$. If, near the edge of the discharge, the fields are close to vacuum fields

$$\frac{\partial B_x}{\partial n} = \frac{\partial B_n}{\partial x}$$

and if x is locally tangent to the field,

$$\frac{\partial B_n}{\partial x} = -\frac{B}{R}$$

where R is the radius of curvature of the field line and is negative if the centre of curvature lies in the direction of increasing n. Now since $\mathrm{d}\phi/\mathrm{d}n = Br$, $\delta v \sim \int(\mathrm{d}l/B^2 rR)$, where r is the radius of the boundary. In hydromagnetic equilibria the flux enclosed by the boundary is constant along the field lines, hence near the edge

$$Br^2 = \text{const}, \quad r \sim B^{-1/2}, \quad \text{and} \quad \delta v \simeq \int \frac{\mathrm{d}l}{B^{3/2}R}$$

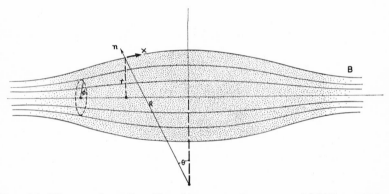

Fig. 6.4. Mirror configuration. Unstable, centre of curvature of field lines within plasma in region of weak field.

We may write $\mathrm{d}l/R$ as the change in the angle $\mathrm{d}\theta$ at the centre of curvature as a point moves along a flux tube. In a mirror configuration, the flux lines outside the plasma must be parallel to those inside, hence in the centre, where the radius of curvature lies inside the plasma, the field is weak, and the contribution to $\delta v = \int(1/B^{3/2})\,\mathrm{d}\theta$ is large and positive while near the ends, where the radius of curvature lies outside the plasma over the same range $\mathrm{d}\theta$, the field is strong, hence the positive contribution exceeds the negative, $v > 0$ and the plasma is unstable.

In the picket-fence, or cusped containing geometry, the field lines curve away from the plasma and form cusps, where, of course, the plasma is not contained. Elsewhere, however, since the radius of curvature lies outside the plasma, v decreases outward and the plasma is stable.

In yet another device, the guarded plasma, rigid conductors lie inside the plasma, so that where the centre of curvature lies within the plasma, the field is strong. This again is stable against convective interchanges.

Not all interchanges need be convective, the flux tubes interchanged need not contain equal fluxes, and an interesting type of interchange occurs when the volumes of the interchanged fluid elements are equal. Then no change in thermal energy occurs, but the magnetic energy may be altered. If the two flux tubes have fluxes ϕ_1 and ϕ_2, and fields B_1 and B_2 so that $B_1 A_1 = \phi_1$, $B_2 A_2 = \phi_2$, then after interchange the flux ϕ_1 will have area A_2, hence the field strength

$$B'_1 = \phi_1/A_2 = B_2\ \phi_1/\phi_2$$

and the final magnetic energy in the flux tube ϕ_1 is

$$(1/8\pi)\int (B'_1)^2 A_2 \mathrm{d}l_2 = (1/8\pi)(\phi_1/\phi_2)^2 \int B_2{}^2 A_2 \mathrm{d}l_2 = (1/8\pi)(\phi^2{}_1/\phi_2)\int B_2 \mathrm{d}l_2$$

The change in magnetic energy is

$$\delta W = (1/8\pi)\{(\phi_1{}^2/\phi_2)\int B_2 \mathrm{d}l_2 + (\phi_2{}^2/\phi_1)\int B_1 \mathrm{d}l_1 - \phi_1 \int B_1 \mathrm{d}l_1 - \phi_2 \int B_2 \mathrm{d}l_2\}$$

$$= (1/8\pi)(\phi_2{}^2 - \phi_1{}^2)[(1/\phi_1)\int B_1 \mathrm{d}l_1 - (1/\phi_2)\int B_2 \mathrm{d}l_2]$$

$$= (1/8\pi)(\phi_2{}^2 - \phi_1{}^2)[\int \mathrm{d}l_1/A_1 - \int \mathrm{d}l_2/A_2]$$

$$= (1/8\pi)(\phi_2 + \phi_1)\int B_1 \mathrm{d}l_1 (\delta\phi/\phi)[1 - (\phi_1/\phi_2)\int B_2 \mathrm{d}l_2 / \int B_1 \mathrm{d}l_1]$$

$$= 2W_M{}^1(\delta\phi/\phi)[(\delta\phi/\phi) - (\delta\int B\mathrm{d}l / \int B\mathrm{d}l)]$$

or since the volume is held fixed

$$\phi = V/\int \mathrm{d}l/B$$

$$\delta W = 2W_M{}^1\delta \log\left(\int \mathrm{d}l/B\right)[\delta \log\left(\int \mathrm{d}l/B\right) + \delta \log\left(\int B\mathrm{d}l\right)] \qquad (6.2.4)$$

On the other hand since

$$V = \int A_1 \mathrm{d}l_1 = \int A_2 \mathrm{d}l_2 = \int A_2(\mathrm{d}l_2/\mathrm{d}l_1)\mathrm{d}l_1$$

$$\delta W = (1/8\pi)(\phi_2{}^2 - \phi_1{}^2)\int (\mathrm{d}l_1/A_1)[1 - (\mathrm{d}l_2/\mathrm{d}l_1)^2]$$

An interesting special case of this occurs when a field-free plasma is supported by an external field, for then

$$\delta W = (1/8\pi)\phi_{ext}{}^2 \int (\mathrm{d}l_1/A_1)[1 - (\mathrm{d}l_{ext}/\mathrm{d}l_{int})^2]$$

and the plasma is unstable if field lines increase in length on leaving the plasma surface, e.g. if their centre of curvature lies within the plasma. On the other hand, if the centre of curvature lies outside the plasma, the configuration is stable.

These remarks already indicate that, while a hole in plasma should be easily maintained by magnetic pressure, it is difficult to contain a plasma by such means. From stability considerations alone, the preferred configuration is one in which the surface is cusped, so that the centre of curvature of the field lines lies everywhere outside the plasma, and such cusped geometries have attracted some attention in thermonuclear research.

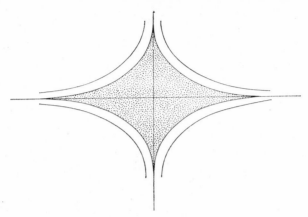

Fig. 6.5. Cusped configuration. Stable, centre of curvature of field lines always outside plasma.

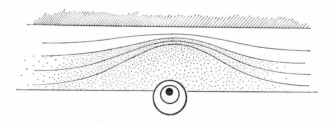

Fig. 6.6. The guarded plasma.

Rayleigh–Taylor Instabilities

A most important type of instability is the magnetohydrodynamic analogue of Rayleigh–Taylor instability, the instability of a dense fluid supported by a less dense one. It can be expected either where a plasma is held against gravity by a magnetic field, i.e. in the sun's atmosphere, or where a plasma is accelerated by a magnetic field, the acceleration acting like an oppositely directed gravitational force. To analyse these, in simple cases, it is enough to add the difference in mechanical potential to the difference in magnetic energy. For example, if a plasma is held up by a horizontal magnetic field, plasma and field can be interchanged with no change in

8

magnetic energy, but a loss of potential. As a second example, consider a plasma held up by a magnetic field whose centre of curvature lies below it. In this case, an interchange will produce an increase of magnetic energy

$$\delta W_m = \frac{1}{8\pi}\phi \int dl_1 B_1 \frac{2\delta z}{R} \tag{6.2.5}$$

where R is the radius of curvature of the field lines, and δz the vertical motion. At the same time, the loss in potential is $\delta W_z = -\int A\, dl\rho g\delta z$, thus the net loss in energy is

$$\delta W_T = -\int A\, dl\delta z\left[\rho g - \frac{B^2}{4\pi R}\right] \tag{6.2.6}$$

and if this is positive the system is unstable. Note that if the radius of curvature lies within the plasma, or if the field lines are straight, the system is unstable. It is not inconceivable that the stability conferred by field curvature may be responsible for the appearance of arches among the solar prominences, these being masses of relatively dense plasma supported by magnetic fields, cf. KIEPENHAUER, especially Figs. 68–71.

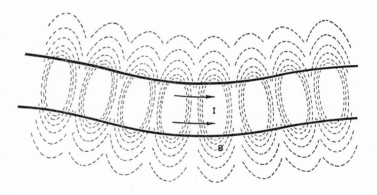

FIG. 6.7. "Wriggle" instability of pinch. On concave side of curved conductor, field lines are crowded, field strength increased and enhanced magnetic pressure increases concavity.

"Wriggle" Instability

A simple instability which can be understood without much formalism, and which is distinct from the interchange mode, is that responsible for the wriggling of a constricted discharge. When a current-carrying conductor is curved, the field lines on the concave side are crowded together, and the magnetic pressure $B^2/8\pi$ is increased, while on the convex side the magnetic pressure is reduced, hence a net force acts on the conductor pushing the convex side outward and increasing the curvature; thus, the conductor is unstable.

To analyse this, let us suppose that the current flows along the centre of a wire. The magnetic field which is related to the current density by

$$B = \int \mathbf{j}(r') \times \frac{(\mathbf{r}-\mathbf{r}')}{|\mathbf{r}-\mathbf{r}'|^3} \, \mathrm{d}^3 r'$$

produces a force at $\mathbf{r}$, $\mathbf{F} = \mathbf{j} \times \mathbf{B}$

$$\mathbf{F} = \mathbf{j}(r) \times \left\{ \int \mathbf{j}(r') \times \frac{(\mathbf{r}-\mathbf{r}')}{|\mathbf{r}-\mathbf{r}'|^3} \right\} \mathrm{d}^3 r'$$

$$= \mathbf{j} \int \cdot \frac{(\mathbf{r}-\mathbf{r}')}{|\mathbf{r}-\mathbf{r}'|^3} \mathbf{j}(r') \, \mathrm{d}^3 r' - \mathbf{j} \cdot \int \mathbf{j}(r') \frac{(\mathbf{r}-\mathbf{r}')}{|\mathbf{r}-\mathbf{r}'|^3} \, \mathrm{d}^3 r'$$

To get the effective force on a wire of radius r_0, we take the mean of $\mathbf{F}$ at $-r_0$ and $+r_0$ about the centre, thus eliminating the forces directed toward the centre of the wire. This is integrated over the wire and we observe that if the wire lies along the curve $[x, \xi(x), 0]$ (a plane curve), then $j = I\delta(z) \times \delta[y-\xi(x)]$, $(1, \mathrm{d}\xi/\mathrm{d}x, 0)$, then to first order in $\xi(x)$,

$$F = I^2 \left\{ \int \frac{x-x'}{[(x-x')^2+r_0^2]^{3/2}} \frac{\partial \xi}{\partial x'}(x') \, \mathrm{d}x' - \int \frac{\xi(x)-\xi(x') \, \mathrm{d}x'}{[(x-x')^2+r_0^2]^{3/2}} \right\}$$

$$= I^2 \left\{ \int_{-\infty}^{\infty} \mathrm{d}u \frac{[\xi(x+u)-\xi(x)-u(\mathrm{d}/\mathrm{d}u)\xi(x+u)]}{(u^2+r_0^2)^{3/2}} \right\}$$

$$= I^2 \left\{ \int_{-a}^{a} \mathrm{d}u \frac{[\xi(x+u)-\xi(x)-u(\mathrm{d}/\mathrm{d}u)\xi(x+u)]}{(u^2+r_0^2)^{3/2}} \right\} +$$

$$+ \int_{a}^{\infty} \mathrm{d}u \frac{\{\xi(x+u)+\xi(x-u)-2\xi(x)-u(\mathrm{d}/\mathrm{d}u)[\xi(x+u)+\xi(x-u)]\}}{(u^2+r_0^2)^{3/2}} \right\}$$

$$\simeq I^2 \left\{ \int_{-a}^{a} \mathrm{d}u \frac{[u\xi'(x)+\frac{1}{2}u^2\xi''(x)+ \dots -u\xi'(x)-u^2\xi''(x)+ \dots]}{(u^2+r_0^2)^{3/2}} \right\} +$$

$$+ \frac{\xi(x+a)+\xi(x-a)-\xi(x)}{a^2} - \int_{a}^{\infty} \frac{\xi(x+u)+\xi(x-u)}{u^3} \right\}$$

$$= -\tfrac{1}{2}I^2 \int_{-a}^{a} \mathrm{d}u \frac{u^2\xi''(x)}{(u^2+r_0^2)^{3/2}} + 0(\xi/a^2) = -I^2(\log 2a/r_0 - 1)\xi''(x) +$$

$$+ 0(\xi/a^2)$$

For small r_0, the dominant term in this is

$$F \simeq -I^2 \log\frac{2a}{r_0}\xi''(x) \qquad (6.2.7)$$

a force which increases the curvature of the wire. To get a numerical value, the curve may be Fourier analysed, and the effect of each harmonic component discovered. The integrals then may be expressed as modified Bessel functions, and for small r_0 the force on the curve $A \sin kx$ becomes

$$F = Ak^2 \sin kx \left[\log\frac{\gamma}{kr_0} - 0.07\right] \qquad (6.2.8)$$

Experimental Evidence for Plasma Instability

It has proved all too easy to demonstrate the existence of instability in a magnetically confined plasma. The first revelation of Soviet controlled thermonuclear research (KURCHATOV, 1956) contained a good photograph

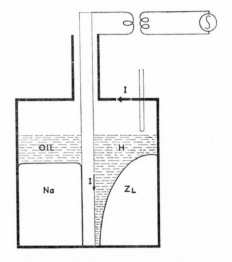

FIG. 6.8. Stability of excluded conductor. Colgate's demonstration of the stability of a liquid metal supported by a magnetic field whose centre of curvature lies without the fluid. r.f. fields from current in central rod forces liquid sodium into stable configuration shown on right. (Colgate *et al. Rev. Mod. Phys.* **32**, 744, 1960.)

of the interchange instability in a simple rapidly collapsing pinch. Photography, of course, requires fast observation techniques since microsecond times are involved, but instabilities may also appear as noise on voltage wave forms, or as fluctuating signals on magnetic probes.

The effect of surface curvature has been demonstrated in sodium experiments performed by COLGATE *et al.* For the first of these experiments a pot containing liquid sodium covered by a layer of oil was prepared having an axial conductor through which an alternating current (a few kilowatts at 100 kc/s) could be passed. The magnetic pressure so produced forced the conducting sodium away leaving a funnel shaped cavity about the conductor. Since the skin depth in the sodium was small ($\sim 0 \cdot 05$ cm), this simulated the effect of a surface current. The sodium could then be frozen and on examination the surface was shown to be smooth and have the shape $r^2(z - z_0) = k$ predicted by hydrostatic equilibrium. Quite different results were obtained when a small billet of solid sodium was placed between pulsed mirror coils producing 20 kg for 200 μsec. For such times and such pressures, solid sodium behaved as a liquid, and was forged to the shape of a mirror of plasma. On the surface, however, were pronounced longitudinal ripples as would be expected from the growth of interchange instabilities. Rather surprisingly, however, in a plasma contained by a mirror field, no signs of instability were observed (POST). A hot plasma was produced by magnetic compression, the particle density increasing from 10^{11}–10^{12} to 10^{13}–10^{14} cm^{-3} while the magnetic field rose from 0–100 g to 10,000–40,000 g, the final electron temperature being 10–25 keV (inferred from energy of escaping electrons). Under these conditions, the characteristic growth time of interchange instabilities is $\sim 0 \cdot 14$ μsec; however, the plasma persisted for 30 msec—the decay times for the fields. This unexpected behaviour has been associated with the fact that lines of force were tied to conducting end plates, so that interchange was prevented.

Guard ring stabilization has been elaborated by BRAGINSKI and KADOMTSEV, and experiments conducted by ORLINSKII on a high current discharge stabilized by metal rods carrying small currents have displayed a dramatic change in the appearance of the discharge when so stabilized.

Cusp experiments in a plasma are somewhat difficult to perform since particles are lost rapidly through the cusped region, the plasma is cooled and diffuses rapidly through the magnetic field. Some experiments by ALLEN, however, in which a high current gas discharge was held in by a "picket fence" coil, i.e. a series of windings with currents alternating in direction, gave spectacular evidence for selective loss at the cusp since the glass containing vessel was etched along the cusp by the escaping plasma.

The Rayleigh–Taylor instability has been demonstrated in liquid sodium, again by COLGATE. By driving liquid sodium out of a vessel with a compressed gas, he produced a hollow jet which was accelerated inward by a rapidly rising (0·2 msec) magnetic field, which persisted for 2 msec. During this interval the sodium surface was illuminated by 2 μsec light pulses and the surface photographed displaying the expected ripples.

CURZON et al. made a careful study of the growth of instability in a straight discharge in argon at pressures 120–1000 μ, with currents ~ 100 kA. A Kerr cell framing camera with 0·4 μsec exposure time took photographs of the plasma through a wire mesh axial return. From the observed size of the column, and the growth of the ripples appearing on it, it was possible to correlate the growth of instability determined by the standard deviation of the discharge radius with the acceleration of the plasma and it was found that ripples grew when the acceleration was directed into the plasma, as is predicted by the theory. The growth rate, too, was in agreement with $\sqrt{(ka)}$, as expected. Under these circumstances the gas is cooled by radiation, the collapse velocity is supersonic, and the Rayleigh–Taylor instability exceeds that produced by gas pressure which grows as $(kv_\theta{}^2/R)^{1/2}$, v_θ being the ion thermal speed and R the radius of curvature of the field line.

The wriggle instability has been photographed in constricted discharges, both in a straight tube and in a torus, e.g. by CARRUTHERS and DAVENPORT. Good photographs were obtained in a discharge of ~ 1500 A in 10^{-3} mm Hg

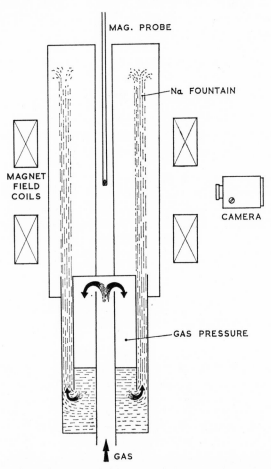

FIG. 6.9. Rayleigh–Taylor instability of a liquid metal. Colgate's demonstration of Rayleigh–Taylor instability. A burst of compressed gas in the lower vessel forces liquid sodium up into a hollow cylindrical jet. This is collapsed by a rising magnetic field from the external coils. Break-up of jet is watched by camera, while axial magnetic probe records magnetic irregularities. (Colgate., U.C.R.L. 4560.)

of He, A and Xe, using an image converter with an 8 μsec exposure. While the current was low and rising, wriggles were not observable, but at current maximum helical disturbances appeared having a wavelength $\sim 2 \times$ tube diameter (9·7 cm). The voltage pulse had a duration of ~ 500 μsec, and in the toroidal tube, the current wave form displayed irregular ripples, typical of unstable discharges.

3. THE FORMAL THEORY OF PLASMA STABILITY

We will now develop the formal procedure sketched in Section 1 and first develop the linearized equations of motion for a small perturbation about an equilibrium. As in the theory of sound, the Lagrangian variable $\boldsymbol{\xi}$ proves useful. We start from a set of fields $\mathbf{B}_0$, pressure p_0, and density ρ_0 which are in equilibrium, i.e. for which

$$-\nabla p_0 = \nabla \frac{1}{8\pi} B_0{}^2 - \frac{1}{4\pi} \mathbf{B}_0 . \nabla \mathbf{B}_0$$

and consider the equations of motion for a disturbance $\boldsymbol{\xi}$.

The equation of continuity takes the form,

$$\rho' = -\nabla . (\rho_0 \boldsymbol{\xi})$$

and the equation of motion,

$$\rho_0 \frac{d^2 \boldsymbol{\xi}}{dt^2} = -\nabla \left(p' + \frac{\mathbf{B}_0 . \mathbf{B}'}{4\pi} \right) + \frac{1}{4\pi} \{ \mathbf{B}_0 . \nabla \mathbf{B}' + \mathbf{B}' . \nabla \mathbf{B}_0 \} \qquad (6.3.1)$$

The magnetic field is determined from flux conservation by

$$\mathbf{B}' = (\mathbf{B}_0 . \nabla) \boldsymbol{\xi} - (\boldsymbol{\xi} . \nabla) \mathbf{B}_0 - \mathbf{B}_0 \operatorname{div} \boldsymbol{\xi} = \operatorname{curl}(\boldsymbol{\xi} \times \mathbf{B}_0) = \mathbf{Q}(\boldsymbol{\xi}) \qquad (6.3.2)$$

while the adiabatic equation of state determines the pressure as

$$p' = -[\gamma p_0 \operatorname{div} \boldsymbol{\xi} + \boldsymbol{\xi} . \nabla p_0] \qquad (6.3.3)$$

for

$$\frac{Dp'}{Dt} = \left(\frac{\partial}{\partial t} p' + \frac{\partial \boldsymbol{\xi}}{\partial t} . \nabla p_0 \right) = \frac{p_0 \gamma}{\rho_0} \frac{D\rho'}{Dt} = -\gamma p_0 \operatorname{div} \frac{\partial \boldsymbol{\xi}}{\partial t}$$

By writing the magnetic force in eq. (6.3.1) as

$$\mathbf{j}_0 \times \mathbf{B}' + \mathbf{j}' \times \mathbf{B}_0 = (\mathbf{j}_0 \times \mathbf{Q}) + \frac{1}{4\pi} (\operatorname{curl} \mathbf{Q}) \times \mathbf{B}_0$$

the equation of motion may be written in the form

$$\rho_0 \ddot{\boldsymbol{\xi}} = \nabla[\gamma p_0 \operatorname{div} \boldsymbol{\xi} + \boldsymbol{\xi} . \nabla p_0] + \mathbf{j}_0 \times \mathbf{Q} + \frac{1}{4\pi} (\operatorname{curl} \mathbf{Q}) \times \mathbf{B}_0 \qquad (6.3.4)$$

where

$$\mathbf{Q}(\boldsymbol{\xi}) = \operatorname{curl}(\boldsymbol{\xi} \times \mathbf{B}_0)$$

If we are interested in the Rayleigh–Taylor problem in which a gravitational potential, ϕ, acts on the plasma, we must add the terms

$$-\rho'\boldsymbol{\nabla}\phi_0-\rho_0\boldsymbol{\nabla}\phi' = \boldsymbol{\nabla}\cdot(\rho_0\,\boldsymbol{\xi})\boldsymbol{\nabla}\phi-\rho_0\boldsymbol{\nabla}(\,\boldsymbol{\xi}\cdot\boldsymbol{\nabla}\phi)$$

The analogue of the first procedure described requires the solution of this equation subject to appropriate boundary conditions, and explicitly determines the rate of growth of a small disturbance $\boldsymbol{\xi}$ about equilibrium.

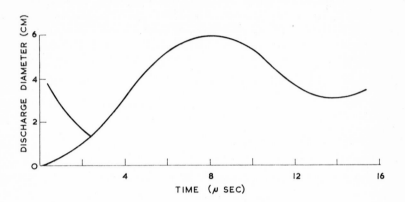

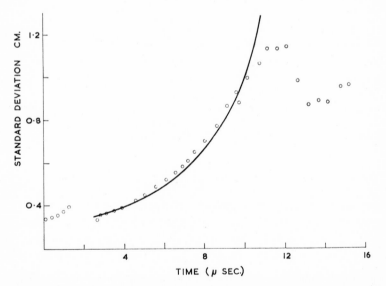

FIG. 6.10. Rayleigh–Taylor instability in a plasma. The upper curve shows the mean radius of a cylindrical plasma as a function of time: when the curvature is negative, the plasma is accelerated by the field. The lower curve shows standard deviation of the plasma radius, made irregular by growing instabilities. Note that this increases only when the field accelerates the plasma. (Curzon *et al.*, *Proc. Soc.* **A257**, 386, 1960.)

It is also possible to develop the analogy to the determination of the variation in potential energy. To do this, note that the energy in the fluid may be written as

$$W = \int d\tau \left(\frac{B^2}{8\pi} + \frac{p}{\gamma - 1} \right) \tag{6.3.5}$$

To calculate the variation in this, we need B' and p' to second order; however, these are easily found from eqs. (6.3.2) and (6.3.3) for

$$\mathbf{B}_2 = \int dt \, \mathrm{curl}(\dot{\boldsymbol{\xi}} \times \mathbf{B}') = \tfrac{1}{2} \mathrm{curl}(\boldsymbol{\xi} \times \mathbf{Q}) \tag{6.3.6}$$

and

$$p_2 = -\int [\gamma p' \, \mathrm{div}\, \dot{\boldsymbol{\xi}} + \dot{\boldsymbol{\xi}} . \nabla p'] \, dt$$

$$= \tfrac{1}{2}\gamma[\gamma p_0 \, \mathrm{div}\, \boldsymbol{\xi} + \boldsymbol{\xi} . \nabla p_0] \, \mathrm{div}\, \boldsymbol{\xi} + \boldsymbol{\xi} . \nabla[\gamma p_0 \, \mathrm{div}\, \boldsymbol{\xi} + \boldsymbol{\xi} . \nabla p_0] \tag{6.3.7}$$

Then to second order

$$W = \int d\tau \left(\frac{B_0^2}{8\pi} + \frac{\mathbf{B}_0 . \mathbf{B}_1}{4\pi} + \frac{\mathbf{B}_1^2}{8\pi} + \frac{\mathbf{B}_0 . \mathbf{B}_2}{4\pi} + \right.$$

$$+ \tfrac{1}{2} \frac{\gamma[\gamma p_0 \, \mathrm{div}\, \boldsymbol{\xi} + \boldsymbol{\xi} . \nabla p_0] \, \mathrm{div}\, \boldsymbol{\xi} + \boldsymbol{\xi} . \nabla[\gamma p_0 \, \mathrm{div}\, \boldsymbol{\xi} + \boldsymbol{\xi} . \nabla p_0]}{\gamma - 1} -$$

$$\left. - \frac{\gamma p_0 \, \mathrm{div}\, \boldsymbol{\xi} + \boldsymbol{\xi} . \nabla p_0}{\gamma - 1} + \frac{p_0}{\gamma - 1} \right) \tag{6.3.8}$$

Since the unperturbed system is in equilibrium the first-order terms must vanish. To demonstrate this we shall need certain vector identities which are most easily written in component form, with the summation convention, i.e. ξ_i = a component of the vector $\boldsymbol{\xi}$, double suffixes are summed, and

$$\xi_{i,j} = \partial \xi_i / \partial x_j$$

Then

$$\int \frac{\mathbf{B}_0}{4\pi} . \mathbf{Q} \, d\tau = \int \frac{d\tau}{4\pi} B_i(\xi_i B_j - \xi_j B_i)_{,j}$$

$$= \int ds \frac{B_i}{4\pi}(\xi_i B_j - \xi_j B_i) n_j - \int \frac{d\tau}{4\pi}(\xi_i B_j - \xi_j B_i) B_{i,j}$$

$$= -\int \frac{d\tau}{4\pi} \Big\{ \xi_i B_j (B_{i,j} - B_{j,i}) \Big\} = -\int d\tau \, \boldsymbol{\xi} . \left\{ \frac{\mathrm{curl}\, \mathbf{B}_0}{4\pi} \times \mathbf{B}_0 \right\}$$

$$= -\int d\tau \, \boldsymbol{\xi} . (\mathbf{j} \times \mathbf{B}_0) \tag{6.3.9}$$

while

$$\int d\tau \frac{[\gamma p_0 \, \mathrm{div}\, \boldsymbol{\xi} + \boldsymbol{\xi} . \nabla p_0]}{\gamma - 1} = \int ds \frac{\gamma p_0 \boldsymbol{\xi} . \mathbf{n}}{\gamma - 1} - \int (\gamma - 1) \frac{\boldsymbol{\xi} . \nabla p_0}{\gamma - 1} \, d\tau$$

the surface terms vanishing since $\boldsymbol{\xi} \cdot \mathbf{n} = 0$ on the perturbed surface, as does $\mathbf{B} \cdot \mathbf{n}$, while in the first integral the dummy suffixes on $B_{i,j}$ have been interchanged:

$$\sum \xi_j B_i B_{i,j} = \sum \xi_i B_j B_{j,i}$$

Hence, the first-order terms are

$$\int \boldsymbol{\xi} \cdot \left(\mathbf{j} \times \mathbf{B} - \boldsymbol{\nabla} p \right) \mathrm{d}\tau = 0$$

The second-order terms may be transformed in a similar way, since

$$\int \mathrm{d}\tau \mathbf{B}_0 \cdot \mathrm{curl}(\boldsymbol{\xi} \times \mathbf{B}) = \int \boldsymbol{\xi} \cdot (\mathbf{B} \times \mathrm{curl}\,\mathbf{B}_0) \mathrm{d}\tau$$

from eq. (6.3.9),

$$\int \mathrm{d}\tau \mathbf{B}_0 \cdot \mathrm{curl}(\boldsymbol{\xi} \times \mathbf{Q}) = 4\pi \int \boldsymbol{\xi} \cdot (\mathbf{Q} \times \mathbf{j}) \mathrm{d}\tau$$

while

$$\int \mathrm{d}\tau\,\gamma\,\frac{[\gamma p_0 \,\mathrm{div}\,\boldsymbol{\xi} + \boldsymbol{\xi} \cdot \boldsymbol{\nabla} p_0]\,\mathrm{div}\,\boldsymbol{\xi} + \boldsymbol{\xi} \cdot \boldsymbol{\nabla}[\gamma p_0 \,\mathrm{div}\,\boldsymbol{\xi} + \boldsymbol{\xi} \cdot \boldsymbol{\nabla} p_0]}{\gamma - 1}$$

$$= \int \mathrm{d}\tau(\gamma - 1)\frac{[\gamma p_0 \,\mathrm{div}\,\boldsymbol{\xi} + \boldsymbol{\xi} \cdot \boldsymbol{\nabla} p_0] \cdot \mathrm{div}\,\boldsymbol{\xi}}{\gamma - 1} - \int \mathrm{d}s \boldsymbol{\xi} \cdot \mathbf{n}\frac{[\gamma p_0 \,\mathrm{div}\,\boldsymbol{\xi} + \boldsymbol{\xi} \cdot \boldsymbol{\nabla} p_0]}{\gamma - 1}$$

hence

$$\delta W = \tfrac{1}{2} \int \mathrm{d}\tau \{ \frac{\mathbf{Q}^2}{4\pi} - \boldsymbol{\xi} \cdot (\mathbf{j} \times \mathbf{Q}) + [\gamma p_0 \,\mathrm{div}\,\boldsymbol{\xi} + \boldsymbol{\xi} \cdot \boldsymbol{\nabla} p_0] \,\mathrm{div}\,\boldsymbol{\xi} \} \qquad (6.3.10)$$

This result would have been obtained by forming the scalar product of the R.H.S. of eq. (6.3.4) with the displacement $\boldsymbol{\xi}$, and integrating over the plasma volume.

If there exists a gravitational potential ϕ acting on the plasma, then the energy too must be modified by a term $-\tfrac{1}{2} \,\mathrm{div}(\rho\boldsymbol{\xi})\boldsymbol{\xi} \cdot \boldsymbol{\nabla}\phi$, the second-order change in the potential energy.

Complications arise if the plasma has a free surface adjoining a vacuum region, for a motion of the surface will alter the magnetic fields in the vacuum. To allow for this, appropriate boundary conditions must be used with eq. (6.3.4). These are:

(1) The normal component of the vacuum field must vanish on the perturbed surface, from flux conservation in the fluids, i.e.

$$\mathbf{B} \cdot \mathbf{n} = 0 \qquad (6.3.11)$$

(2) There must exist pressure balance between the tangential components of the fields, i.e.

$$\left[\frac{1}{8\pi}B^2\tan^{in}+p\right] = \left[\frac{1}{8\pi}B^2\tan^{out}\right] \qquad (6.3.12)$$

on the perturbed surfaces.

Of course, the vacuum field itself must satisfy another appropriate boundary condition, either on a wall or at infinity.

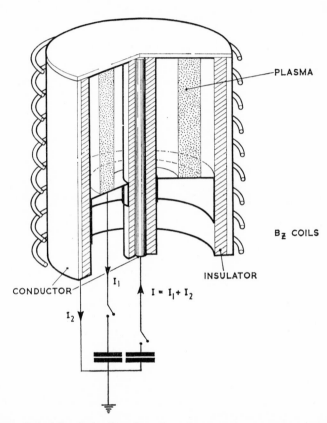

FIG. 6.11. Principle of the "hard-core" or "unpinch" experiment. Plasma is confined in a cylindrical sheet between internal and external fields. If the plasma current is less than the axial current, the configuration is magnetohydrodynamically stable. (Aitken *et al.*, *Proc. 4th. Int. Conf. on Ion. Phen. in Gases* 1960.)

Since we are interested in low-frequency behaviour, it is not usually necessary to solve Maxwell's equations in the vacuum since the quasi-static representation suffices. Thus, the components of the field must be harmonic and divergence-free.

In the energy integral the requirements are even less stringent. Indeed, the perturbed vacuum field need only satisfy eq. (6.3.11), but contributes to the energy integral a term (cf. Bernstein *et al.*)

$$\delta W_{\text{vac}} = (1/8\pi) \int (B'_v)^2 \, d\tau \qquad (6.3.13)$$

The volume integral may be taken over the unperturbed volume, if there is added a surface contribution to the energy

$$\delta W_s = \tfrac{1}{2} \int ds \, (\mathbf{n} \cdot \boldsymbol{\xi})^2 \left[\mathbf{n} \cdot \boldsymbol{\nabla} \frac{B^2}{8\pi} + p \right]$$

representing the work done in displacing the surface, where $[x]$ represents the increase in x on crossing the surface, and the integral extends over the plasma–vacuum interface.

As an illustration of these two methods, we will consider first a configuration in which a plasma is held up against a gravitational field by a magnetic field. This problem has been considered for a field-free plasma with a surface current (cf. KRUSKAL and SCHWARZSCHILD). Instead we will consider a system in which the plasma extends to a lower boundary, but contains a thick layer of uniform current, the density increasing from zero, while the current and its associated magnetic field vanish above some layer z_0 in the plasma. Specifically, we consider an isothermal plasma in a gravitational field $(0, 0, -g)$, containing a uniform current $(j, 0, 0)$ and a magnetic field $(0, B, 0)$, where $B = B_0 - 4\pi jz$ in $0 < z < z_0 = B_0/4\pi j$. The density is then

$$\rho = \frac{1}{4\pi} \frac{B_0^2}{kT} \frac{1}{\alpha z_0} \left[\left(1 + \frac{1}{\alpha z_0} \right) [1 - \exp(-\alpha z)] - z/z_0 \right] \qquad (6.3.15)$$

where $\alpha = g/kT$.

To apply the energy method it is not necessary to consider all perturbations, it is enough to display a single one for which $\delta W < 0$. Consider then a perturbation $\boldsymbol{\xi}$ for which div $\boldsymbol{\xi} = 0$, and $\boldsymbol{\xi} = [\xi_x, 0, \xi_z(x, z)]$. Then

$$\mathbf{Q} = \mathbf{B} \cdot \boldsymbol{\nabla}\boldsymbol{\xi} - \boldsymbol{\xi} \cdot \boldsymbol{\nabla}\mathbf{B} = [0, -\xi_z(\partial B/\partial z), 0] = (0, 4\pi j\xi_z, 0)$$

and

$$\mathbf{j} \cdot \mathbf{Q} \times \boldsymbol{\xi} = jQ_y\xi_z = 4\pi j^2\xi_z^2$$

and the magnetic contribution $Q^2/4\pi - \mathbf{j} \cdot \mathbf{Q} \times \boldsymbol{\xi} = 0$. Since div $\boldsymbol{\xi} = 0$, the thermal energy of the gas contributes nothing to δW, and the sole surviving term is that arising from the gravitational potential, $-(\boldsymbol{\xi} \cdot \boldsymbol{\nabla}\phi \text{ div } \rho\boldsymbol{\xi})$ $= -\xi_z^2 g(\partial\rho/\partial z)$, hence eq. (6.3.10) yields $\delta W = -\tfrac{1}{2} \int d\tau g(\partial\rho/\partial z)\xi_z^2$, which is negative if $\xi_z \neq 0$ only where $\partial\rho/\partial z > 0$. With fixed lower boundaries, the surface and vacuum terms vanish, and the system has been shown unstable, $\delta W < 0$.

To use the normal modes procedure, it is again not necessary to obtain the most general solution to the equations of motion if a particular exponentially growing solution can be obtained.

To do this simply we may consider an incompressible perturbation varying only across the magnetic field. Using the value of $\mathbf{Q}$ above (6.3.4) becomes

$$\rho_0\ddot{\xi}_x = \frac{\partial\xi_z}{\partial x}\left[\frac{\partial}{\partial z}(p_0+B_0{}^2/8\pi)-\rho_0 g\right] = -2\rho_0 g\frac{\partial\xi_z}{\partial x}$$

$$\rho_0\ddot{\xi}_z = \frac{\partial\xi_z}{\partial z}\left[\frac{\partial}{\partial z}(p_0+B_0{}^2/8\pi)-\rho_0 g\right]+\xi_z\frac{\partial}{\partial z}\left[\frac{\partial}{\partial z}(p_0+B_0{}^2/8\pi)+\rho_0 g\right]$$

$$= -2\rho_0 g\frac{\partial\xi_z}{\partial z}$$

(6.3.16)

where the equilibrium conditions have been used, i.e.

$$\frac{\partial}{\partial z}(p_0+B_0{}^2/8\pi)+\rho_0 g = 0$$

The divergence-free condition may be satisfied by deriving ξ from a stream function, ψ

$$\xi_x = -\frac{\partial\psi}{\partial z}, \ \xi_z = \frac{\partial\psi}{\partial x}$$

whereupon the equations of motion 6.3.16 reduce to

$$(\partial^2/\partial x^2 + \partial^2/\partial z^2)\psi = 0. \qquad \ddot{\psi} = -2g\,\partial\psi/\partial z$$

which are satisfied by

$$\psi_2\exp\left(-lz\pm ilx\right)\exp\sqrt{(2gl)}t$$

an exponentially growing solution. For large l the disturbance vanishes for large positive z, while below $z = 0$ the vacuum field suffers a local harmonic perturbation. Thus the system is unstable against rippling of the lower boundary, the perturbations growing as $\sqrt{(2gl)}t$, l being the wave number.

4. THE STABILITY OF CYLINDRICAL CONFINED PLASMAS

Cylindrical equilibria of confined plasmas have been studied in considerable detail, partly in an effort to discuss the stability of toroidal systems of large aspect ratio (R_{max}/R_{min} large), of which it has been hoped the infinite cylinder forms a reasonable, though incomplete, representation, and partly to study actual cylindrical systems operating between electrodes.

In such systems the equilibrium quantities are considered as functions of the distance r from the axis of the cylinder, and include the gas pressure p, and the axial and azimuthal components of the magnetic field and current $[B_\theta(r), B_z(r)], [j_\theta(r), j_z(r)]$. It is usual to take advantage of the symmetry of the undisturbed system to Fourier analyse the perturbation $\boldsymbol{\xi}(r, \theta, z)$ as $\boldsymbol{\xi}(r, m, k)\exp(im\theta)\exp(ikz)$, and use the linearity of the analysis to discuss the harmonic components of $\boldsymbol{\xi}$ one at a time. To form the energy integral with these quantities, it is necessary to make $\boldsymbol{\xi}(r, \theta, z)$ real by adding $\boldsymbol{\xi}(r, m, k)$ and $\boldsymbol{\xi}^*(r, m, k)$, and when the integrations over the harmonic terms are carried out, the surviving parts contain only products of $\boldsymbol{\xi}$ and $\boldsymbol{\xi}^*$.

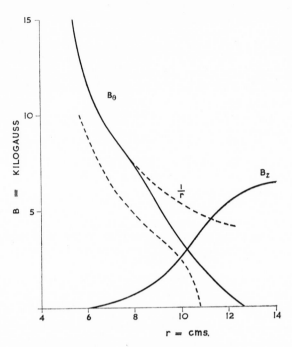

FIG. 6.12. Fields in the "unpinch". Since B_θ falls off more rapidly than $1/r$, the configuration is magnetohydrodynamically stable (Aitken *et al.*, *op. cit.*).

Specifically, if $\mathbf{B} = (0, B_\theta, B_z)$

$$\boldsymbol{\xi} \times \mathbf{B} = [\xi_\theta B_z - \xi_z B_\theta, \; -\xi_r B_z, \; \xi_r B_\theta]$$

$$\mathbf{Q} = \boldsymbol{\nabla} \times (\boldsymbol{\xi} \times \mathbf{B}) = \left\{ \left(i\frac{mB_\theta}{r} + ikB_z \right)\xi_r, \; \left(i\frac{mB_\theta}{r} + ikB_z \right)\xi_\theta - B_\theta \operatorname{div}\boldsymbol{\xi} - \right.$$

$$\left. -r\xi_r\frac{\mathrm{d}}{\mathrm{d}r}(B_\theta/r), \; \left(i\frac{mB_\theta}{r} + ikB_z \right)\xi_z - B_z \operatorname{div}\boldsymbol{\xi} - \xi_r\frac{\mathrm{d}B_z}{\mathrm{d}r} \right\} \qquad (6.4.1)$$

and using the equilibrium conditions,

$$j = \left[0, \; -\frac{\partial B_z}{\partial r}, \; \frac{1}{r}\frac{\partial}{\partial r}(rB_\theta) \right]$$

$$\frac{\partial p}{\partial r} = -\frac{1}{2}\frac{\partial}{\partial r}(B_\theta^2 + B_z^2) - \frac{B_\theta^2}{r}$$

the second-order variation in plasma energy induced by a displacement $\boldsymbol{\xi}$ becomes

$$\delta W_p = \frac{\pi}{2}L \int_0^{r_0} dr \cdot r\left\{\left(\frac{mB_\theta}{r} + kB_z\right)^2 (\boldsymbol{\xi} \cdot \boldsymbol{\xi}^*) + (B_\theta^2 + B_z^2 + \gamma p)(\operatorname{div}\boldsymbol{\xi})(\operatorname{div}\boldsymbol{\xi}^*) - \right.$$

$$- 2B_\theta \frac{d}{dr}(B_\theta/r)\xi_r\xi_r^* - 2B_\theta^2/r\{\xi_r(\operatorname{div}\boldsymbol{\xi}^*) + \xi_r^* \operatorname{div}\boldsymbol{\xi}\} +$$

$$+ i\left(m\frac{B_\theta}{r} + kB_z\right)[(2B_\theta/r)(\xi_r^*\xi_\theta - \xi_\theta^*\xi_r) - B_\theta(\xi_\theta \operatorname{div}\boldsymbol{\xi}^* - \xi_\theta^* \operatorname{div}\boldsymbol{\xi}) -$$

$$\left. - B_z(\xi_z \operatorname{div}\boldsymbol{\xi}^* - \xi_z^* \operatorname{div}\boldsymbol{\xi})]\right\} \tag{6.4.2}$$

Since this involves only $\boldsymbol{\xi}$ and $\operatorname{div}\boldsymbol{\xi} = (1/r)[\partial(r\xi_r)/\partial r] + (im/r)\xi_\theta + ik\xi_z$, it is independent of the derivatives of ξ_θ and ξ_z, and is minimized by values of ξ_θ and ξ_z satisfying the two algebraic equations

$$\left(m\frac{B_\theta}{r} + kB_z\right)^2 \xi_\theta - \frac{im}{r}\left[(B_\theta^2 + B_z^2 + \gamma p) \operatorname{div}\boldsymbol{\xi} - \frac{2B_\theta^2}{r}\xi_r + \right.$$

$$\left. + i\left(m\frac{B_\theta}{r} + kB_z\right)(B_\theta\xi_\theta + B_z\xi_z)\right] + i\left(m\frac{B_\theta}{r} + kB_z\right)\left[B_\theta \operatorname{div}\boldsymbol{\xi} - 2\frac{B_\theta}{r}\xi_r\right] = 0$$

and

$$\left(m\frac{B_\theta}{r} + kB_z\right)^2 \xi_z - ik\left[(B_\theta^2 + B_z^2 + \gamma p) \operatorname{div}\boldsymbol{\xi} - 2\frac{B_\theta^2}{r}\xi_r + \right.$$

$$\left. + i\left(m\frac{B_\theta}{r} + kB_z\right)(B_\theta\xi_\theta + B_z\xi_z)\right] + i\left(m\frac{B_\theta}{r} + kB_z\right)B_z \operatorname{div}\boldsymbol{\xi} = 0$$

These may be solved for ξ_θ and ξ_z, and the results substituted in eq. (6.4.2). If $mB_\theta/r + kB_z \not\equiv 0$, eq. (6.4.2), takes the form

$$\delta W = \frac{\pi}{2}L \int_0^{r_0} dr \cdot r\left\{\left[\left(\frac{m}{r}B_\theta + kB_z\right)^2 - \frac{2B_\theta}{r^2}\frac{d}{dr}(rB_\theta)\right]\xi_r^2 + \right.$$

$$\left. + \left[\left(kB_z - \frac{m}{r}B_\theta\right)\xi_r + \left(kB_z + \frac{m}{r}B_\theta\right)r\frac{d\xi_r}{dr}\right]^2 / [m^2 + k^2 r^2]\right\} \tag{6.4.3}$$

The only term which can make this negative is the second one

$$-2\frac{B_\theta}{r}\frac{d}{dr}(rB_\theta) \, \xi_r^2$$

Since $(1/r)[\mathrm{d}(rB_\theta)/\mathrm{d}r] = 4\pi j_z$, while $B_\theta = 2I_z{}^{(r)}/r$ where I is the total current enclosed within a cylinder of radius r, this de-stabilizing term is

$$-16\frac{\pi I_z}{r}j_z(r)\xi_r^2 \qquad (6.4.4)$$

hence if the current density in the plasma is everywhere opposite to the total current, δW is positive and the plasma is stable. This is the basis of the "hardcore" confinement scheme in which a plasma contained between two coaxial conductors carries a current opposite in direction and less in magnitude than a current in the central conductor.

Although the plasma energy has been expressed entirely in terms of ξ_r, we must still show that the surface and vacuum energy can be so expressed. It is clear that this can be done for the surface energy for from eq. (6.3.14), it involves only $(\mathbf{n} . \boldsymbol{\xi}) = \xi_r$. Indeed, since

$$\frac{\partial}{\partial r}(8\pi p + B_z{}^2 + B_\theta{}^2) + 2B_\theta{}^2/r = 0 \qquad \text{inside}$$

$$\frac{\partial}{\partial r}(B_z{}^2 + B_\theta{}^2) + 2B_\theta{}^2/r = 0 \qquad \text{outside}$$

and

$$[\mathbf{n} . \boldsymbol{\nabla}(8\pi p + B_z{}^2 + B_\theta{}^2)] = \frac{2}{r_0}[(B_\theta{}^i)^2 - (B_\theta{}^o)^2]$$

where r_0 is the radius of the plasma cylinder, and $B_\theta{}^o$ and $B_\theta{}^i$ the strength of the azimuthal field component just outside and inside the plasma surface; hence the surface energy becomes

$$\delta W_s = \frac{1}{8} . \xi_r^2(r_0)[(B_\theta{}^i)^2 - (B_\theta{}^o)^2] \qquad (6.4.5)$$

To obtain the vacuum field we must insist that the normal component of B vanishes on the surface to first order in the displacement ξ. The perturbed surface is $0 = r - r_0 - \xi_r(r_0)\exp(im\theta + ikz)$, hence its normal

$$\mathbf{n} = \boldsymbol{\nabla} . f = [1 - (\partial \xi_r/\partial r), -(im/r)\xi_r, -ik\xi_r] \qquad (6.4.6)$$

and the normal component of the unperturbed field is

$$B_n{}^o = \left(-\frac{im}{r}\xi_r B_\theta{}^o - ik\xi_r B_z{}^o\right)\exp(im\theta + ikz)$$

hence the perturbed field must satisfy

$$B_n{}^1 = B_r{}^1(r_0) = \left[\frac{im}{r}B_\theta{}^o + ikB_z{}^o\right]\xi_r$$

Externally $\mathbf{B}$ is derivable from a harmonic scalar field as $\mathbf{B} = \text{grad } \psi$ and the boundary condition on the plasma surface is

$$\partial\psi(r_0)/\partial r = [(im/r)B_\theta{}^0 + ikB_z{}^0]\xi_r$$

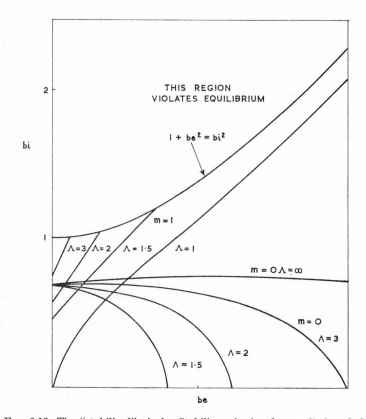

FIG. 6.13. The "stabilized" pinch. Stability criterion for a cylinder of plasma containing an axial magnetic field and confined by an azimuthal one, with a surface current. Curves in normalized internal axial field (B_z^i), external axial field B_z^0 plane, for various ratios Λ of the confining tube radius R to the plasma radius r_0. Plasma is stable above the lower curves, but no non-negative pressure equilibrium is possible above the upper curve. (Tayler, *Proc. Phys. Soc.* **B 70**, 31, 1957)

If ψ is harmonic

$$\psi \simeq \psi(r) \exp(im\theta + ikz)$$

where

$$\psi(r) = [\psi_1 I_m(kr) + \psi_2 K_m(kr)] \tag{6.4.7}$$

If the plasma–vacuum region is surrounded by a perfectly conducting cylindrical wall at a distance $R = \Lambda r_0$, the boundary conditions determining ψ_1 and ψ_2 become

9

$$\psi_1 I_m{}'(k\Lambda r_0) + \psi_2 K_m{}'(k\Lambda r_0) = 0$$

$$k[\psi_1 I_m{}'(kr_0) + \psi_2 K_m{}'(kr_0)] = i[(m/r_0)B_\theta{}^0 + kB_z{}^0]\xi_r \qquad (6.4.8)$$

whence

$$\psi(r) = -\frac{i}{k}\frac{I_m{}'(\Lambda kr_0)K_m(kr) - K_m{}'(\Lambda kr_0)I_m(kr)}{I_m{}'(\Lambda kr_0)K_m{}'(kr_0) - K_m{}'(\Lambda kr_0)I_m{}'(kr_0)}\left[\frac{m}{r_0}B_\theta{}^0 + kB_z{}^0\right]\xi_r \qquad (6.4.9)$$

The vacuum integral then becomes

$$\delta W_v = \frac{\pi}{2}L \cdot \int_{r_0}^{\Lambda r_0} r\left[\frac{\partial\psi}{\partial r}\frac{\partial\psi^*}{\partial r} + \left(\frac{m^2}{r^2} + k^2\right)\psi^2\right]dr$$

$$= \frac{\pi}{2}L\left[r\psi\frac{\partial\psi}{\partial r}\Big|_{r_0}^{\Lambda r_0} - \int r\psi\left[\frac{1}{r}\frac{\partial}{\partial r}(r\psi) - \left(\frac{m^2}{r^2} + k^2\right)\psi\right]dr\right]$$

Since ψ is harmonic the integrand vanishes and

$$\delta W_v = -\frac{\pi}{2}L\xi_r{}^2\frac{(mB_\theta{}^0 + kr_0 B_z{}^0)^2}{kr_0}\left[\frac{I'_m(\Lambda kr_0)K_m(kr_0) - K'_m(\Lambda kr_0)I_m(kr_0)}{I'_m(\Lambda kr_0)K'_m(kr_0) - K'_m(\Lambda kr_0)I'_m(kr_0)}\right] \qquad (6.4.10)$$

As an application of this scheme, consider the "stabilized pinch", in which the plasma contains only a constant axial magnetic field B_z, while outside the plasma, there is a helical field $B_\theta{}^0$, $B_z{}^0$, and finally a perfectly conducting wall—a problem solved independently by TAYLER, ROSENBLUTH and SHAFRANOV. For perturbations with $k \neq 0$, eq. (6.4.3) is applicable in the plasma and becomes

$$\delta W_p = \frac{\pi}{2}L\int_0^{r_0} dr \cdot r\left\{k^2 B_z{}^2\xi_r{}^2 + \frac{k^2 B_z{}^2}{m^2 + k^2 r^2}\left(\xi_r + r\frac{d\xi}{dr}\right)^2\right\} \qquad (6.4.11)$$

$$= \frac{\pi}{2}Lk^2 B_z{}^2\int_0^{r_0} dr \cdot r\left\{\xi_r{}^2 + \frac{[d(r\xi)\,dr]^2}{m^2 + k^2 r^2}\right\} = K\int_0^{r_0} dr \cdot \mathcal{L}$$

We can minimize this with respect to $r\xi_r$ by

$$\frac{d}{dr}\frac{\partial\mathcal{L}}{\partial(r\xi)'} - \frac{\partial\mathcal{L}}{\partial(r\xi)} = \frac{d}{dr}\left(\frac{rd(r\xi_r)/dr}{m^2 + k^2 r^2}\right) - \xi_r = 0 \qquad (6.4.12)$$

This is satisfied by $\xi = dI_m(kr)/dr$, for since

$$\frac{1}{r}\frac{d}{dr}\left\{r\frac{d}{dr}[I_m(kr)]\right\} = \left(\frac{m^2}{r^2} + k^2\right)I_m(kr)$$

eq. (6.4.12) is satisfied. Further $r\xi(0) = 0$, and we may normalize to the surface value of $\xi(r_0) = \xi_1$, thus $\xi = \xi_1[I_m'(kr)/I_m'(kr_0)]$.

The second integral in eq. (6.4.11) may be written

$$\int dr . r\frac{[d(r\xi)/dr]^2}{m^2+k^2r^2} = \int dr . \left(\frac{d}{dr}r\xi\right)r\frac{d(r\xi)/dr}{m^2+k^2r^2}$$

$$= r\xi\left[\frac{r\,d(r\xi)/dr}{m+k^2r^2}\right]_0^{r_0} - \int dr . r\xi\frac{d}{dr}\frac{rd(r\xi)/dr}{m^2+k^2r^2} = r\xi_r\left[\frac{d(r\xi)/dr}{m^2+k^2r^2}\right]_0^{r_0} - \int dr . r\xi^2$$

using eq. (6.4.12); hence

$$\delta W_p = \frac{1}{8}Lkr_0B_z^2\frac{I_m(kr_0)}{I'_m(kr_0)}\xi_r^2 \tag{6.4.13}$$

From eq. (6.4.5)

$$\delta W_s = -\frac{1}{8}L\xi_r^2(B_\theta^0)^2$$

and using eq. (6.4.10)

$$\delta W_T = \delta W_p + \delta W_s + \delta W_v$$

$$= \frac{1}{8}L\xi_1^2\left\{kr_0B_z^2\frac{I_m(kr_0)}{I'_m(kr_0)} - (B_\theta^0)^2 - \frac{(mB_\theta^0+kr_0B_z^0)^2}{kr_0}\times\right.$$

$$\left.\times\left(\frac{I'_m(\Lambda kr_0)K_m(kr_0) - K'_m(\Lambda kr_0)I_m(kr_0)}{I'_m(\Lambda kr_0)K'_m(kr_0) - K'_m(\Lambda kr_0)I'_m(kr_0)}\right)\right\}$$

and the stability criterion for this system becomes

$$(B_z^i)^2 . kr_0\frac{I_m(kr_0)}{I'_m(kr_0)} > (B_\theta^0)^2 + \frac{(mB_\theta^0+kr_0B_z^0)^2}{kr_0}\times$$

$$\times\left\{\frac{I'_m(\Lambda kr_0)K_m(kr_0) - K'_m(\Lambda kr_0)I_m(kr_0)}{I'_m(\Lambda kr_0)K'_m(kr_0) - K'_m(\Lambda kr_0)I'_m(kr_0)}\right\}$$

This criterion is plotted in Fig. 6.13, where the fields are normalized to B_θ^0 so that $B_z^i = b^iB_\theta^0$, $B_z^0 = b^eB_\theta^0$, and the stable region is shown. There is an upper limit to b^i and b^e demanded by pressure balance, for since the pressure must be positive, and

$$p + \frac{B_z^2}{8\pi} = \frac{1}{8\pi}[(B_\theta^0)^2 + (B_z^0)^2], \; 1 + (b^e)^2 > (b^i)^2$$

Further developments of stability theory have been concerned with removing artificiality of the surface current in this model.

5. SURFACE INSTABILITIES AND STABILITY CRITERION

The minimizing of eq. (6.4.3) involves a certain subtlety due to the possible importance of singular perturbations. We may write eq. (6.4.3) as

$$\delta W_p = \frac{\pi}{2}L \int\limits_0^R \mathrm{d}r \cdot r\left[\frac{(fr\xi'+g\xi)^2}{m^2+k^2r^2} + (f^2-h)\xi^2\right] = \frac{\pi}{2}L \int\limits_0^R \mathscr{L}\,\mathrm{d}r$$

where $\xi = \xi_r$, $f = kB_z+(mB_\theta/r)$, $g = kB_z-(mB_\theta/r)$ and $h = (2B_\theta/r)j_z$, and on forming the Euler–Lagrange equations which determine the minimum of δW_p with respect to ξ, namely,

$$0 = \frac{\mathrm{d}}{\mathrm{d}r}\frac{\partial\mathscr{L}}{\partial\xi'} - \frac{\partial\mathscr{L}}{\partial\xi}$$

$$= \frac{\mathrm{d}}{\mathrm{d}r}2r\left[\frac{fr}{m^2+k^2r^2}(fr\xi'+g\xi)\right] - \frac{2gr}{m^2+k^2r^2}(fr\xi'+g\xi)-2(f^2-h)\xi$$

i.e.

$$= \frac{\mathrm{d}2}{\mathrm{d}r}\left[\frac{f^2r^3}{m^2+k^2r^2}\xi'\right] + 2\left[r\left(h-f^2-\frac{g^2}{m^2+k^2r^2}\right) + \frac{\mathrm{d}}{\mathrm{d}r}\left(\frac{fgr^2}{m^2+k^2r^2}\right)\right]\xi$$

$$\tag{6.5.2}$$

we observe that these equations are singular at the point $f = 0$, i.e.

$$kB_z(r)+(m/r)B_\theta(r) = 0 \quad \text{or where} \quad (\mathbf{B}\cdot\boldsymbol{\nabla})\boldsymbol{\xi} = 0$$

At that point the Euler solutions need not be well behaved, although to be permissible they must be normalized, e.g. so that

$$\int\limits_0^R \xi^2 r\,\mathrm{d}r = 1$$

This suggests that special interest is attached to disturbances which are localized near the point r_0 where $kB_z(r_0)+(m/r)B_\theta(r_0) = 0$, and by examining such local perturbations SUYDAM has produced a necessary condition for the stability of a cylindrical plasma. Consider disturbances which differ from zero only in a neighbourhood ϵ of r_0, but are square integrable and differentiable in this interval, the first derivatives, however, being of order $1/\epsilon$. Introduce $r = r_0+\epsilon x$, whereupon δW becomes

$$\delta W = \frac{\pi}{2} L r_0 \epsilon \int\limits_{-1}^{1} dx \left\{ \frac{[\epsilon r_0 f' x \xi'/\epsilon + g\xi]^2}{m^2 + k^2 r_0^2} - h\xi^2 \right\} + O(\epsilon^2)$$

$$= \frac{\pi}{2} L r_0 \epsilon \int\limits_{-1}^{1} dx \left\{ \frac{[r_0 f'(r_0) x \xi' + g\xi]^2}{m^2 + k^2 r_0^2} - h\xi^2 \right\}$$

The term

$$\sim \int\limits_{-1}^{1} x\xi'\xi = \int\limits_{-1}^{1} \tfrac{1}{2} x \frac{d}{dx}(\xi^2) = \xi^2 \frac{x}{2} \bigg]_{-1}^{1} - \int\limits_{-1}^{1} \tfrac{1}{2}\xi^2 = - \int\limits_{-1}^{1} \tfrac{1}{2}\xi^2$$

since $\xi(-1) = \xi(1) = 0$; and we may write

$$\delta W = \frac{\pi}{2} L \frac{r_0^3 f'^2}{m^2 + k^2 r_0^2} \epsilon \int\limits_{-1}^{1} dx[(x\xi')^2 + A\xi^2] \qquad (6.5.3)$$

where

$$A = \frac{1}{r_0^2 f'^2}[-g r_0 f'(r_0) + g^2 - h(m^2 + k^2 r_0^2)],$$

or using

$$\frac{m}{r_0} B_\theta + k B_z = 0$$

so that

$$\frac{m}{k} = -\frac{B_z}{B_\theta} r_0, \qquad g = 2k B_z$$

$$f' = k B_z \left[\frac{B_z'}{B_z} - \frac{r}{B_\theta} \left(\frac{B_\theta}{r} \right)' \right] = -k B_z \frac{d}{dr} \log \left(\frac{B_\theta}{r B_z} \right) = -k B_z \left(\frac{\mu'}{\mu} \right)$$

where $\mu = B_\theta/r B_z$

$$A = -\frac{2}{r_0 B_z^2} \left(\frac{\mu'}{\mu} \right)^{-2} [B_z B_z' + B_\theta B_\theta' + (B_\theta^2/r)] = \frac{(2p'/r_0 B_z^2)}{(\mu'/\mu)^2}$$
$$(6.5.4)$$

Now we may invoke the following theorem: given a function ξ which is integrable and differentiable in $-1 \leqslant x \leqslant 1$, and for which $\xi(-1) = \xi(1) = 0$, then

$$\int\limits_{-1}^{1} x^2(\xi')^2 \, dx \geqslant \tfrac{1}{4} \int\limits_{-1}^{1} \xi^2 \, dx \qquad (6.5.5)$$

for consider the Schwartz inequality

$$l \int_0^l f^2 \, dx \geq [\int_0^l f \, dx]^2$$

applied to the function $f = 2x\xi' + \xi$. Then

$$2 \int_{-1}^1 [2x\xi' + \xi]^2 \, dx = 2[\int_{-1}^1 (4x^2\xi'^2 + \xi^2) \, dx + 4 \int_{-1}^1 x\xi\xi' \, dx]$$

but

$$\int_{-1}^1 x\xi\xi' \, dx = \tfrac{1}{2} \int_{-1}^1 x \frac{d}{dx}(\xi^2) \, dx = \tfrac{1}{2}x\xi^2 \Big|_{-1} - \int_{-1} \tfrac{1}{2}\xi^2 \, dx$$

hence

$$2 \int_{-1}^1 [2x\xi' + \xi]^2 \, dx = 8 \int_{-1}^1 x^2\xi'^2 \, dx - 2 \int_{-1}^1 \xi^2 \, dx.$$

From the Schwartz inequality this is not less than

$$[\int_{-1}^1 (2x\xi' + \xi) \, dx]^2 = [\int_{-1}^1 \xi \, dx + 2x\xi \Big|_{-1} - 2 \int_{-1}^1 \xi \, dx]^2 = [\int_{-1}^1 \xi \, dx]^2$$

Therefore

$$\int_{-1}^1 x^2\xi'^2 \, dx - \tfrac{1}{4} \int_{-1}^1 \xi^2 \, dx \geq \tfrac{1}{8}[\int_{-1}^1 \xi \, dx]^2 \geq 0$$

Hence

$$\delta W = \tfrac{1}{8}Lr_0^3 \frac{f'^2}{m^2 + k^2r^2} \epsilon \Big\{ \int_{-1}^1 [(x\xi')^2 + A\xi^2] \, dx \geq \int_{-1}^1 (A + \tfrac{1}{4})\xi^2 \, dx \Big\}$$

(This argument I owe to R. J. Tayler.)

Since the first factor is positive definite and ξ^2 is positive definite, the sign of δW is that of $A + \tfrac{1}{4}$; hence for stability it is necessary that Suydam's condition be satisfied;

$$\frac{8\pi p'}{B_z^2} + \tfrac{1}{4}r\left(\frac{\mu'}{\mu}\right)^2 \geq 0 \tag{6.5.6}$$

The Suydam criterion is useful and easily applied, but although necessary is not sufficient. There is a more powerful necessary and sufficient condition for stability due to NEWCOMB which, however, is much more difficult to apply. It depends upon the properties of the solution to the Euler equation of (6.5.1). The singularities at the points r_i where $f(r_i) = 0$ again play an important role, and it is first necessary to discover how the solution behaves at these points. Near a singularity we may form the Euler equation of (6.5.3) and investigate the behaviour of the solution near $r = r_i$. Here the Euler equation becomes, with $r = r_i + x$,

$$\frac{d}{dx}\left(x^2 \frac{d\xi}{dx}\right) - A\xi = 0$$

and near $x = 0$ is satisfied by $\xi \sim x^n$ where

$$n(n-1) + 2n - A = 0; \qquad n = \tfrac{1}{2}[-1 \pm \sqrt{(1+4A)}]$$

and if Suydam's condition is satisfied, $1+4A > 0$ and n is real. Of these solutions, both of which make a positive contribution to the energy, that for which $|n|$ is smaller makes the smallest contribution i.e. $n = \tfrac{1}{2}\sqrt{[(1+4A)-1]}$, and we concentrate our attention on this solution. The singularities divide the region $0 < r < r_0$ into sub-regions $r_i < r < r_{i+1}$ between the singularities which may be considered separately. The contribution to the energy integral from the singularity is

$$\sim \int (n^2+A)x^{2n}\, dx = \frac{n^2+A}{2n+1}x^{2n+1}\bigg| = \frac{n^2+A}{2n+1}x^{\sqrt{1+4A}}$$

and goes to zero as $x \to 0$. For an Euler solution ξ, the energy integral may be evaluated explicitly, for the integral may be written as

$$\delta W_p = \int dr\left\{\xi' r^2 \frac{f(fr\xi'+g\xi)}{m^2+k^2r^2} + \frac{gr\xi(fr\xi'+g\xi)}{m^2+k^2r^2} + (f^2-h)r\xi^2\right\}$$

and on integrating the first term by parts

$$\delta W_p = \frac{r^2 f(fr\xi'+g\xi)\xi}{m^2+k^2r^2}\bigg|_{r_1}^{r_2} - \int dr\left\{\xi\left[\frac{d}{dr}\frac{r^2 f(fr\xi'+g\xi)}{m^2+k^2r^2} - \frac{gr(fr\xi'+g\xi)}{m^2+k^2r^2} - (f^2-h)r\xi\right]\right\}$$

where, however, the quantity under the integral sign vanishes for an Euler solution in virtue of eq. (6.5.2), and

$$\delta W_p(r_1, r_2, \xi_E) = r^2 f\frac{(fr\xi'_E + g\xi_E)}{(m^2+k^2r^2)}\xi_E\bigg|_{r_1}^{r_2} \qquad (6.5.7)$$

We may now consider the solution which is small at r_1. In general, this will not be small at r_2, and will contribute a positive term to the energy. If however this solution vanishes in (r_1, r_2) then the system cannot be more than marginally stable, for at an ordinary point r where $\xi_E = 0$, $\delta W_p = 0$, and ξ may be taken as zero in the rest of the plasma. However, if $\xi_E(r_3) = 0$

for some r_3, $r_1 < r_3 < r_2$, then the plasma is unstable, for instead of continuing from r_3 by $\xi = 0$, so that the entire solution is not an Euler solution, we may continue from $\xi_4 < \xi_3$ by a further Euler solution ξ_E', thus minimizing the value of δW over a wider interval. Since, however, the first choice of ξ, $\xi = \xi_E(r)$, $r_1 < r < r_3$, $\xi = 0$, $r_3 < r < r_2$, reduced δW to zero, the second, for which $\xi = \xi_E$, $r_1 < r < r_4 (> r_3)$, $\xi_1 = \xi_E'$, $r_4 < r < r_2$ and $\xi_E(r_4) = \xi_E'(r_4)$, reduces it below zero, hence the plasma is unstable.

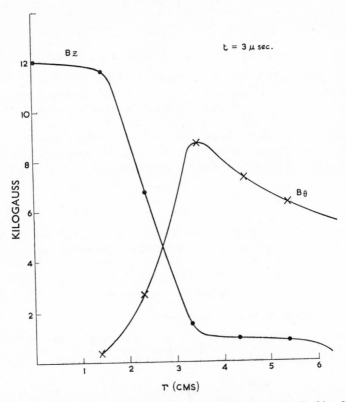

Fig. 6.14. Gross stability of the stabilized pinch. Fields in the Burkhardt and Lovberg experiment showing restriction of currents to a layer near the surface. (Burkhardt and Lovberg, *Progress in Nuclear Energy* XI, Vol. I, p. 405.)

Thus we may enunciate Newcomb's theorem. If $r_1 \ldots r_n$ are singular points $f(r_i) = 0$, the plasma may be divided into regions $0 < r_1 < \ldots < r_n < r_0$ in which the contribution to the plasma energy δW may be considered separately, the r_i depending on the choice of m, k. At the singular points r_i, there are two possible solutions

$$\xi_{1,2} \sim x^{[-1 \pm \sqrt{(1+4A)}]/2}$$

and if Suydam's condition is satisfied the larger of these gives a positive contribution to the energy, while the smaller contributes nothing. If the Euler solution small at r_i has no zero in the range $r_i < r < r_{i+1}$ for all i the system is necessarily stable; while if in any interval such a solution has a zero the system is necessarily unstable. A full proof of this has been given by NEWCOMB, while here a mere sketch has had to suffice.

Although a powerful statement, this theory can be applied only with difficulty since all values of m and k must be considered and the Euler equation solved in each region. It has, however, been applied by NEWCOMB and KAUFMANN and by WHITEMAN and COPLEY.

A modification of the argument was applied (before Newcomb's theorem was stated) by ROSENBLUTH in order to demonstrate the conditions under which a plasma cylinder supported by a thin current sheet, but not a surface current, was stable. This requires a reversed external axial field and a rather carefully designed current layer.

The stability theory of a plasma cylinder has had a doubtful success; i.e. predictions of instability have been verified, but no completely stable configurations have been found.

The suppression of the sausage instability by an axial field, and of the gross "wriggle" by conducting walls occurs as predicted; however, "stabilized" pinches (see for example BUTT et al.) still display the high power consumption and brief energy containment indicative of instability, while magnetic probe traces show high frequency flutter.

An attempt to confirm the detailed theory of Suydam was made by BURKHARDT and LOVBERG, using a linear pinch with an axial stabilizing field into which probes could be inserted for magnetic field sampling. It was possible to vary the axial magnetic field so that the conditions for gross stability could be met or violated. Simultaneous magnetic traces were then made on four probes spaced at 15 mm separation at a constant distance from the axis. Any large scale instability would appear as a set of correlated magnetic traces, while local instabilities would appear as random noise. When the gross stability criterion was satisfied, only local instabilities appeared, but it was not possible to produce a Suydam stable configuration.

On the other hand, experiments with the "hard core" or unpinch device, in which eq. (6.4.4) is satisfied and which should therefore be stable, do not show stability. Although the onset of instability is delayed when compared with that in a similar pinch device, fluctuations do appear on magnetic probe traces. At the time of writing the reason for this is obscure. Finite conductivity, omitted from the theory, or the distorting effect of the magnetic probes themselves on the magnetic field or plasma temperature distribution have been suggested.

6. THERMAL CONVECTION IN A MAGNETIC FIELD

The stability analysis presented in the earlier parts of this chapter has had a considerable mathematical development, but is based on a rather artificial model of the plasma; in particular all transport processes have been omitted. When these dissipative effects are included the analysis loses a good deal of its formal elegance, and relatively little has been accomplished.

B$_{\bar{z}}$ = 2000 GROSSLY STABLE.

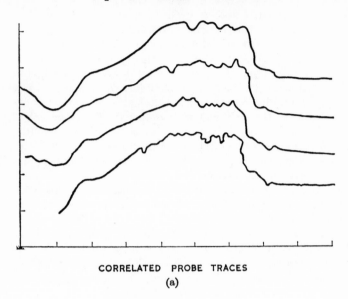

CORRELATED PROBE TRACES
(a)

B$_{\bar{z}}$ = 1000g GROSSLY UNSTABLE

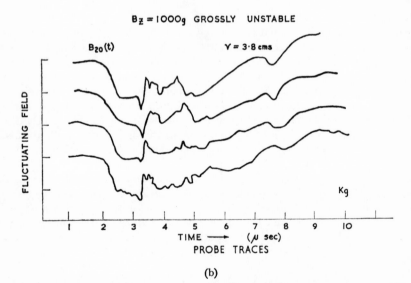

FIG. 6.15. Gross stability of the stabilized pinch. Correlated probe traces, showing magnetic field fluctuations (in arbitrary units) vs. times at neighbouring points in a constricted discharge. (a) when stability conditions are satisfied showing lack of correlation and (b) when stability conditions are violated, where correlation in probe traces indicates large scale instabilities.

One problem which has attracted some attention is that of the influence of a magnetic field on the thermal convection of a conducting fluid. The first and simplest approach to this problem involves applying the interchange criterion (5.2.3); however, if transport processes are included, more elaborate and less stringent criteria are obtained.

A variational principle of a rather special character has been developed for solving this problem (CHANDRASEKHAR), but we will restrict ourselves here to consideration of a simple problem for which the method of normal modes is convenient. Moreover, instead of considering a compressible plasma we will consider an incompressible fluid with a coefficient of thermal expansion, α. JEFFREYS has shown that the results of this analysis in the normal hydrodynamic case can be taken over for the compressible fluid simply by replacing the temperature gradient by the super adiabatic gradient, the difference (6.2.3). Specifically we consider a layer of incompressible fluid of density ρ in a vertical magnetic field B which is heated from below so that the temperature $T \sim -\beta z$. The fluid is assumed to have a coefficient of thermal expansion α, thermometric conductivity K, kinematic viscosity ν, and electrical resistivity η, and to be located in a vertical gravitational field $-g$.

The relevant equations of motion become

$$\operatorname{div} \mathbf{v} = 0 \qquad (6.6.1)$$

$$\rho = \rho^0(1 - \alpha T) \qquad (6.6.2)$$

$$\rho \frac{D\mathbf{v}}{Dt} - \rho\nu\nabla^2\mathbf{v} = -\boldsymbol{\nabla}\left(p + \frac{B^2}{8\pi}\right) + \frac{(\mathbf{B}.\boldsymbol{\nabla})\mathbf{B}}{4\pi} + \rho\mathbf{g} \qquad (6.6.3)$$

$$\frac{D\mathbf{B}}{Dt} + \mathbf{B}\operatorname{div}\mathbf{v} - (\mathbf{B}.\boldsymbol{\nabla})\mathbf{v} = \eta\nabla^2\mathbf{B} \qquad (6.6.4)$$

$$\frac{DT}{Dt} = K\nabla^2 T \qquad (6.6.5)$$

In equilibrium $\mathbf{v} = 0$, $T = T_0 - \beta z$, $\mathbf{B} = \mathbf{B}_0$. We now linearize the equations introducing $\mathbf{v}$, T^1, $\mathbf{B}^1$, p^1, $\rho^1 = -\rho^0\alpha T^1$, whereupon the linearized equations for the perturbations become

$$\rho_0\left[\frac{\partial\mathbf{v}}{\partial t} - \nabla\nu^2\mathbf{v}\right] = -\boldsymbol{\nabla}\left(p^1 + \frac{\mathbf{B}_0.\mathbf{B}^1}{4\pi}\right) + \frac{\mathbf{B}_0.\boldsymbol{\nabla}\mathbf{B}^1}{4\pi} - \rho^0\alpha T^1\mathbf{g} \qquad (6.6.6)$$

$$\left(\frac{\partial}{\partial t} - \eta\nabla^2\right)\mathbf{B}^1 = (\mathbf{B}_0.\boldsymbol{\nabla})\mathbf{v} \qquad (6.6.7)$$

$$\left(\frac{\partial}{\partial t} - K\nabla^2\right)T^1 = \beta v_z \qquad (6.6.8)$$

Now in eq. (6.6.6) we make a further simplification, noting that the variation in ρ_0 is itself usually small so we can replace ρ_0 by ρ^0 and treat it, ν, K and

η as constants. We may now begin eliminating p, $\mathbf{B}^1$, and $\mathbf{v}$ from eqs. (6.6.6) and (6.6.8), ending with an equation for T^1. Operating on eq. (6.6.6) with curl curl eliminates p^1 leaving

$$\left(\frac{\partial}{\partial t} - \nu\nabla^2\right)\nabla^2\mathbf{v} = \frac{(\mathbf{B}_0.\boldsymbol{\nabla})}{4\pi\rho_0}\nabla^2\mathbf{B}^1 - \alpha[\mathbf{g}\nabla^2 - \boldsymbol{\nabla}(\mathbf{g}.\boldsymbol{\nabla})]T^1$$

and operating on this with $(\partial/\partial t) - \eta\nabla^2$, and using eq. (6.6.7) to eliminate $\mathbf{B}^1$ yields

$$\left(\frac{\partial}{\partial t} - \eta\nabla^2\right)\left(\frac{\partial}{\partial t} - \nu\nabla^2\right)\nabla^2\mathbf{v} - \left(\frac{\mathbf{B}_0.\boldsymbol{\nabla}}{4\pi\rho_0}\right)^2\nabla^2\mathbf{v} = -\alpha\left(\frac{\partial}{\partial t} - \eta\nabla^2\right).[\mathbf{g}\nabla^2 - \boldsymbol{\nabla}(\mathbf{g}.\boldsymbol{\nabla})]T^1$$

and finally eliminating v_z from the zz component of this yields

$$\left[\left(\frac{\partial}{\partial t} - \eta\nabla^2\right)\left(\frac{\partial}{\partial t} - \nu\nabla^2\right) - C_A{}^2(\mathbf{b}.\boldsymbol{\nabla})^2\right]\left(\frac{\partial}{\partial t} - K\nabla^2\right)\nabla^2 T^1 -$$

$$-\alpha g\beta\left(\frac{\partial}{\partial t} - \eta\nabla^2\right)\left(\nabla^2 - \frac{\partial^2}{\partial z^2}\right)T^1 = 0 \qquad (6.6.9)$$

For simplicity we will first consider the problem of marginal stability in the absence of viscosity, i.e. setting $\partial/\partial t$ and $\nu = 0$ in eq. (6.6.9), which is then reduced to

$$[C_A{}^2(\mathbf{b}.\boldsymbol{\nabla})^2.K\nabla^2]\nabla^2 T^1 + \alpha g\beta\eta\nabla^2\left(\nabla^2 - \frac{\partial^2}{\partial z^2}\right)T^1 = 0$$

or

$$\left[C_A{}^2(\mathbf{b}.\boldsymbol{\nabla})^2 K\nabla^2 + \alpha g\eta\beta\left(\nabla^2 - \frac{\partial^2}{\partial z^2}\right)\right]\nabla^2 T^1 = 0 \qquad (6.6.10)$$

We may now look for a solution of the form $T^1 \sim \exp i(lx + my + sz)$ $= \exp i\mathbf{k}.\mathbf{x}$, whereupon eq. (6.6.10) yields the dispersion relation

$$[KC_A{}^2(\mathbf{b}.\mathbf{k})^2k^2 - \alpha g\beta\eta(k^2 - s^2)] = 0 \qquad (6.6.11)$$

or writing

$$\Lambda = \frac{\alpha g\beta\eta}{KC_A{}^2}$$

$$(\mathbf{b}.\mathbf{k})^2k^2 = \Lambda(k^2 - s^2)$$

For a vertical field

$$(l^2 + m^2 + s^2)s^2 = \Lambda(l^2 + m^2)$$

while for a horizontal field

$$(l^2 + m^2 + s^2)l^2 = \Lambda(l^2 + m^2)$$

In either case s is determined by boundary conditions on $z = 0$ and $z = d$. A suitable simple set is that used by RAYLEIGH in the absence of a magnetic field: $v_z = 0$, and $T^1 = 0$ on the bounding surface. These are satisfied if $T^1(z) \sim \sin \pi z/d$ thus $s^2 = \pi^2/d^2$. Thus, the eigenvalue, $\Lambda(l^2, m^2)$, is determined in the case of a vertical field as

$$\Lambda = \frac{\pi^2}{d^2}\left[1 + \frac{\pi^2}{d^2}\frac{1}{l^2 + m^2}\right]$$

and for a horizontal field as

$$\Lambda = l^2\left[1 + \frac{\pi^2}{d^2}\frac{1}{l^2 + m^2}\right]$$

In the first case, and if $l^2 + m^2 \to \infty$, i.e. if the horizontal wavelength of the disturbance $\to 0$, then

$$\Lambda \to \frac{\pi^2}{d^2}$$

for a vertical field and

$$\Lambda \to l^2$$

for a horizontal field.

For an infinite plane $l \to 0$ the horizontal field has no effect on the critical temperature gradient, while the vertical field prohibits motion until the negative temperature gradient exceeds the value β_0:

$$\beta_0 = \frac{\pi^2}{d^2}\frac{KC_A^2}{\alpha g \eta}$$

or

$$R' = \frac{\beta \alpha g \eta \, d^2}{KC_A^2} > \pi^2 \tag{6.6.12}$$

for instability.

If we include the effects of viscosity, but restrict our attention to marginal instability, and again use a solution for which $T \sim \sin \pi z/d$, which now requires free slip at the walls and is somewhat artificial, eq. (6.6.10) must be replaced by

$$\left\{[\nu\eta\nabla^4 - C_A^2(\mathbf{b}.\boldsymbol{\nabla})^2]K\nabla^2 - \alpha g \beta\eta\left(\nabla^2 - \frac{\partial^2}{\partial z^2}\right)\right\}\nabla^2 T^1 = 0$$

and eq. (6.6.11) by

$$[\Lambda(k^2 - s^2) - (\mathbf{b}.\mathbf{k})^2 k^2 - \Gamma k^6]T^1 = 0$$

where

$$\Gamma = \frac{\nu\eta}{C_A^2}$$

whence

$$\Lambda = \frac{(\mathbf{b}.\mathbf{k})^2 k^2 + \Gamma k^6}{(k^2 - s^2)}$$

If B is horizontal, the displacements may satisfy $\mathbf{b} . \mathbf{k} = 0$;

hence
$$\Lambda = \frac{\Gamma k^6}{k^2 - s^2} = \frac{\Gamma (m^2 + s^2)^3}{m^2}$$

This has its minimum at $m^2 = \frac{1}{2}s^2$, where

$$\Lambda = \frac{27}{4}\Gamma s^4 \quad \text{or} \quad R = \frac{\beta \alpha g}{K\nu}\,\mathrm{d}^4 > \frac{27}{4}\pi^4 \tag{6.6.13}$$

which is Rayleigh's result in the absence of a field.

If the field is vertical

$$\Lambda = \frac{s^2 k^2 + \Gamma k^6}{k^2 - s^2}$$

which has its minimum at the value of k^2 for which

$$(s^2 + 3\Gamma k^4)(k^2 - s^2) - (s^2 k^2 + \Gamma k^6) = 0$$

or introducing $x = \frac{2}{3}k^2/s^2$, where

$$x^2(x-1) = 4/(27\Gamma s^2)$$

The resulting value for β may be written in a rather neat form, for observing the similarity between eqs. (6.6.12) and (6.6.13) suggests the introduction of a "magnetic viscosity" ν_H defined as so that

$$R(\nu_H) = R', \quad \text{thus} \quad \nu_H = \frac{4}{27}\frac{\mathrm{d}^2}{\pi^2}\frac{C_A^2}{\eta} \tag{6.6.14}$$

Then $4/27\Gamma s^2 = \nu_H/\nu$, and the critical temperature gradient is determined by

$$\Lambda = s^2 \frac{(k^2/s^2) + \Gamma s^2 (k^2/s^2)^3}{(k^2/s^2) - 1} = s^2 \left[x \frac{(1 + \frac{9}{4}\Gamma s^2 x^2)}{(x - \frac{2}{3})} \right]$$

$$= s^2 \frac{x\ (x - 1 + \frac{1}{3})}{(x - \frac{2}{3})\ (x - 1)} = s^2 \frac{x}{x - 1} = s^2 \left((1 + \frac{x^2 \nu}{\nu_H}) \right)$$

and the critical gradient becomes therefore

$$\beta = \frac{27}{4}\frac{K}{\alpha g}\frac{\pi^4}{\mathrm{d}^4}(x^2 \nu + \nu_H) = (x^2 \beta_\nu + \beta_H) \tag{6.6.15}$$

where β_ν and β_H are the critical gradient of a viscous fluid with no field and an inviscid fluid in a field.

We will now attempt to examine the dynamical behaviour of the instability and in particular to examine the assumption of static marginal stability. We will show that there do exist conditions under which convection sets in as growing oscillations rather than as a steady flow. To do this we introduce into eq. (6.6.9) a time-dependent solution of the form

$$\exp i(lx+my) \sin(\pi z/d) \exp(\Omega t)$$

and consider the particular case of a vertical field. The dispersion relation derived from eq. (6.6.9) has the form

$$k^2(\Omega + Kk^2)[(\Omega + \eta k^2)(\Omega + \nu k^2) + C_A{}^2 s^2] - \alpha g \beta (\Omega + \eta k^2)(k^2 - s^2) = 0$$

$$(6.6.16)$$

This has the form

$$\Omega^3 + A\Omega^2 + B\Omega + C = 0$$

For a real positive $\Omega \to 0$, $C < 0$; while for a complex root with a positive real part $AB - C < 0$, thus, the condition that instabilities appear as growing oscillations is

$$AB - C < 0 < C$$

or,

$$(K+\eta+\nu)\{[C_A{}^2 s^2 + (K\nu + K\eta + \eta\nu)k^4]k^2 - \alpha g \beta(k^2 - s^2)\} - [(C_A{}^2 s^2 + \eta\nu k^4)Kk^2 -$$
$$- \eta\alpha g \beta(k^2 - s^2)]$$
$$< 0 < (C_A{}^2 s^2 + \eta\nu k^4)Kk^2 - \eta\alpha g \beta(k^2 - s^2)$$

or

$$\frac{\eta+\nu}{K+\nu}[C_A{}^2 s^2 + (K\nu + K\eta + \eta\nu)k^4]k^2 < \alpha g \beta(k^2 - s^2) < (C_A{}^2 s^2 + \eta\nu k^4)\frac{K}{\eta}k^2$$

hence a necessary condition on the constants of the material is

$$\frac{K}{\eta} > \frac{\eta+\nu}{K+\nu}; \quad \text{or} \quad K > \eta$$

For most normal materials this is not satisfied, e.g. for solid copper $K/\eta = 1\cdot4$, but for plasmas $K/\eta \simeq n\lambda f^2 e^2/mc^2$ and at high densities and temperatures this ratio may be very large. In high magnetic fields however and at low densities, the thermal conductivity is reduced; thus only in the interior of stars is oscillating convection likely.

The inhibition of thermal convection by a magnetic field has been observed in mercury (NAGAKAWA). A container of mercury heated from below was placed between the poles of a large magnet, and the temperature difference between top and bottom plotted as a function of the heat input. This curve appeared as two straight lines, the change in slope occurring at

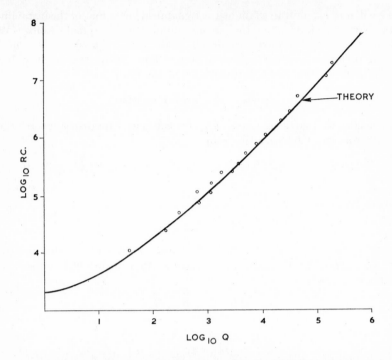

FIG. 6.16. Thermal convection in a magnetic field. Critical Rayleigh number $Rc = (g\alpha\beta d^4/K\nu)$ vs. $Q = (d^2B^2/4\pi^3\rho\eta\nu)$ for the onset of thermal convection as determined by increase in the effective heat conduction. Solid lines shows theoretical value. (Nagakawa, *Proc. Roy. Soc.* **A240**, 108, 1957).

the onset of thermal convection. By varying the field strength the critical gradient for the onset of convection was determined as a function of field strength and satisfactory agreement with theory was obtained. Instead of plotting the values of β directly, Nagakawa, for example, observes that in strong fields we may write

$$\beta \to \frac{27}{4}\frac{K}{\alpha g}\frac{\pi^4}{d^4} \cdot \frac{4}{27}\frac{d^2}{\pi^2}\frac{B^2}{4\pi\eta\rho} = \frac{K\nu}{\alpha g\,d^4} \cdot \frac{d^2B^2}{4\pi^3\rho\nu\eta}\pi^4$$

hence the critical Rayleigh number $R_c = g\alpha\beta d^4/K\nu$, the dimensionless number characterizing the onset field-free convection, approaches $\pi^4 Q$ where

$$Q = \frac{d^2B^2}{4\pi^3\rho\eta\nu}$$

He then plots R_c vs. Q for variations of magnetic field strength and fluid depth (cf. Fig. 6.16), obtaining the predicted asymptotic behaviour.

BIBLIOGRAPHY

Convective instabilities

KADOMTSEV, B. B. (1959). *Plasma Physics and the problem of Controlled Thermo-nuclear Reactions, Volume III*. LEONTOVITCH, M. A. (ed.) Pergamon Press, London, p.340.

ROSENBLUTH, M. N. and LONGMIRE, C. I. (1957). *Am. J. phys.* **1**, 120.

KADOMTSEV, B. B. and BRAGINSKI, S. I. (1958). *Proc. 2nd Geneva Conf.* P/2212 *Prog. Nuc. En.* XI, **1**, 565.

"Wriggle"

ROBERTS, S. J., STURROCK, P. A., THOMPSON, W. B. and WHIPPLE, R. T. P. (1955). A.E.R.E.T/R 1792 H.M. Stationery Office.

THOMPSON, W. B., EDWARDS, S. F., HUBBARD, J. and ROBERTS, S. J. (1958). *Proc. 2nd Geneva Conf.* P/2 *Prog. Nuc. En.* XI, **1**, 416.

FRIEDRICHS, K. O. (1960). *Rev. Mod. Phys.* **32**, 889.

Cusp

BERKOWITZ, J., GRAD, H. and RUBIN, H. (1958). *Proc. 2nd Geneva Conf.* **31**, p.177.

Rayleigh Taylor

KRUSKAL, M. D. and SCHWARZSCHILD, M. (1954). *Proc. Roy. Soc.* **A223**, 348.

KUIPER, G. P. (ed.) (1953). "The Sun" Ch. 6. KIEPENHAUR, K. D. "Solar Activity" University of Chicago Press, Chicago.

Experimental Evidence

KURCHATOV, I. (1956). *Nucleonics* **14**, 636.

COLGATE, S. A., FURTH, H. P. and HALLIDAY, F. V. (1960). *Rev. Mod. Phys.* **32**, 744.

POST, R. F., ELLIS, R. E., FORD, F. C. and ROSENBLUTH, M. N. (1960). *Phys. Rev. Letters* **4**, 166.

ORLINSKII, D. V., *Plasma Physics and Controlled Thermonuclear Reactions IV*, 149.

COLGATE, S. A. (1955). U.C.R.L. 4560 University of California Radiation Laboratory, Livermore, California.

LANDSHOFF, R. K. M. (ed.) (1957). *Magnetohydrodynamics*, Stanford University Press, Stanford, p.104.

CURZON, F. L., FOLKIERSKI, A., LATHAM, R. and NATION, J. A. (1960). *Proc. Roy. Soc.* **A257**, 386.

CARRUTHERS, R. and DAVENPORT, P. A. (1957). *Proc. Phys. Soc.* **B70**, 49.

BERNSTEIN, I. B., FRIEMAN, E. A., KRUSKAL, M. D. and KULSRUD, R. M. (1958). *Proc. Roy. Soc.* **A244**, 17.

Cylindrical Plasma

KRUSKAL, M. D. and SCHWARZSCHILD, M. *op. cit.*

KRUSKAL, M. D. and TUCK, J. L. (1958). *Proc. Roy. Soc.* **A245**, 222.

TAYLER, R. J. (1957). *Proc. Phys. Soc.* **B70**, 31.

SHAFRANOV, V. D. (1957) *J. Nuc. En.* **5**, 86.

ROSENBLUTH, M. N. (1956) U.S.A.E.C. Report LA–2030.

TAYLER, R. J. (1957). *Proc. Phys. Soc.* **B70**, 1049.

SUYDAM, B. *2nd Geneva Conf.* **31**, P1354, p.157.

ROSENBLUTH, M. N. *2nd Geneva Conf.* **31**, P1347, p.85.

NEWCOMB, W. (1959). U.C.R.L. 5447. University of California, Radiation Lab., Livermore.

AITKEN, K. L., BURCHAM, J. N., REYNOLDS, P. (1960). *Proc. 4th Int. Conf. on Ionization Phenomena* Vol. II, p.896.

BIRDSALL, D. H., COLGATE, S. A., FURTH, H. P. (1960). *ibid*, p.888, 892.

BURKHARDT, L. C. and LOVBERG, R. H. (1958). *Proc. 2nd Geneva Conf.*, P/2395, *Prog. Nuc. En.* XI, **1**, 405.

Convection

THOMPSON, W. B. (1951). *Phil. Mag.* **42**, 1417.

CHANDRASEKHAR, S. (1952). *Phil. Mag.* **43**, 501.

CHANDRASEKHAR, S. (1954). *Phil. Mag.* **45**, 1117.

Convection (*continued*)
  JIRLOW, K. (1956). *Tellus* **8**, 252.
  NAGAKAWA, K. (1957). *Proc. Roy. Soc.* A**240**, 108.
  JEFFREYS, H. (1926) *Phil. Mag.* **2**, 833.
  RAYLEIGH (1916) *Phil. Mag.* **32**, 529.

General
  International Summer Course in Plasma Physics 1960
    p.119 *et seq*. Risö Report 18.
    Danish Atomic Energy Commission, Risö Roskilde, Denmark.
  TAYLER, R. J. Lectures on Plasma Stability. A.E.R.E. Harwell.

CHAPTER 7

PLASMA DYNAMICS AND PARTICLE MOTIONS

In the last three chapters we have explored in some detail the consequences of a particular representation of the plasma, magnetohydrodynamics, without inquiring too closely into its validity. From now on, however, we shall attempt to consider the plasma in a somewhat more directly physical manner, and we shall investigate the basis and the limitations of the magnetohydrodynamic representation. In doing this we shall find that, while not a completely adequate description, magnetohydrodynamics is a useful guide to plasma behaviour although the relation between the properties of the fluid and the underlying atomic system is quite different from that for normal gases. The differences arise in several ways. In the first place, the electric forces acting between ions and electrons are of long range, and the neat distinction between intermolecular and macroscopic forces which can often be drawn, becomes blurred, magnetohydrodynamic-like behaviour often arising simply through the response of the electrons and the ions to macroscopic fields, which their distribution and motion, of course, may alter. Thus it is often possible to describe the dynamics of a diffuse plasma by assuming that individual ions and electrons move independently in macroscopic fields which, in turn, are determined or modified by their combined motion, the interaction between individual particles being entirely neglected. If, moreover, particle interaction must be considered in detail, the long-range nature of the interaction prevents us, even in a dilute plasma, from considering only binary encounters. Indeed, an attempt to do so leads immediately to nonsensical results; and, even at its most dilute, the plasma shares some properties with a liquid rather than a gas.

In the present chapter, we will consider these equations only in an informal way, using the simplest of physical arguments, while in the next chapter we shall employ a little of the formal apparatus of kinetic theory and discover certain refinements. However, before embarking on the study of particle motions in inhomogeneous magnetic fields, which will lead us towards the basis of magnetohydrodynamics, we will consider a simpler but nevertheless important problem, which lies beyond that subject; this is the response of a magnetized plasma to an applied alternating electric field, from which we will deduce the dielectric behaviour of the plasma.

1. THE DIELECTRIC BEHAVIOUR OF A MAGNETIZED PLASMA

In Chapter 2 we described the phenomenon of plasma oscillations in the absence of a steady magnetic field, and deduced that to a plasma could be attributed a frequency dependent dielectric coefficient $\epsilon(\omega) = 1 - (\omega_0^2/\omega^2)$. We also observed that this, becoming negative for $\omega < \omega_0$, implied that low frequency oscillations could not be transmitted through the plasma, which for $\omega < \omega_0$ behaved as an electric conductor.

In the presence of a magnetic field the transmission phenomenon becomes much more complex, but we will attempt to analyse it first in the same simple manner, deferring a more sophisticated treatment to the next chapter. Thus, as before, we consider the motion of a charged particle in an oscillating electric field, and a steady uniform magnetic field. The motion is determined by the Lorentz force, thus (Gaussian units)

$$m\dot{\mathbf{v}} = e(\mathbf{E} + \mathbf{v}/c \times \mathbf{B})\qquad(7.1.1)$$

What we wish to do is to find asymptotic solutions of this, and determine the currents induced by the electric field $\mathbf{E}$. We introduce a Cartesian coordinate system with $OX||B$, then by writing $v_x = u$, $v_y + iv_z = w$, $v_y - iv_z = w^*$, replace the three equations (7.1.1) by the equivalent set

$$\dot{u} = \frac{e}{m}E_x$$

$$\dot{w} = \frac{e}{m}(E_y + iE_z) - i\frac{eB}{mc}w\qquad(7.1.2)$$

$$\dot{w^*} = \frac{e}{m}(E_y - iE_z) + i\frac{eB}{mc}w^*$$

Now, if we assume all quantities vary with time as $\exp(i\omega t)$

$$u = \frac{e}{m}\frac{E_x}{i\omega}$$

$$w = \frac{e}{m}\frac{(E_y + iE_z)}{i(\omega + \Omega)}$$

$$w^* = \frac{e}{m}\frac{(E_y - iE_z)}{i(\omega - \Omega)}$$

where $\Omega = eB/mc$.

The Y and Z components of velocity are $v_y = \frac{1}{2}(w + w^*)$ and $v_z = \frac{1}{2i}(w - w^*)$; hence, asymptotically at least,

$$v_x = \frac{e}{m}\frac{E_x}{i\omega}$$

$$v_y = \frac{1}{i}\frac{e}{m}\frac{\omega E_y - i\Omega E_z}{\omega^2 - \Omega^2}\qquad(7.1.3)$$

$$v_z = \frac{1}{i}\frac{e}{m}\frac{\omega E_z + i\Omega E_y}{\omega^2 - \Omega^2}$$

We may now form the currents, including the contribution from the electrons and ions of mass M, charge e_+

$$j_x = \left(\frac{ne^2}{m}\frac{1}{i\omega} + \frac{n_+e_+^2}{M}\frac{1}{i\omega}\right)E_x$$

$$j_y = \frac{ne^2}{m}\frac{1}{i}\frac{\omega E_y - i\Omega E_z}{\omega^2 - \Omega^2} + \frac{n_+e_+^2}{M}\frac{1}{i}\frac{\omega E_y - i\Omega_+ E_z}{\omega^2 - \Omega_+^2} \qquad (7.1.4)$$

$$j_z = \frac{ne^2}{m}\frac{1}{i}\frac{\omega E_z + i\Omega E_y}{\omega^2 - \Omega^2} + \frac{n_+e_+^2}{M}\frac{1}{i}\frac{\omega E_z + i\Omega_+ E_y}{\omega^2 - \Omega_+^2}$$

Since the induced current, while still proportional in magnitude to the electric field, is no longer parallel to it, the dielectric coefficient becomes a tensor; however, it may still be simply defined, for the first of Maxwell's equations

$$\text{curl }\mathbf{B} = \frac{4\pi\mathbf{j}}{c} + \frac{1}{c}\frac{\partial\mathbf{E}}{\partial t} = \frac{1}{c}\frac{\partial\mathbf{D}}{\partial t} = \frac{1}{c}\frac{\partial}{\partial t}\boldsymbol{\epsilon}\cdot\mathbf{E}$$

implies

$$\epsilon_{ij}E_j = D_i = E_i + 4\pi j_i/i\omega$$

and on introducing

$$\omega_p = \frac{4\pi ne^2}{m} \qquad \omega_{p+} = \frac{4\pi n_+ e_+^2}{M}$$

$$\boldsymbol{\epsilon} = \begin{vmatrix} 1 - \left(\dfrac{\omega_p^2}{\omega^2} + \dfrac{\omega_{p+}^2}{\omega^2}\right) & 0 & 0 \\[3mm] 0 & 1 - \dfrac{\omega_p^2}{\omega^2 - \Omega^2} - \dfrac{\omega_{p+}^2}{\omega^2 - \Omega_+^2} & +\dfrac{i\omega_p^2\Omega}{\omega(\omega^2 - \Omega^2)} + \dfrac{i\omega_{p+}^2\Omega_+}{\omega(\omega^2 - \Omega_+^2)} \\[3mm] 0 & -\left(\dfrac{i\omega_p^2\Omega}{\omega(\omega^2 - \Omega^2)} + \dfrac{i\omega_{p+}^2\Omega_+}{\omega(\omega^2 - \Omega_+^2)}\right) & 1 - \dfrac{\omega_p^2}{\omega^2 - \Omega^2} - \dfrac{\omega_{p+}^2}{\omega^2 - \Omega_+^2} \end{vmatrix}$$

$$(7.1.5)$$

At high frequencies $\epsilon \to 1$, and at low frequencies

$$\boldsymbol{\epsilon} \to \begin{vmatrix} -\left(\dfrac{\omega_p^2 + \omega_{p+}^2}{\omega^2}\right) & 0 & 0 \\[3mm] 0 & 1 + \dfrac{4\pi\rho c^2}{B^2} & 0 \\[3mm] 0 & 0 & 1 + \dfrac{4\pi\rho c^2}{B^2} \end{vmatrix} \qquad (7.1.6)$$

since

$$\frac{\omega_p^2}{\Omega^2} + \frac{\omega_{p+}^2}{\Omega_+^2} = \frac{4\pi n_- e_-^2}{m_-(e_-^2 B^2/m_-^2 c^2)} + \frac{4\pi n_+ e_+^2}{M_+(e_+^2 B^2/M_+^2 c^2)} = \frac{4\pi(n_- m_- + n_+ M_+)c^2}{B^2}$$

while

$$\frac{1}{c}\left[\frac{\omega_p^2}{\Omega} + \frac{\omega_{p+}^2}{\Omega_+}\right] = 4\pi\left(\frac{n_- e_-}{B} + \frac{n_+ e_+}{B}\right) = 0$$

from quasi-neutrality.

At these low frequencies the motion of the charges is, from eq. (7.1.2),

$$\frac{e}{m}(E_y + iE_z) - i\frac{eB}{mc}(v_y + iv_z) = 0$$

i.e.

$$v_y = \frac{E_z}{B}c, \qquad v_z = -\frac{E_y c}{B}$$

or

$$\frac{\mathbf{v}}{c} = \frac{\mathbf{E} \times \mathbf{B}}{B^2} \tag{7.1.7}$$

This motion, which is common to both ions and electrons, is exactly that experienced by a fluid transmitting Alfvén waves.

The dielectric coefficient (7.1.6) may be used to discuss the transmission properties of a uniform magnetized plasma and, as may be imagined, these are much more complex than those of a field-free plasma. The first aim must be to derive a relationship between frequency and wavelength—a dispersion relation. We assume that we are interested in plane waves of the form $\sim \exp i(\mathbf{k} \cdot \mathbf{x} + \omega t)$, whereupon Maxwell's equations become

$$\mathbf{k} \times \mathbf{B} = \frac{\omega}{c}\boldsymbol{\epsilon} \cdot \mathbf{E}, \qquad \mathbf{k} \times \mathbf{E} = -\frac{\omega}{c}\mathbf{B}$$

$$\mathbf{k} \cdot \mathbf{B} = 0, \qquad \mathbf{k} \cdot \boldsymbol{\epsilon} \cdot \mathbf{E} = 0$$

The first two imply

$$\mathbf{k} \times (\mathbf{k} \times \mathbf{E}) = -\frac{\omega^2}{c^2}\boldsymbol{\epsilon} \cdot \mathbf{E}$$

or

$$k^2\mathbf{E} - \mathbf{k}(\mathbf{k} \cdot \mathbf{E}) = \frac{\omega^2}{c^2}\boldsymbol{\epsilon} \cdot \mathbf{E}$$

If we write $\boldsymbol{\epsilon}$ as

$$\begin{vmatrix} 1-\alpha & 0 & 0 \\ 0 & 1-\beta & i\gamma \\ 0 & -i\gamma & 1-\beta \end{vmatrix}$$

and introduce $\mathbf{K} = c\mathbf{k}/\omega$, and a unit vector $\mathbf{b}$ in the direction of the steady magnetic field, this may be written

$$[K^2 - (1-\beta)]\mathbf{E} - K(\mathbf{K} \cdot \mathbf{E}) + (\alpha - \beta)(\mathbf{b} \cdot \mathbf{E})\mathbf{b} + i\gamma(\mathbf{b} \times \mathbf{E}) = 0 \qquad (7.1.8)$$

It proves most convenient to replace the three equations (7.1.8) in the components of $\mathbf{E}$ by three others in the variables $X = \mathbf{K} \cdot \mathbf{E}$, $Y = \mathbf{b} \cdot \mathbf{E}$, and $Z = \mathbf{K} \cdot \mathbf{b} \times \mathbf{E}$, which on introducing θ, the angle between $\mathbf{b}$ and $\mathbf{K}$, may be written

$$(1-\beta)X + (\beta - \alpha)K \cos\theta \cdot Y - i\gamma Z = 0$$

$$K \cos\theta \cdot X - [K^2 - (1-\alpha)]Y = 0$$

$$i\gamma X - i\gamma K \cos\theta \cdot Y - [K^2 - (1-\beta)]Z = 0$$

By eliminating Y and Z, we obtain a homogeneous equation for X which is solvable only if the subsidiary condition,

$$[K^2 - (1-\beta)] \cdot [K^2(1 - \alpha\cos^2\theta - \beta\sin^2\theta) - (1-\alpha)(1-\beta)] +$$

$$+ \gamma^2[K^2 \sin^2\theta - (1-\alpha)] = 0 \qquad (7.1.9)$$

is satisfied.

At very low frequencies

$$\beta \to = \frac{-4\pi\rho c^2}{B^2} = \frac{-c^2}{C_A^2}, \quad \gamma \to 0$$

and

$$\alpha \to \frac{\omega_p^2}{\omega^2}\left(1 + \frac{m}{M}\right)$$

thus, eq. (7.1.9) becomes

$$[K^2 - (1 + c^2/C_A^2)]\{K^2[1 + \sin^2\theta \cdot c^2/C_A^2 - (1 + m/M)\cos^2\theta \cdot \omega_p^2/\omega^2] -$$

$$- (1 + c^2/C_A^2)[1 - (1 + m/M)\omega_p^2/\omega^2]\} = 0 \qquad (7.1.10)$$

which has the roots

$$K^2 = 1 + \left(\frac{c^2}{C_A^2}\right),$$

$$K^2 = \frac{(1 + c^2/C_A^2)(1 + m/M - \omega^2/\omega_p^2)}{(1 + m/M)\cos^2\theta - (\omega^2/\omega_p^2)\{1 + (c^2/C_A^2)\sin^2\theta\}} \simeq \frac{1 + c^2/C_A^2}{\cos^2\theta}$$

and the phase velocities ($V = \omega/k$)

$$V^2 = \frac{C_A^2}{1 + C_A^2/c^2}$$

or

$$V^2 = \frac{C_A^2}{1 + C_A^2/c^2}\cos^2\theta$$

If $\cos^2\theta = 0$ the second root becomes $K^2 = -(\omega_p^2/\omega^2)$, and the corresponding wave does not propagate. For propagation parallel to the magnetic field $\theta = 0$ and eq. (7.1.9) becomes

$$(1-\alpha)[\{K^2-(1-\beta)\}^2 - \gamma^2] = 0 \qquad (7.1.11)$$

i.e. $\alpha = 1$ corresponding to the longitudinal plasma oscillations that occur in the absence of a magnetic field, and

$$K^2 = (1-\beta) \pm \gamma \qquad (7.1.12)$$

The corresponding wave is described by eq. (7.1.8). If we consider $\mathbf{E} \perp \mathbf{K}$, and $\mathbf{K}||\mathbf{b}$, eq. (7.1.8) becomes

$$[K^2-(1-\beta)]\mathbf{E} + i\gamma(\mathbf{b} \times \mathbf{E}) = 0 \qquad (7.1.13)$$

thus if the field is circularly polarized, $\mathbf{E} = (0,\, E \cos \omega t,\, E \sin \omega t)$, or in complex representation $E_z = \pm i E_y$, then $i \,.\, (\mathbf{b} \times \mathbf{E}) = \pm \mathbf{E}$ and eq. (7.1.12) implies (7.1.13). Since at low frequencies $\gamma \to 0$, both waves have the same velocity, $V^2 = [C_A^2/(1+C_A^2/c^2)]$, but interesting features appear at higher frequencies. If we write $\omega_p^{+2} = (m/M)Z\omega_p^2$, $\Omega_+ = -(m/M)Z\Omega$, Z being the ionic charge, eq. (7.1.12) may be written (for $\omega > 0$)

$$K_+^2 = 1 - \frac{\omega_p^2(1+\alpha m/M)}{[\omega+(\alpha m/M)\Omega](\omega-\Omega)} \simeq \frac{\omega_p^2}{\omega\Omega} \text{ for } \Omega_+ \ll \omega \ll \Omega$$

$$K_-^2 = 1 - \frac{\omega_p^2(1+Zm/M)}{(\omega+\Omega)[\omega-(Zm/M)\Omega]} \qquad (7.1.14)$$

where for transmission, the R.H.S. must be positive. For K_+ transmission is possible until $\omega \to \Omega$ where K goes to infinity positively, and appears again at $\omega = \Omega$ from $-$infinity passing through zero at $\omega \simeq \omega_p + \frac{1}{2}\Omega$ (if $\Omega \ll \omega_p$), or $\omega \simeq \Omega[1+(\omega_p/\Omega)^2]$ for $\Omega \gg \omega_p$—then proceeding to its asymptotic value $K^2 = 1$. The other wave has its singularity at $\omega = Zm\Omega/M$, and passes through zero at $\omega = \omega_p - \frac{1}{2}\Omega$. It is the first wave, which is highly dispersive at low frequencies, that has been held responsible for "whistlers", a naturally occurring radio noise, in the form of a whistle dropping in pitch. The whistler has been interpreted as the Fourier analysis of the signal produced by a lightning flash at the magnetic antipodes transmitted in the K_+ mode along magnetic field lines through the ionized outer layers of the atmosphere (STOREY).

If the waves are transverse to the magnetic field, eq. (7.1.9) becomes

$$[K^2-(1-\alpha)]\{(1-\beta)[K^2-(1-\beta)] - \gamma^2(1-\alpha)\} = 0$$

hence there are two possible waves, for one of which $K^2 = 1-\alpha$, representing the transmission of a transverse wave with its electric field along the magnetic field, while for the other

$$K^2 = 1-\beta+\gamma^2\frac{(1-\alpha)}{1-\beta} \qquad (7.1.15)$$

This, unlike the longitudinal wave, has no singularities at the gyrofrequencies; however, it has singularities at the points where $1 - \beta = 0$. If $\omega^2 \ll \omega_p{}^2$ there is such a singularity at $\omega_p{}^2 = \Omega^2 Zm/M = \Omega_+ \Omega_-$ while if $\omega^2 \approx \omega_p{}^2$ and $\omega_p{}^2 \gg \Omega^2$, a second one at $\omega^2 = (\omega_p{}^2 + \Omega^2)$; these being the two hybrid resonances.

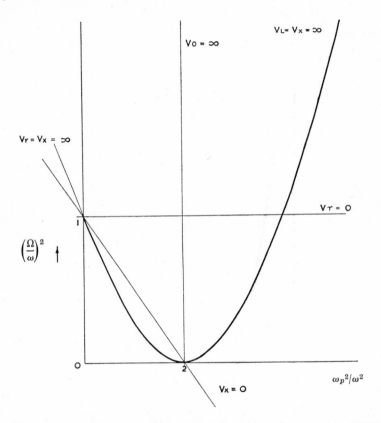

Fig. 7.1. Propagation through a magnetized plasma. Curves in the $(\Omega/\omega)^2$ vs. $(\omega_p/\omega)^2$ plane showing critical lines where phase velocity vanishes or becomes infinite, V_L, V_R for left and right handed waves, V_X, V_O for extraordinary and ordinary waves. (Brown, *Proc. 4th Int. Conf. on Ion. Phen. in Gases*, 1960.)

The stop bands, where the phase velocity ($\sim 1/K$) becomes infinite, are given by

$$(1-\alpha)[(1-\beta)^2 - \gamma^2] = 0 \qquad (7.1.16)$$

i.e.

$$\omega = \omega_p$$

$$\omega \simeq \omega_p \pm \tfrac{1}{2}\Omega$$

In general, eq. (7.1.9) may be written as a quadratic in K^2, i.e. as $AK^4 + BK^2 + C = 0$ with

$$A = 1 - \alpha \cos^2\theta - \beta \sin^2\theta$$

$$B = -\{(1-\beta)[(1-\alpha\cos^2\theta-\beta\sin^2\theta)+(1-\alpha)]-\gamma^2\sin^2\theta\}$$

$$C = (1-\alpha)[(1-\beta)^2-\gamma^2]$$

and the roots

$$K^2 = \frac{-B \pm \sqrt{(B^2-4AC)}}{2A}$$

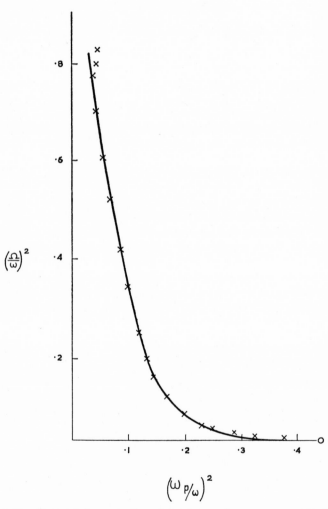

FIG. 7.2. Experimental demonstration of electron cyclotron resonance. Radiation emitted from a plasma near frequency Ω. (Brown, *op. cit.*)

We may now examine the behaviour of this quantity at the cyclotron resonances. Consider first $\omega = \Omega_+ - \epsilon$ as $\epsilon \to 0$. A then has a singularity of order $1/\epsilon$ and $A \sim (\omega_p^2/2\Omega_+\epsilon)\sin^2\theta$; hence only if a singularity of order $1/\epsilon^2$ persists in the numerator is K singular. However, $\beta \to (\omega_p^2/2\Omega_+\epsilon)$ and $\gamma \to (\omega_p^2/2\Omega_+\epsilon)$, hence the terms of order $1/\epsilon^2$ cancel in both B and C, and except for waves propagating along the field, K^2 has no singularities at the cyclotron frequencies. There is, however, a singularity at the vanishing point of A, i.e. where

$$1 - \alpha\cos^2\theta - \beta\sin^2\theta = 0$$

$$\omega^2 = \tfrac{1}{2}(\Omega^2 + \omega_p^2)[1 \pm \sqrt{[1 - 4\omega_p^2\Omega^2\cos^2\theta/(\Omega^2 + \omega_p^2)^2]}]$$

$$\simeq \omega_p^2 + \Omega^2\sin^2\theta, \text{ or } \Omega^2\cos^2\theta \text{ if } \Omega^2 < < \omega_p^2$$

or
$$\omega^2 = \Omega^2_+(1 - (m/M)\tan^2\theta)$$

One of the difficulties in comprehending the transmission characteristics of the magnetized plasma arises from the number of parameters involved. S. C. BROWN has an elegant representation in which he uses as ordinate and abscissa $(\Omega/\omega)^2$ and $(\omega_p/\omega)^2$ plotting the singular lines for which the phase velocity $V = \omega/k$ is either zero or infinite. He considers only the electron effects, and introduces a somewhat arbitrary description of the modes, e.g. the wave with $\mathbf{E} \| \mathbf{B}$ is unaffected by the magnetic field and called the "ordinary" wave. Waves propagating along B are "right-handed" or "left-handed" depending on whether or not the electrons rotate in the same direction as the electric field. Finally the "extraordinary" wave is that involving a longitudinal as well as a transverse component, and propagates across the field. V_0 is infinite at the plasma frequency, V_r vanishes at the plasma frequency; V and V_x become infinite and V_x vanishes along certain curves in the B, n plane (Fig. 7.1). Experiments were made showing the relation between absorption and emission of radiation from a plasma, which from Kirchhoff's laws should be similar in form, then measurements were made of the emitted radiation, which at low pressures showed a definite resonance; finally, the location of the resonance was plotted and found in rough agreement with the theoretical predictions.

WHARTON has measured the radiation from the plasma confined in a magnetic mirror by using a fixed frequency detector. As the magnetic field decayed he discovered resonances not only at the electron gyro-frequency, but at its first three harmonics. These last are due to the high temperature of the confined plasma (cf. Chapter 8). The peak fields were ~ 10 kg, and the frequency ~ 24 kMc/s and the radiation was observed both along and across the magnetic field, with polarization parallel and perpendicular to the field.

The ion cyclotron absorption has been observed by STIX in a helically wound stellerator B-65. The plasma was produced by a current of ~ 2000 A in $2\ \mu$ He in a confining field of 4–20 kg. The power absorbed was plotted as a function of field strength and frequency, and two resonances were found; one corresponding to He++, and a second to H+. Since the measurements were made late in the 600 μsec current pulse the hydrogen probably came from the walls.

The simple theory presented here may be extended by including in a phenomenological way the effect of interparticle collisions. The equations of motion (7.1.1) may be considered as approximate representations of the mean motion of the particles, the effect of interparticle collisions may be

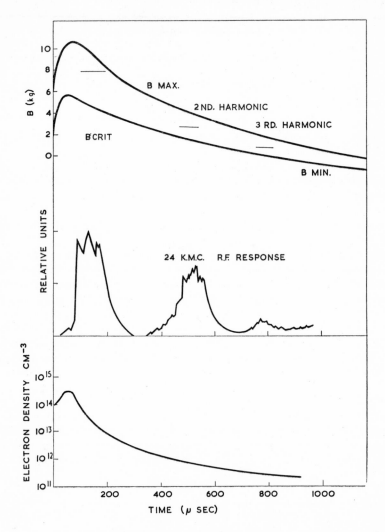

FIG. 7.3. Electron resonance and harmonics. Radiation emitted at fixed frequency from a hot plasma in a varying magnetic field. Horizontal bars show region of cyclotron resonance, first and second harmonics. (Wharton, *Proc. 4th Int. Conf. on Ion. Phen. in Gases*, 1959.)

approximately represented by a frictional resistance, so that the equation of motion becomes

$$\dot{\mathbf{v}} + \frac{1}{\tau}\mathbf{v} = \frac{e}{m}\left[\mathbf{E} + \frac{\mathbf{v}}{c}\times\mathbf{B}\right]$$

τ being the effective collision time for momentum transfer between ions and electrons. We then discover that the gas can abstract energy from the

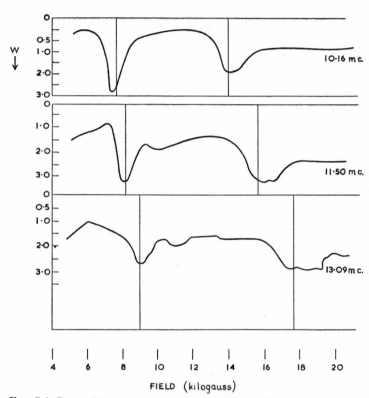

$$W = \frac{\text{POWER ABSORBED BY PLASMA}}{\text{POWER ABSORBED BY COIL OF } Q = 300}$$

FIELD (kilogauss)

FIG. 7.4. Ion cyclotron resonance. Power absorbed by a magnetized Helium plasma. Higher peak represents resonance due to He^{++}, lower due to H^+, a contaminant from the tube walls. (Stix, *Phys. Fluids* **1**, 446, 1958.)

oscillating field; for example, if $B = 0$ the current $j = [ne^2E/m(i\omega + 1/\tau)]$ and the mean rate at which energy is abstracted becomes

$$\frac{d\mathscr{E}}{dt} = \langle \mathbf{j} \cdot \mathbf{E}\rangle = \tfrac{1}{2}\frac{\omega_p^2}{(\omega^2 + 1/\tau^2)\tau}\cdot(\mathbf{E}\cdot\mathbf{E^*})$$

For the circularly polarized waves propagating parallel to the magnetic field the energy added to the gas becomes

$$\frac{d\mathscr{E}_+}{dt} = \frac{1}{\tau}\left\{\frac{\omega_p{}^2}{(\omega-\Omega)^2+(1/\tau)^2} + \frac{\omega_{p+}{}^2}{(\omega+\Omega_+)^2+(1/\tau)^2}\right\}\tfrac{1}{2}(\mathbf{E}\cdot\mathbf{E}^*)$$

and

$$\frac{d\mathscr{E}_-}{dt} = \frac{1}{\tau}\left\{\frac{\omega_p{}^2}{(\omega+\Omega)^2+(1/\tau)^2} + \frac{\omega_{p+}{}^2}{(\omega-\Omega_+)^2+(1/\tau)^2}\right\}\tfrac{1}{2}(\mathbf{E}\cdot\mathbf{E}^*)$$

The energy abstracted from a given spectrum is greatest near a resonance; for example, near the ion cyclotron resonance $\omega \to \Omega_+$, in the second wave, it is possible to abstract $\sim\tfrac{1}{2}\tau\omega_p{}^2{}_+(\mathbf{E}\cdot\mathbf{E}^*)$. This, of course, depends on the wave being propagated into the plasma. Much attention has been given to the problem of heating a plasma by using this mode of propagation in a slowly varying magnetic field. At the ion cyclotron frequency, there is added attraction from the viewpoint of those interested in thermonuclear fusion, since the energy is added selectively to the ions.

2. MEAN FREE PATHS IN A PLASMA

The analysis of the dielectric behaviour has been presented in a manner which has almost neglected the effect of collisions. We have yet to show in what sense this neglect can be extended from high-frequency phenomena to low-frequency phenomena, where magnetohydrodynamic-like behaviour can be expected. To do this we must consider the size of the mean free path in a plasma and its relation to other important lengths. Strictly speaking, the introduction of a mean free path is scarcely justified because of the long-range nature of the Coulomb interaction. Indeed, the differential cross section for the scattering of a pair of charged particles is

$$\sigma(\theta, v)\,d\Omega = \frac{e_1{}^2e_2{}^2}{4(mv^2)^2}\operatorname{cosec}^4\frac{\theta}{2}\,d\Omega \tag{7.2.1}$$

where θ is the scattering angle, v the relative velocity, m the reduced mass and e_1, e_2 the charges. To calculate the mean free path we need the momentum transfer cross section, Q, between particles, which requires averaging the loss of momentum in the direction of initial relative motion $mv(1-\cos\theta)$ over the differential cross section (7.2.1), thus

$$Q = \int \sigma(\theta, v)(1-\cos\theta)\,d\Omega = \frac{e_1{}^2e_2{}^2}{4m^2v^4}\int \operatorname{cosec}^4\tfrac{1}{2}\theta\,.\,(1-\cos\theta)\sin\theta\,d\theta\,d\phi$$

$$= 4\pi\frac{e_1{}^2e_2{}^2}{(mv^2)^2}\,.\,\log(\sin\tfrac{1}{2}\theta)\Big|_0^\pi \tag{7.2.2}$$

If the lower limit is taken as zero, Q diverges, a consequence of the long-range nature of the interaction; however, as will be shown in the next chapter, the effect of the remaining particles in the plasma is to screen the interaction at a characteristic distance, the Debye length, $\lambda_D = v_\theta/\omega_p$, where v_θ = electron thermal speed, and ω_p plasma frequency. This distance while small is usually much greater than the interparticle spacing, indeed

$$\lambda_D n^{1/3} = \left(\frac{v_\theta^2}{\omega_p^2}n^{2/3}\right)^{1/2} = \left(\frac{mv_\theta^2}{4\pi ne^2}n^{2/3}\right)^{1/2} = \left(\frac{\frac{1}{2}mv_\theta^2}{2\pi e^2 n^{1/3}}\right)^{1/2} \simeq \left(\frac{T}{V}\right)^{1/2}$$

where T and V are the mean kinetic and mean interparticle potential energies. If $V \gg T$, the ions and electrons can recombine and the gas becomes neutral; thus for highly ionized gases $\lambda_D \gg n^{-1/3}$. The origin of the screening effect is then easily seen. A particle going past a point target at a distance l produces a time-varying field at the target which may be Fourier analysed into harmonic components, these becoming extremely weak for frequencies greater than v/l. If the distance l is large, the plasma between particle and target must be considered as a medium with a frequency-dependent dielectric coefficient $\epsilon(\omega) = 1 - (\omega^2/\omega_p^2)$, which will not transmit signals below ω_p. If $l = \lambda_D$ the characteristic frequency of the typical particle becomes $v_\theta/\lambda_D = \omega_p$, hence at greater distances the interaction between particles is screened.

When the screening length is used, Q is reduced to

$$Q = 4\pi\frac{e_1^2 e_2^2}{(mv^2)^2}\log\Lambda$$

with $\Lambda^2 = \lambda_D^2(mv^2/e^2)^2$, and the mean free path

$$l_f = \frac{1}{nQ} \simeq \frac{10^{13}}{n\log\Lambda}W^2 \text{ cm},$$

W being the temperature in electron volts. Approximate values of this quantity for a number of plasmas of astrophysical and laboratory importance are given in Table 1, a table which indicates that in laboratory plasmas at least the mean free path is usually *macroscopic*. In many astrophysical situations this is not the case, since the scales of the phenomena are so large.

In a magnetic field a second length becomes important, the Larmor radius, r_L, i.e. the radius of the circle formed by the particle orbit about the magnetic field lines, $r_L = v_\perp/\Omega = mv_\perp c/eB$ ($\simeq 3\cdot7(\sqrt{W}/B)$ cm for electrons, $\simeq 159(\sqrt{W}/B)$ for protons where B is in gauss). This is tabulated in Table 1, which indicates that except in the solar atmosphere $r_L \ll l_f$.

The ratio of these quantities $r_L/l_f \simeq 3 \times 10^{-13}(n \log \Lambda)/BW^{3/2}$ for electrons, $\sim 1\cdot6 \times 10^{-11}(n\log\Lambda)/BW^{3/2}$ for protons, thus at high temperatures, high magnetic fields, and low densities $r_L \ll l_f$, and under these conditions the behaviour of the plasma is determined rather by the interaction of the charged particles with the external magnetic field than by interaction between pairs of particles. For the next few sections, we shall be concerned primarily with an approximation to the behaviour of a plasma in which all interparticle collisions are ignored—the collisionless plasma—and the

Table 1. *Approximate Magnitudes in Typical Plasmas*

Plasma	Density n cm^{-3}	Temperature T °K	Plasma frequency ω_p sec^{-1}	Debye length λ_D cm	Particles in Debye sphere $n\lambda_D^3$	Collision frequency ν sec^{-1}	Ratio $\nu/\omega_p = \lambda_D/l_f$	Magnetic field B gauss	Gyro frequency Electron Ω sec^{-1}	Gyro frequency Proton Ω sec^{-1}	Larmor Electron r_L cm	Radius Proton r_{L+} cm
Interstellar gas	1	10^4	$5.6\ 10^4$	10^3	10^9	$5.2\ 10^{-5}$	$9.3\ 10^{-10}$	10^{-6}	16.0	$8.7\ 10^{-3}$	$3.7\ 10^6$	$1.6\ 10^8$
Gaseous nebula	10^3	10^4	$1.8\ 10^6$	30	$2.7\ 10^9$	$4.3\ 10^{-2}$	$7.7\ 10^{-8}$	10^{-5}	$1.6\ 10^2$	$8.7\ 10^{-2}$	$3.7\ 10^5$	$1.6\ 10^7$
Solar corona	10^6	10^6	$5.6\ 10^7$	10	10^9	$5.2\ 10^{-2}$	$9.3\ 10^{-10}$	10^{-4}	$1.6\ 10^3$	0.87	$3.7\ 10^5$	$1.6\ 10^7$
Solar atmosphere	10^{14}	10^4	$5.6\ 10^{11}$	10^{-4}	10^2	$1.2\ 10^9$	$3.0\ 10^{-4}$	10^3	$1.6\ 10^{10}$	$8.7\ 10^6$	$3.7\ 10^{-3}$	0.16
Gas discharge	10^{14}	10^4	$5.6\ 10^{11}$	$3.2\ 10^{-4}$	10^2	$1.2\ 10^9$	$3.0\ 10^{-4}$	10^3	$1.6\ 10^{10}$	$8.7\ 10^6$	$3.7\ 10^{-3}$	0.16
Hot plasma	10^{14}	10^5	$5.6\ 10^{11}$		$3.2\ 10^3$	$6.4\ 10^{-4}$	$1.14\ 10^{-4}$	10^3	$1.6\ 10^{10}$	$8.7\ 10^6$	$1\ 10^{-3}$	$4.2\ 10^{-2}$
Diffuse hot plasma	10^{12}	10^6	$5.6\ 10^{10}$	10^{-2}	10^6	$3.5\ 10^4$	$6.2\ 10^{-7}$	10^3	$1.6\ 10^{10}$	$8.7\ 10^6$	$3.7\ 10^{-2}$	1.6
Dense hot plasma	10^{16}	10^6	$5.6\ 10^{12}$	10^{-4}	10^4	$2.3\ 10^8$	$4.1\ 10^{-5}$	10^4	$1.6\ 10^{11}$	$8.7\ 10^7$	$3.7\ 10^{-3}$	0.16
Thermonuclear plasma	10^{16}	10^8	$5.6\ 10^{12}$	10^{-3}	10^7	$3.2\ 10^5$	$5.7\ 10^{-8}$	$3\cdot 10^5$	$4.8\ 10^{12}$	$2.61\ 10^9$	$1.2\ 10^{-3}$	$5\ 10^{-2}$

origin of magnetohydrodynamic behaviour will be sought in the interaction between independent charged particles and macroscopic electric and magnetic fields, where instead of a short mean free path we shall assume that the Larmor radius of the particle orbit is small.

3. THE APPROXIMATE TREATMENT OF PARTICLE ORBITS

In pursuance of this scheme we must first discover the effect of slowly varying fields on the motion of particles. In doing this we shall make use of the smallness of the Larmor radius, and assume that all quantities vary slowly i.e. that $\Omega = eB/mc \gg$ any other frequency and $r_L = v/\Omega \ll$ any other length, e.g. $(1/\Omega)(1/B)(\partial B/\partial t) \ll 1$ and $(r_L/B)(\partial B/\partial x) \ll 1$. In addition to these constraints there is a further more or less arbitrary one that must be imposed if any hydrodynamic behaviour is to appear; that is that variations of quantities in the direction of the magnetic field and accelerations along the field lines should be small. In default of this, localized phenomena cannot be expected, since the magnetic field itself will not locate particles along a field line.

With these constraints in mind we will proceed to produce approximate solutions to the equations of motion,

$$\dot{\mathbf{v}} = \frac{e}{m}\left(\mathbf{E} + \frac{\mathbf{v}}{c}\times\mathbf{B}\right) + \mathbf{F} \tag{7.3.1}$$

where $\mathbf{F}$ is any non-electric acceleration experienced by the particles. We will first consider the case where $\mathbf{E}$ and $\mathbf{F}$ have no component parallel to $\mathbf{B}$, and where $\mathbf{B}$ is uniform.

If we introduce $\mathbf{v} = \mathbf{v}_E + \mathbf{v}_F + \mathbf{v}_1$, where

$$\mathbf{v}_E = \frac{\mathbf{E}\times\mathbf{B}}{B^2}c, \qquad \mathbf{v}_F = \frac{m}{e}\frac{\mathbf{F}\times\mathbf{B}}{B^2}c \tag{7.3.2}$$

then

$$\frac{\mathbf{v}_E}{c}\times\mathbf{B} = \frac{(\mathbf{E}\times\mathbf{B})\times\mathbf{B}}{B^2} = \frac{(\mathbf{E}.\mathbf{B})\,\mathbf{B}}{B^2} - \mathbf{E} = -\mathbf{E}$$

and

$$\frac{\mathbf{v}_F}{c}\times\mathbf{B} = -\frac{m}{e}\mathbf{F}$$

Thus, provided $\mathbf{E}$ and $\mathbf{F}$ are not time-dependent, the introduction of these two velocities reduces (7.3.1) to

$$\dot{\mathbf{v}}_1 = \frac{e}{m}\left(\frac{\mathbf{v}_1}{c}\times\mathbf{B}\right) \tag{7.3.3}$$

If, on the other hand, $\mathbf{E}$ or $\mathbf{F}$ are time-dependent, $\mathbf{v}_E$ and $\mathbf{v}_F$ are also time-dependent and eq. (7.3.1) becomes

$$\dot{\mathbf{v}}_E + \dot{\mathbf{v}}_F + \dot{\mathbf{v}}_1 = \frac{e}{m}\left(\frac{\mathbf{v}_1}{c}\times\mathbf{B}\right) \qquad (7.3.4)$$

or

$$\frac{c[\dot{\mathbf{E}}+(m/e)\dot{\mathbf{F}}]\times\mathbf{B}}{B^2} + \dot{\mathbf{v}}_1 = \frac{e}{m}\left(\frac{\mathbf{v}_1}{c}\times\mathbf{B}\right)$$

Now let us write $\mathbf{v}_1 = \mathbf{v}_{\dot{E}} + \mathbf{v}_2$, and reduce eq. (7.3.2) to

$$\left\{\frac{(\dot{\mathbf{E}}+(m/e)\dot{\mathbf{F}})c}{B^2} - \frac{e}{m}\frac{\mathbf{v}_{\dot{E}}}{c}\right\}\times\mathbf{B} + \dot{\mathbf{v}}_{\dot{E}} + \dot{\mathbf{v}}_2 = \frac{e}{m}\frac{\mathbf{v}_2}{c}\times\mathbf{B}$$

and if

$$\mathbf{v}_{\dot{E}} = \frac{mc^2\dot{\mathbf{E}}/e + c^2 m^2 \dot{\mathbf{F}}/e^2}{B^2} \qquad (7.3.5)$$

eq. (7.3.4.) is reduced to

$$\dot{\mathbf{v}}_{\dot{E}} + \dot{\mathbf{v}}_2 = \frac{e}{m}\frac{\mathbf{v}_2}{c}\times\mathbf{B}$$

Since the electric field contribution to $\mathbf{v}_{\dot{E}} = mc^2\dot{\mathbf{E}}/eB^2 = (mc/eB)(c\dot{\mathbf{E}}/B)$ $\simeq (\omega/\Omega)\,\mathbf{v}_E$, $\dot{\mathbf{v}}_{\dot{E}} \sim (\omega^2/\Omega)\mathbf{v}_E$, while $\dot{\mathbf{v}}_2 \sim \Omega\mathbf{v}_2$, thus $\dot{\mathbf{v}}_{\dot{E}} \sim (\omega^2/\Omega^2)\dot{\mathbf{v}}_2$, to first order in ω/Ω may be neglected, and eq. (7.3.4) reduced to the form of (7.3.3). This last drift $\mathbf{v}_{\dot{E}}$ is responsible for the low-frequency form of the dielectric constant, since it induces a current density $\mathbf{j} = (nmc^2/B^2)\dot{\mathbf{E}}$ and a dielectric constant $\epsilon = 1+4\pi\rho c^2/B^2$, which is just the low-frequency limit of the dielectric constant for transverse fields discovered in Section 1.

We must now consider the effect of variations of the magnetic field on eq. (7.3.1). If the magnetic field is uniform and steady, the orbit forms a helix about the magnetic lines with radius $r_L = v_\perp/\Omega$. If the field varies in time, Ω becomes time-dependent, but in addition, Maxwell's equations require the appearance of an electric field. Indeed, there will be an e.m.f. about the orbit of the particle, whose magnitude is

$$\mathcal{E} = \oint \mathbf{E}\,.\,\mathbf{dl} = -\frac{1}{c}\frac{\partial}{\partial t}\int \mathbf{B}\,.\,\mathbf{dA} \simeq -\frac{1}{c}\frac{\partial}{\partial t}(B\pi r_L^2)$$

We may then equate the rate of gain of angular momentum of the particle to the torque acting upon it, thus

$$\frac{\mathrm{d}}{\mathrm{d}t}(mr_L^2\Omega) = er_L\,.\,E_\phi = \frac{e}{2\pi}\oint \mathbf{E}\,.\,\mathbf{dl} = -\frac{1}{2\pi}\frac{e}{c}\frac{\mathrm{d}}{\mathrm{d}t}\pi(Br_L^2)$$

$$= -\tfrac{1}{2}\frac{\mathrm{d}}{\mathrm{d}t}(mr_L^2\Omega)$$

hence, to this order,

$$\frac{d}{dt}(r_L{}^2\Omega) \sim \frac{d}{dt}\left(\tfrac{1}{2}\frac{mv_\perp{}^2}{B}\right) \equiv \frac{d(\mu)}{dt} = 0 \qquad (7.3.6)$$

and the magnetic moment $\mu = \tfrac{1}{2}mv_\perp{}^2/B$ is an approximate constant of the motion. This is an example of an adiabatic invariant for a quasi-periodic system. Suppose that a quantity r may be determined as a power series in a small parameter ϵ, and is periodic in zero order, i.e. r satisfies

$$\ddot{r} + \Omega^2 r = \epsilon g(r, t)$$

then the quantity

$$\alpha(r_0) = \oint \dot{r}\,dr$$

is a constant to second order in ϵ; for introducing $r_0 + \epsilon r_1$ into α yields

$$\frac{d}{dt}[\alpha(r_0 + \epsilon r_1)] = \frac{d}{dt}\oint (\dot{r}_0 + \epsilon \dot{r}_1)^2\,dt$$

$$= \frac{d}{dt}\oint \dot{r}_0{}^2\,dt + 2\epsilon \oint (\ddot{r}_0 \dot{r}_1 + \dot{r}_0 \ddot{r}_1)\,dt + O(\epsilon^2)$$

The first term vanishes from the periodicity of $r_0(t)$, and integrating the second term by parts yields

$$\epsilon(\dot{r}_0 \dot{r}_1)\Big|_a^b - \oint (\ddot{r}_1 \dot{r}_0 - \dot{r}_0 \ddot{r}_1)\,dt = 0$$

the integrated part vanishing at the two limits a, b where $\dot{r}_0 = 0$. Thus $d\alpha(r)/dt = O(\epsilon^2)$. In terms of the frequency Ω,

$$\alpha(r) = \oint \dot{r}_0\,dr_0 = \Omega \oint \left(\frac{dr}{d\theta}\right)^2 d\theta = \tfrac{1}{2}\Omega a^2$$

where a is the amplitude of r_0, and where, moreover, we need not insist that $\Omega(t)$ be constant, only that $\dot{\Omega}(t) = O(\epsilon)$. For changes in a magnetic field $\alpha = \tfrac{1}{2}\Omega r_L{}^2 \sim \tfrac{1}{2}mv_\perp{}^2/B$.

Such adiabatic invariants play an important role in the analysis of quasi-periodic orbits and have been the subject of much study. For example, the magnetic moment represents the first approximation to an adiabatic invariant which may be expanded in powers of ϵ, $\alpha = \mu + \epsilon \cdot f(\partial B/\partial x \ldots) + \epsilon^2 + \ldots$, and which is constant to all orders in ϵ. This does not imply that α is a constant, but only that its time variation is non-analytic in ϵ, e.g. it could have the form $\alpha \sim \exp[-f(t)/\epsilon]$ which is small for small ϵ, but not expansible about $\epsilon = 0$ (KRUSKAL, 1957).

If the magnetic field varies in space, there are nine separate terms to be considered, although only eight of these are independent, i.e. we have

$$
\begin{pmatrix}
\dfrac{\partial B_x}{\partial x} & \dfrac{\partial B_x}{\partial y} & \dfrac{\partial B_x}{\partial z} \\[2ex]
\dfrac{\partial B_y}{\partial x} & \dfrac{\partial B_y}{\partial y} & \dfrac{\partial B_y}{\partial z} \\[2ex]
\dfrac{\partial B_z}{\partial x} & \dfrac{\partial B_z}{\partial y} & \dfrac{\partial B_z}{\partial z}
\end{pmatrix}
$$

subject to the constraint $\partial B_x/\partial x + \partial B_y/\partial y + \partial B_z/\partial z = 0$. Since we intend to linearize in these parameters they may be considered separately. The most important effect of introducing spatial gradients is to induce certain further drifts, and the principal effects can be understood fairly simply. For example, if B is not constant in direction, so that the field lines curve, while the guiding centres are constrained in lowest order to move along the field lines, the particles experience a centripetal acceleration $\mathbf{n} \cdot v_\parallel^2/R$ where R is the radius of curvature of the field line and $\mathbf{n}$ the principal normal. If we use this as $-\mathbf{F}$ in eq. (7.3.2) it is apparent that a drift

$$
\mathbf{v}_R = -\frac{m}{e}\frac{\mathbf{n} \times \mathbf{B}}{B^2}c \cdot \frac{v_\parallel^2}{R} = \frac{1}{\Omega}\frac{v_\parallel^2}{R}\mathbf{b} \times \mathbf{n} \tag{7.3.7}
$$

will appear, where $\mathbf{b}$ is a unit vector $\parallel \mathbf{B}$

If, on the other hand, not the direction but the magnitude of B varies, two effects are produced. If the magnitude of B varies in the direction normal to $\mathbf{b}$, i.e. $\mathbf{b} \times \nabla|B| \neq 0$, then, writing a component of the motion normal to the field as

$$
v_x = v_\perp \cos \int \Omega \, \mathrm{d}t = v_\perp \cos\left[\Omega_0 t + \int\left[\frac{\partial \Omega}{\partial y}y_0 + \frac{\partial \Omega}{\partial x}x_0\right] \mathrm{d}t\right]
$$

and expanding

$$
v_x = v_\perp \cos \Omega_0 t - v_\perp \sin \Omega_0 t \cdot \left[\int\int\left(\frac{\partial \Omega}{\partial x}\frac{v_\perp}{\Omega_0} \sin \Omega_0 t - \frac{\partial \Omega}{\partial y}\frac{v_\perp}{\Omega_0} \cos \Omega_0 t\right) \mathrm{d}t\right]
$$

$$
= v_\perp \cos \Omega_0 t - v_\perp \sin \Omega_0 t \cdot \left[-\frac{\partial \Omega}{\partial x}\frac{v_\perp}{\Omega_0{}^2} \cos \Omega_0 t - \frac{\partial \Omega}{\partial y}\frac{v_\perp}{\Omega_0{}^2} \sin \Omega_0 t\right]
$$

which has the average value over a cycle of $\frac{1}{2}v_\perp^2(1/\Omega_0^2)\partial\Omega/\partial y$; hence, a gradient in field strength produces a drift

$$
\mathbf{v}_B = \mathbf{b} \times \nabla \log B \cdot \frac{\frac{1}{2}v_\perp^2}{\Omega} \tag{7.3.8}
$$

If, on the other hand, the magnitude of $\mathbf{B}$ varies in the direction of $\mathbf{B}$, i.e. $\mathbf{b} \cdot \nabla|B| \neq 0$, then the constancy of $\mu = v_\perp^2/B$ demands that the particle experiences an acceleration along the field line, for if the fields are steady $v_\parallel{}^2 + v_\perp{}^2 = \text{const}$, but since $v_\perp{}^2/B = \text{const}$

$$\frac{\partial}{\partial x}\frac{v_\perp{}^2}{B} = \frac{1}{B}\frac{\partial v_\perp{}^2}{\partial x_\parallel} - \frac{v_\perp{}^2}{B^2}\frac{\partial B}{\partial x_\parallel} \quad \text{or} \quad \frac{\partial v_\perp{}^2}{\partial x_\parallel} = \frac{v_\perp{}^2}{B}\frac{\partial B}{\partial x_\parallel}$$

hence

$$\dot{v}_\parallel = v_\parallel\frac{\partial v_\parallel}{\partial x_\parallel} = -\tfrac{1}{2}\frac{\partial}{\partial x_\parallel}v_\perp{}^2 = -\tfrac{1}{2}\frac{v_\perp{}^2}{B}\frac{\partial B}{\partial x_\parallel}$$

and

$$m\dot{v}_\parallel = -\mu\frac{\partial B}{\partial x_\parallel} \tag{7.3.9}$$

This, however, is exactly the force experienced by a dipole of moment μ oriented along the field line, and since the particle in its Larmor orbit forms a current loop of moment μ, we may consider its motion as just that of an oriented dipole.

The aperiodic effects of electric fields and of magnetic field gradients are summarized in the following statements about the motion of the guiding centre:

(1) an adiabatic invariant is $\mu = \tfrac{1}{2}mv_\perp{}^2/B$;
(2) the guiding centre moves along the magnetic field subject to the acceleration $m\dot{v}_\parallel = (eE_\parallel + F_\parallel) - \mu\partial|B|/\partial x_\parallel$;
(3) the guiding centre also drifts across the magnetic field with a drift velocity having components

$$\mathbf{v}_E = \frac{\mathbf{E}\times\mathbf{B}}{B^2}c$$

$$\dot{\mathbf{v}}_F = \frac{m}{e}\frac{\mathbf{F}\times\mathbf{B}}{B^2}c$$

$$\mathbf{v}_{\dot{E}} = \frac{(\dot{\mathbf{E}}+m\dot{\mathbf{F}}/e)}{B}mc^2/e$$

$$\mathbf{v}_R = \frac{1}{\Omega}\frac{v_\parallel{}^2}{R}\mathbf{b}\times\mathbf{n} = \frac{1}{\Omega}v_\parallel{}^2\mathbf{b}\times(\mathbf{b}\,.\,\boldsymbol{\nabla})\mathbf{b}(r)$$

$$\mathbf{v}_B = \tfrac{1}{2}\frac{v_\perp{}^2}{\Omega}\,\mathbf{b}\times\boldsymbol{\nabla}(\log B)$$

The best evidence for the constancy of the adiabatic invariant is probably provided by the long confinement of a diffuse plasma in a mirror machine (Post). One experiment involved an 18 in. dia. highly evacuated chamber with low confining fields $\sim 20\ G$. Into this was injected a low energy plasma which was confined for times ~ 8 msec, which was that expected if collisional diffusion alone removed particles. Further evidence is provided by a high-temperature, high-compression experiment in which the electron density distribution could be compared with that calculated on the basis of diffusion theory, and agreement was again found (POST *et al.*).

4. A FORMAL DERIVATION OF THE DRIFTS

In order to calculate these drifts in a more formal fashion we will solve eq. (7.3.3) in the form and in e.m.u.

$$\dot{\mathbf{v}} = \left[\left(\frac{e}{m}\mathbf{E}+\mathbf{F}\right) \cdot \mathbf{b}\right]\mathbf{b}+\frac{e}{m}\mathbf{v}\times\mathbf{B} \tag{7.4.1}$$

where $[(e/m)\mathbf{E}+\mathbf{F}] \cdot \mathbf{b}$ and $\boldsymbol{\nabla} \cdot \mathbf{B}$ are small of order ϵ.

It proves convenient to consider the components of eq. (7.4.1) on a triad of orthogonal unit vectors $\mathbf{e}_1$, $\mathbf{e}_2$, $\mathbf{e}_3$ containing some information about the magnetic field geometry. We select these as the unit tangent, principle normal and binormal,

$$\mathbf{e}_1 = \mathbf{b}, \qquad \mathbf{e}_2 = R(\mathbf{b} \cdot \boldsymbol{\nabla})\mathbf{b}, \qquad \mathbf{e}_3 = \mathbf{e}_1\times\mathbf{e}_2$$

Among the useful properties of these vectors are

$$\text{div } \mathbf{e}_1 = -\frac{1}{|B|}\mathbf{e}_1\cdot\boldsymbol{\nabla}|B| = -\frac{1}{B}\frac{\partial}{\partial x_1}-|B| \tag{7.4.2}$$

$$\mathbf{e}_1 \cdot \left[\frac{\partial\mathbf{e}_2}{\partial x_2} + \frac{\partial\mathbf{e}_3}{\partial x_3}\right] = -\text{div } \mathbf{e}_1 = \frac{1}{B}\frac{\partial}{\partial x_1}|B| \tag{7.4.3}$$

To prove the first of these observe that

$$0 = \text{div } \mathbf{B} = \boldsymbol{\nabla} \cdot |B|\mathbf{e}_1 = |B|(\boldsymbol{\nabla} \cdot \mathbf{e}_1)+\mathbf{e}_1 \cdot \boldsymbol{\nabla}|B|$$

while for the second

$$\mathbf{e}_1 \cdot \left[\frac{\partial\mathbf{e}_2}{\partial x_2} + \frac{\partial\mathbf{e}_3}{\partial x_3}\right] = \mathbf{e}_1 \cdot \left[\frac{\partial}{\partial x_2}(\mathbf{e}_3\times\mathbf{e}_1)+\frac{\partial}{\partial x_3}(\mathbf{e}_1\times\mathbf{e}_2)\right]$$

$$= \mathbf{e}_1 \cdot \left[\mathbf{e}_2\times\mathbf{e}_1\left(\mathbf{e}_2 \cdot \frac{\partial}{\partial x_2}\mathbf{e}_3\right)+\mathbf{e}_3\times\mathbf{e}_2\left(\mathbf{e}_2 \cdot \frac{\partial}{\partial x_2}\mathbf{e}_1\right)+ \right.$$

$$\left. +\mathbf{e}_3\times\mathbf{e}_2\left(\mathbf{e}_3 \cdot \frac{\partial\mathbf{e}_1}{\partial x_3}\right)+\mathbf{e}_1\times\mathbf{e}_3\left(\mathbf{e}_3 \cdot \frac{\partial}{\partial x_3}\mathbf{e}_2\right)\right]$$

$$= -\left[\mathbf{e}_2 \cdot \frac{\partial\mathbf{e}_1}{\partial x_2}+\mathbf{e}_3 \cdot \frac{\partial\mathbf{e}_1}{\partial x_3}\right] = -\text{div } \mathbf{e}_1$$

The remaining terms

$$\mathbf{e}_3\left[\mathbf{e}_2 \cdot \frac{\partial}{\partial x_2}\mathbf{e}_3\right]+\mathbf{e}_2\left[\mathbf{e}_3 \cdot \frac{\partial}{\partial x_3}\mathbf{e}_2\right]$$

are produced by the rotation of the normal and binormal, and are of no great interest.

Representing the velocity by its projections v_1, v_2, v_3 on this triad means that the acceleration becomes

$$\dot{v}_1\mathbf{e}_1+\dot{v}_2\mathbf{e}_2+\dot{v}_3\mathbf{e}_3+v_1\dot{\mathbf{e}}_1+v_2\dot{\mathbf{e}}_2+v_3\dot{\mathbf{e}}_3$$

where $\dot{\mathbf{e}} = (\mathbf{v} \cdot \nabla)\mathbf{e}$.

In zero order, $\dot{\mathbf{e}}= 0$ and the components of eq. (7.4.1) become

$$\dot{v}_1 = 0$$

$$\dot{v}_2 = \Omega v_3$$

$$\dot{v}_3 = -\Omega v_2$$

$v_1 = $ const, $v_2 = v_\perp \sin \Omega t$, $v_3 = v_\perp \cos \Omega t$ where the irrelevant phase of t has been selected for convenience. In first order then

$$v_1\dot{\mathbf{e}}_1+v_2\dot{\mathbf{e}}_2+v_3\dot{\mathbf{e}}_3 = v_1{}^2\frac{\partial \mathbf{e}_1}{\partial x_1}+\tfrac{1}{2}v_\perp{}^2\left[\frac{\partial \mathbf{e}_2}{\partial x_2} + \frac{\partial \mathbf{e}_3}{\partial x_3}\right]+$$

$$+\text{periodic terms};$$

and neglecting the torsion of the fields,

$$= v_1{}^2\frac{\mathbf{e}_2}{R}+\tfrac{1}{2}v_\perp{}^2\mathbf{e}_1\frac{1}{|B|}\frac{\partial}{\partial x_1}|B|$$

Similarly, on the R.H.S.

$$\Omega\mathbf{v}\times\mathbf{e}_1 = (\Omega_0+\nabla\Omega \cdot \mathbf{r}_0)\mathbf{v}\times\mathbf{e}_1$$

$$= \Omega_0\mathbf{v}^1\times\mathbf{e}_1+\frac{\partial\Omega}{\partial x_2}\langle r_2v_3\rangle\mathbf{e}_2-\frac{\partial\Omega}{\partial x_3}\langle r_3v_2\rangle\mathbf{e}_3$$

$$= \Omega_0\mathbf{v}^1\times\mathbf{e}_1-\frac{1}{2}\frac{v_\perp{}^2}{\Omega}\left[\left(\mathbf{e}_2\frac{\partial}{\partial x_2}+\mathbf{e}_3\frac{\partial}{\partial x_3}\right)\Omega\right]+$$

$$+\text{periodic terms} \qquad (7.4.4)$$

and eq. (7.4.1) becomes

$$\dot{\mathbf{v}}_1{}^{(1)} = \left(\frac{e}{m}E_\parallel+F_\parallel\right)-\tfrac{1}{2}\frac{v_\perp{}^2}{|B|}\frac{\partial}{\partial x_1}|B|+ \cdots$$

$$\dot{\mathbf{v}}_2{}^{(1)} = \Omega_0\mathbf{v}_3{}^{(1)}-v_1{}^2\frac{1}{R}-\tfrac{1}{2}\frac{v_\perp{}^2}{B}\frac{\partial}{\partial x_2}|B|+ \cdots \qquad (7.4.5)$$

$$\dot{\mathbf{v}}_3{}^{(1)} = -\Omega_0\mathbf{v}_2{}^{(1)}-\tfrac{1}{2}\frac{v_\perp{}^2}{B}\frac{\partial}{\partial x_3}|B|+ \cdots$$

where the remaining terms are periodic. The aperiodic terms in the second and third equations may be handled exactly as was an electric field, by introducing drifts

$$v_{03} = \frac{v_{\parallel}^2}{\Omega R} + \frac{1}{2}\frac{v_{\perp}^2}{\Omega B}\frac{\partial}{\partial x_2}|B| \qquad (7.4.6)$$

$$v_{02} = -\frac{1}{2}\frac{v_{\perp}^2}{\Omega B}\frac{\partial}{\partial x_3}|B|$$

which are exactly the drifts of Section 3. The added acceleration in the first of eq. (7.4.5) permits the formation of an energy integral in the steady state

$$\mathscr{E}_{\parallel} = \tfrac{1}{2}mv_{\parallel}^2 + \mu B - \int(eE_{\parallel} + mF_{\parallel})\,dx_{\parallel} \qquad (7.4.7)$$

The existence of the invariant μ implies that particles may be trapped between regions of high B where $\mu B = \mathscr{E}_{\parallel}$. If so, the orbits along the field lines become periodic and there exists a second adiabatic invariant

$$\alpha_2 = \oint v_{\parallel}\,dl_{\parallel}$$

which is frequently important.

5. MACROSCOPIC EFFECTS OF PARTICLE MOTION

We may now inquire into the macroscopic effects of particle motions and attempt to discover what gross phenomena are to be expected from the summed motion of a large number of particles. Before making use of the information from the last section we must briefly recall the relationship between macroscopic and microscopic motions. Suppose then that we have a large number of particles having masses m_i, charges q_i moving with velocities $\mathbf{v}_i$, then clearly the mean density of matter ρ in a macroscopic volume $\mathscr{V}$ is simply

$$\rho = \frac{\Sigma m_i}{\mathscr{V}} \qquad (7.5.1)$$

where the sum extends over all those particles which happen to be in the volume $\mathscr{V}$ at any instant. The electric charge density is similarly

$$Q = \frac{\sum q_i}{\mathscr{V}} \qquad (7.5.2)$$

The total momentum in any macroscopic volume is $\Sigma m_i\mathbf{v}_i$, from which it is possible to define a mean velocity through

$$\rho\mathbf{V} = \sum m_i\mathbf{v}_i/\mathscr{V} \qquad (7.5.3)$$

hence $\mathbf{V}$ is the mean velocity of the particles weighted by particle mass.

The total current density J may be defined in a similar way, although here the weighting is by charge

$$\mathbf{J} = \frac{\sum q_i \mathbf{v}_i}{\mathscr{V}} \tag{7.5.4}$$

Frequently, it is useful to distinguish between the convection current

$$\mathbf{J}_{conv} = Q\mathbf{V} \tag{7.5.5}$$

and the net current

$$\mathbf{j} = \mathbf{J} - \mathbf{J}_{conv} \tag{7.5.6}$$

To write the equations of motion in a macroscopic form it is often convenient to consider the rate of change of momentum in a given volume of space. This contains two contributions, a part representing the instantaneous rate of change of momentum of the particles within the volume and a part representing the momentum carried into the volume by particles entering it. Of these the first is $\partial(\sum m_i \mathbf{v}_i)/\partial t$, and the second div $\sum \mathbf{v}(m\mathbf{v})$. Hence the total rate of change of momentum is

$$\frac{\partial}{\partial t}(\rho \mathbf{V}) + \nabla \cdot \sum \mathbf{v}_i(m_i \mathbf{v}_i)$$

In the second term, we may introduce the random velocity $\mathbf{c}_i = \mathbf{v}_i - \mathbf{V}$ and write

$$\nabla \cdot \mathbf{V}(\rho \mathbf{V}) + \nabla \cdot \sum \mathbf{c}_i m_i \mathbf{c}_i$$

In hydrodynamics, the last term here, which represents the momentum carried by the random velocity plays the role of the pressure tensor, provided that random interparticle forces are small, i.e.

$$\mathbf{p} = \sum m\mathbf{c}\mathbf{c} \tag{7.5.7}$$

Observing that the conservation of mass implies

$$\frac{\partial \rho}{\partial t} + \operatorname{div} \rho \mathbf{V} = 0 \tag{7.5.8}$$

it is apparent that the equation for the conservation of momentum may be written

$$\frac{\partial}{\partial t}\rho \mathbf{V} + \nabla \cdot \mathbf{V}(\rho \mathbf{V}) + \nabla \cdot \mathbf{p}$$

$$= \mathbf{V}\left[\frac{\partial \rho}{\partial t} + \nabla \cdot (\rho \mathbf{V})\right] + \rho\left[\frac{\partial V}{\partial t} + \mathbf{V} \cdot \nabla \mathbf{V}\right] + \nabla \cdot \mathbf{p} = \mathbf{F}$$

or

$$\rho\left[\frac{\partial \mathbf{V}}{\partial t} + (\mathbf{V} \cdot \nabla)\mathbf{V}\right] = -\nabla \cdot \mathbf{p} + \mathbf{F} \tag{7.5.9}$$

F being the force per unit volume acting on the particles, i.e. $\Sigma F_i / \mathscr{V}$. We are now in a position to consider the gross effects of the motion of a large number of charged particles in a magnetic field.

First, to zero order in field gradients the particles move in circles about the field lines, thus giving rise to current loops with dipole moments $\mu = \frac{1}{2} m v_\perp^2 / B$, hence the plasma is diamagnetic with a moment density parallel to the applied field, $M = \Sigma \mu = W_\perp / B$, $W_\perp$ being the kinetic energy density associated with the gyromotion about the magnetic field lines. If the particle orbits are not phased, $W_\perp$ is associated with a random motion and the components of the pressure tensor associated with directions X, Y, normal to the magnetic field are

$$p_{xx} = n \langle m v_\perp^2 \cos^2\theta \rangle = \tfrac{1}{2} n m v_\perp^2 = W_\perp$$

$$p_{yy} = n \langle m v_\perp^2 \sin^2\theta \rangle = \tfrac{1}{2} n m v_\perp^2 = p_{xx} = p_\perp$$

$$p_{xy} = p_{yx} = n \langle m v_\perp^2 \sin\theta \cos\theta \rangle = 0$$

The particle motion along the magnetic field line is unspecified, and the component of the pressure tensor associated with this, $p_{zz} = \Sigma n m v_\parallel^2 = p_\parallel$ has no necessary connection with $p_\perp$. Clearly $p_{xz} = n \langle m v_\perp v_\parallel \cos\theta \rangle = 0$ as does p_{yz} and the pressure tensor has the form

$$\mathbf{p} = p_\perp \mathbf{1} + (p_\parallel - p_\perp)\mathbf{bb} \tag{7.5.10}$$

where **1** is the unit tensor, i.e.

$$\mathbf{p} = \begin{pmatrix} p_\perp & & \\ & p_\perp & \\ & & p_\parallel \end{pmatrix}$$

If the plasma experiences an electric field **E** normal to the magnetic field all charged particles will experience a common motion $\mathbf{V}_E$ such that

$$\mathbf{E} + \mathbf{V}_E \times \mathbf{B} = 0 \tag{7.5.11}$$

and to this order the fields within the plasma are related as though the plasma were a perfect conductor. If some non-electric force **F** is also present, a second drift $\mathbf{V}_F$ which, however, is charge dependent, appears, i.e.

$$\mathbf{V}_F = \frac{\mathbf{F} \times \mathbf{B}}{B^2} \frac{cm}{e} \tag{7.5.12}$$

Since this is charge dependent it produces a current

$$\mathbf{j}_F = \sum \frac{e}{c} \mathbf{V}_F = n \frac{\mathbf{F} \times \mathbf{B}}{B^2} \tag{7.5.13}$$

such that

$$\mathbf{B} \times \mathbf{j}_F = \mathbf{F}_{2\perp} \tag{7.5.14}$$

F being the force per unit volume. If the positive and negative particles have unequal mass, eq. (7.5.12) might be expected to contribute to the drift velocity; however, in many circumstances this does not occur, instead an additional polarization field $\mathbf{E}_F$ appears which introduces a drift $\mathbf{V}_E$ compensating that produced by $\mathbf{F}$. The appearance of such a polarization field is often required by the conservation of total momentum.

If we consider the effect of gradients we note first that the effect of magnetization contributes a current

$$\mathbf{j}_M = \boldsymbol{\nabla} \times \mathbf{M} = -\boldsymbol{\nabla} \times \left(\frac{p_\perp \mathbf{B}}{B^2}\right) \tag{7.5.15}$$

There are additional currents arising from the drift velocities $\mathbf{v}_R$, $\mathbf{v}_B$

$$\mathbf{j}_R = \sum \frac{e}{c}\frac{1}{\Omega}\frac{v_\parallel{}^2}{R}\mathbf{b} \times \mathbf{n} = \sum \frac{m}{B}v_\parallel{}^2\frac{\mathbf{b}}{R} \times \mathbf{n} = p_\parallel \frac{\mathbf{b} \times \mathbf{n}}{BR} \tag{7.5.16}$$

$$\mathbf{j}_B = \frac{p_\perp}{B^2}\mathbf{b} \times \boldsymbol{\nabla}|B| \tag{7.5.17}$$

If these are added, we obtain

$$\mathbf{j}_T = \mathbf{j}_M + \mathbf{j}_R + \mathbf{j}_B = -\boldsymbol{\nabla} \times \left(\frac{p_\perp \mathbf{B}}{B^2}\right) + p_\parallel\frac{\mathbf{b} \times \mathbf{n}}{BR} + \frac{p_\perp}{B^2}\mathbf{b} \times \boldsymbol{\nabla}|B| \tag{7.5.18}$$

an expression which is more readily intelligible in the form

$$-\mathbf{B} \times \mathbf{j}_T = \boldsymbol{\nabla}_\perp p_\perp + p_\perp\boldsymbol{\nabla}_\perp\log|B| - p_\perp\frac{\mathbf{n}}{R} + p_\parallel\frac{\mathbf{n}}{R} - p_\perp\boldsymbol{\nabla}_\perp\log|B|$$

where $\boldsymbol{\nabla}_\perp = \boldsymbol{\nabla} - \mathbf{b}(\mathbf{b} \cdot \boldsymbol{\nabla})$, or

$$\mathbf{j}_T \times \mathbf{B} = \boldsymbol{\nabla}_\perp p_\perp + (p_\parallel - p_\perp)\frac{\mathbf{n}}{R} = (\boldsymbol{\nabla} \cdot \mathbf{p})_\perp \tag{7.5.19}$$

If the pressure tensor is isotropic this becomes the familiar expression for magnetohydrostatic equilibrium, thus it is through the appearance of anisotropies in the pressure tensor that a diffuse plasma first differs from a simple magnetohydrodynamic system.

If field gradients are negligible, it is possible to develop a zero-order equation of state for the plasma, for the constancy of μ, $\frac{1}{2}mv_\perp{}^2/B = \text{const}$, implies that for displacements normal to the lines of force, for which

$$\frac{\delta B}{B} \simeq -\frac{\delta A}{A}, \quad \text{and} \quad \frac{\delta n}{n} \simeq -\frac{\delta A}{A}$$

$$\frac{\delta p_\perp}{p_\perp} = \frac{\delta n}{n} + \frac{\delta v_\perp{}^2}{v_\perp{}^2} = \frac{\delta n}{n} + \frac{\delta B}{B} = -2\frac{\delta A}{A}$$

or

$$p_\perp V^2 = \text{const}, \quad V \text{ being the specific volume} \tag{7.5.20}$$

for displacements perpendicular to the field, while for displacements parallel to the field $v_\perp{}^2 = \text{const}$, $\partial n/n \sim \delta l/l$, thus

$$p_\perp V = \text{const. for displacements parallel to the field.} \qquad (7.5.21)$$

To obtain a similar expression for $p_\parallel$ one must either consider in detail the external boundary conditions, or restrict oneself to situations in which particles are trapped between regions of strong fields. In such situations, the orbit of particles along the magnetic field lines is also quasi-periodic, and again an adiabatic invariant may be formed,

$$\alpha = \oint v_\parallel \, dl \qquad (7.5.22)$$

Hence, in the mean along a field line $v_\parallel L = \text{const}$ where L is the length of the closed orbit, and

$$\frac{\delta v_\parallel}{v_\parallel} = -\frac{\delta l}{l}$$

while

$$\frac{\delta n}{n} \sim -\frac{\delta l}{l}$$

thus

$$\frac{\delta p_\parallel}{p_\parallel} = \frac{2\delta v_\parallel}{v_\parallel} + \frac{\delta n}{n} \sim \frac{-3\delta l}{l}$$

and for parallel compression

$$p_\parallel V^3 = \text{const} \qquad (7.5.23)$$

while for perpendicular compression

$$p_\parallel V = \text{const.} \qquad (7.5.24)$$

On this level then the plasma behaves as a perfectly conducting fluid in which the stress tensor is diagonal, but not isotropic, having the form (7.5.10), the two components of the pressure tensor satisfying the equation of state specified by eqs. (7.5.20)–(7.5.24), or more briefly

$$\delta p_\perp = -p_\perp \left[\frac{\partial \xi_\parallel}{\partial x_\parallel} + \frac{2\partial . \boldsymbol{\xi}_\perp}{\partial \mathbf{x}_\perp} \right]$$

$$\delta p_\parallel = -p_\parallel \left[\frac{3\partial \xi_\parallel}{\partial x_\parallel} + \frac{\partial . \boldsymbol{\xi}_\perp}{\partial \mathbf{x}_\perp} \right] \qquad (7.5.25)$$

where $\boldsymbol{\xi}$ is the displacement of an element of plasma, $\xi_\parallel = \mathbf{b} . \boldsymbol{\xi}$,

$$\boldsymbol{\xi}_\perp = \boldsymbol{\xi} - \mathbf{b} . \boldsymbol{\xi}_\parallel, \quad \frac{\partial}{\partial x_\parallel} = \mathbf{b} . \boldsymbol{\nabla} \quad \text{and} \quad \frac{\partial}{\partial \mathbf{x}_\perp} = \boldsymbol{\nabla} - \mathbf{b} \frac{\partial}{\partial x_\parallel}$$

This is the double-adiabatic, or Chew–Goldberger–Low approximation for the properties of a plasma.

6. SOME CONSEQUENCES OF THE MAGNETIC MOMENT

The existence and approximate conservation of the adiabatic invariants has several important consequences which are not predicted by the simple magnetohydrodynamic theory.

(a) Mirror Containment

The first of these is the possibility of containing plasma between two regions of high field, the field lines leaving the plasma surfaces.

Suppose a magnetic field line runs out in both directions from a region where the field strength is B_0 to regions where it has the larger value B_m. The constancy of μ then requires that, as a particle runs along a field line from the centre plane where $B = B_0$, and its transverse kinetic energy is $W_\perp(0)$, at any point x,

$$\frac{W_\perp(x)}{B(x)} = \frac{W_\perp(0)}{B_0}$$

hence

$$W_\perp(x) = W_\perp(0)\frac{B(x)}{B_0}$$

However, in steady conditions the total energy is a constant and the increase in $W_\perp$ must be subtracted from $W_\parallel$, hence when $W_\perp(x) = W_T = W_\perp(0) + W_\parallel(0)$, the particle must stop moving along the field line and be reflected. The most distant point from the centre plane reached by a particle is then x_0, where

$$W_\perp(x_0) = W_\perp(0)\frac{B(x_0)}{B_0} = W_\perp(0) + W_\parallel(0)$$

or

$$\frac{W_\perp(0)}{W_\perp(0) + W_\parallel(0)} = \sin^2\theta(0) = \frac{B_0}{B(x_0)} \qquad (7.6.1)$$

where $\theta(0)$ is the angle between the orbit and the magnetic field line on the central plane. It follows that all those particles for which $\theta(0) > \theta_0$, where

$$\sin^2\theta_0 = \frac{B_0}{B_m} \qquad (7.6.2)$$

are trapped between magnetic mirrors. This trapping is, of course, temporary since interparticle collisions will scatter particles into the loss cone in velocity space (where $\theta(0) < \theta_0$); however, at high particle energies the Coulomb scattering cross section is small ($Q \sim 1/W^2$), and at low densities and high energies the mean scattering time $\tau \sim W^{\frac{3}{2}}/n \simeq 10^6\,T^{\frac{3}{2}}/n$ (eV, cm^{-3} sec) becomes very small ($n = 10^{14}$, $W = 100$ keV, $\tau = 0.3$ sec).

A good deal of experimental effort has been devoted to the production of a plasma confined between magnetic mirrors.

One procedure is to inject a cold diffuse plasma which is heated and compressed by increasing the mirror fields, a process in which the second adiabatic invariant

$$\oint v_{\parallel} \, dl$$

plays an essential role. This procedure has had considerable success, but since it produces a dense plasma, has so far produced confinement only for brief periods.

The success of this operation, however, gives good evidence for the validity of the hydrodynamic-like behaviour of the diffuse plasma, for from the loss rates and the radial distribution and energy of the lost electrons POST *et al.* have shown that the compression must be a collisionless process; while mirror confinement itself depends on the unimportance of scattering.

An alternative procedure is to form the plasma between the mirrors by changing the charge state of a high energy beam of injected particles. Attempts have been made using singly ionized molecular hydrogen which is stripped to the atomic ion by scattering off background gas or off ions in an arc introduced between the mirrors. Alternatively beams of fast neutrals have been used. This method of producing plasma is made extremely difficult by the large value of the charge exchange cross sections between ions and neutral atoms or molecules, so that a small residual gas pressure in the vacuum vessel can transform fast ions into fast neutrals and slow ions, both of which escape (SIMON).

(b) *Particle Acceleration*

A second fascinating application of the adiabatic invariant has been in the theory of the acceleration of cosmic ray particles. Even for relativistic particles the adiabatic invariant $p_{\perp}^2/B$ exists, where p is now the relativistic momentum, hence changed particles can be reflected from magnetic mirrors. If the mirrors are moving, then on an elastic collision particles gain or lose energy, and if collisions occur at random there is a slight tendency for a net gain in energy, head-on collisions being more common. On any encounter a relativistic particle gains energy at a rate proportional to the energy which it already has. This process was proposed by FERMI as a mechanism for accelerating particles to cosmic ray energies. In interstellar space there is evidence for the presence of magnetic fields and of moving clouds of diffuse matter, often ionized. Fermi suggested that such clouds could be regions of higher than average magnetic field, and that in colliding with these, particles would gain energy. If the rate of gain of energy is proportional to energy and the probability of being lost is independent thereof, the observed form of the spectrum of cosmic rays can be produced, i.e.

$$n(E) \, dE \sim E^{-\gamma} \, dE \tag{7.6.3}$$

for the energy of a particle after time $t \sim E(t) \simeq \exp(t/\tau_c)$, where τ_c is an effective collision time, while the distribution of ages $n(t) \sim \exp(-t/\tau)$.

Combining these we obtain the spectrum

$$n(E)\,\mathrm{d}E = n[t(E)]\,\mathrm{d}E = \exp[(-\tau_c/\tau)\log E]\,\mathrm{d}E$$
$$n(E)\,\mathrm{d}E = E^{-(\tau_c/\tau)}\,\mathrm{d}E$$

(7.6.4)

A serious difficulty in this theory is that unless some non-adiabatic process occurs the particle gains energy solely in $W_{\parallel}$, hence becomes less and less susceptible to collisions. If non-adiabatic processes can occur, however, acceleration processes of this kind may be of great astronomical importance.

7. A STABILITY PROBLEM

With these elementary pictures of particle drifts it is possible to study simple stability problems. Consider for example the case of a layer of plasma held against gravity by a magnetic field. Near the plasma surface there are at least two currents flowing, that supporting the pressure gradient

$$\mathbf{B} \times \mathbf{j}_p = -\nabla_\perp p \tag{7.7.1}$$

and that produced by the gravitational force

$$\mathbf{j}_F = \rho \frac{\mathbf{g} \times \mathbf{B}}{B_2} c \tag{7.7.2}$$

As long as the surface remains plane and normal to g, the configuration remains one of equilibrium; however, if the surface should be rippled in the form $y = A \cos kx$, where y = vertical displacement of the surface, initially in the plane $y = 0$, with magnetic field B_z, then the current j_F can no longer flow without interruption; instead a surface charge of τ will begin to grow at a rate

$$\dot{\tau} = \mathbf{j}_F \cdot \frac{\mathrm{d}y}{\mathrm{d}x} = \frac{\rho \mathbf{g} \times \mathbf{B}}{B^2} ckA \sin kx \tag{7.7.3}$$

This charge in turn will produce an electric field E which must be harmonic

$$E_y = E_0 \sin kx \exp(-ky)$$
$$E_x = -E_0 \cos kx \exp(-ky)$$

Boundary conditions require $E_y = 4\pi\tau/\epsilon$ on the surface, hence

$$\dot{E}_0 = 4\pi\rho \frac{\mathbf{g} \times \mathbf{B}}{B^2} \frac{ckA}{c^2 C_A{}^2} = \mathbf{g} \times \mathbf{B} \frac{kA}{c}$$

and

$$\dot{E}_x = -\mathbf{g} \times \mathbf{B} \frac{kA}{c} \cos kx \exp(-ky) \tag{7.7.4}$$

This in turn produces a drift velocity

$$\dot{v}_y = gk \cdot A \cos kx \exp(-ky) \tag{7.7.5}$$

and the rate at which the surface moves appears as

$$\ddot{y} = \dot{v} = gky \tag{7.7.6}$$

thus the ripple grows exponentially, $y \sim \exp(\gamma t)$, at a rate

$$\gamma = \sqrt{(gk)} \tag{7.7.7}$$

which is just the result obtained by the magnetohydrodynamic theory.

Although this treatment has reproduced the magnetohydrodynamic result, it has given insight into the physical mechanisms underlying the instability process. It also suggests a possible explanation for the failure of the simple theory of interchange instability to account for the fast compression mirror results (POST *et al.*). If in this problem the magnetic lines of force had run through rigid conductors before leaving the plasma, then the surface charge responsible for the instability could have been removed by currents along the magnetic field lines. No instability electric field would have developed and the instability could not grow.

BIBLIOGRAPHY

General
1. SPITZER, L. (1956). *Physics of Fully Ionized Gases.* Interscience, New York,
2. CHANDRASEKHAR, S. (1960). *Lectures on Plasma Physics.* (Notes by S. K. TREHAN.) University of Chicago Press, Chicago.

A thorough treatment of the approach to plasma dynamics sketched in this chapter.

Dielectric behaviour
ALLIS, W. P. *Proc. of Conf. on Plasma Oscillations,* Linde Company, Indianapolis, Indiana.
BERNSTEIN, I. B. and TREHAN, S. K. *Nuclear Fusion,* **1,** 3.
BROWN, S. C. (1960). *Proc. 4th Int. Conf. on Ionization Phenomena in Gases,* II, p.691.
WHARTON, C. (1960). *ibid,* p.737.
RATCLIFFE, J. A. (1959). *The Magneto-Ionic Theory and its Applications to the Ionosphere.* Cambridge University Press, Cambridge.
STOREY, L. P. U. (1953). *Phil. Trans.* A**246,** 113.
STIX, T. (1958). *Phys. Fluids,* **1,** 446.

Adiabatic Theory
ALFVÉN, H. (1950) *Cosmical Electrodynamics,* Clarendon Press, Oxford.
KRUSKAL, M. D. (1957). *Proc. 3rd Int. Conf. on Ion. Phen. in Gases.* Venice.
BERKOWITZ, J. and GARDNER, C. (1957). NYO 7975, Inst. Math. Sci. N.Y. University, New York.
WATSON, K. M. (1956). *Phys. Rev.* **102,** 12.
RUDAKOV, L. J. and SAGDEEV, R. Z. (1959.) *Plasma Physics and the Problem of Controlled Thermonuclear Reactions,* Vol. III, p. 321, Pergamon Press, Oxford.
POST, R. F. *Proc. 2nd Geneva Conf.* p.377.
POST, R. F., ELLIS, R. E., FORD, F. L. and ROSENBLUTH, M. N. (1960). *Phys. Rev. Letters,* **4,** 166.

Macroscopic effects
CHEW, G., GOLDBERGER, M. L. and LOW, F. E. (1956). *Proc. Roy. Soc.* A**256,** 12.
FERRARO, V. C. A. (1955). *Proc. Roy. Soc.* A**233,** 310.
ROSENBLUTH, M. N. and LONGMIRE, C. I. (1957). *An. of Phys.* **1,** 120.
FERMI, E. (1949). *Phys. Rev.* **75,** 1169.
THOMPSON, W. B. (1955). *Proc. Roy. Soc.* A**233,** 402.
SIMON, A. (1960). *An Introduction to Thermonuclear Research,* Pergamon Press, Oxford.

CHAPTER 8

KINETIC THEORY OF THE PLASMA

1. TRANSPORT EQUATIONS AND HYDRODYNAMICS

In this chapter a brief introduction will be given to the kinetic theory of diffuse plasmas, beginning with a survey of the general methods to be employed. The starting point for the formal kinetic theory is the transport equation, the equation of motion for the distribution function $f(\mathbf{x}, \mathbf{v}, t)$. The Boltzmann distribution function describes the probability of finding a particle in the phase space $\mathbf{x}, \mathbf{v}$; i.e.

$$f(\mathbf{x}, \mathbf{v}, t) \, \mathrm{d}^3x \, \mathrm{d}^3v$$

is the probability of finding a particle within the volume element d^3x about $\mathbf{x}$, with velocity in the range d^3v about $\mathbf{v}$. Frequently the same symbol and language will be used to describe the probable number of particles in the same phase space volume, the difference being one of normalization, in one case $\iint f \, \mathrm{d}^3x \, \mathrm{d}^3v = 1$, in the other $\iint f \, \mathrm{d}^3x \, \mathrm{d}^3v = N$, the total number of particles in the system, and it is the second we shall normally use.

It is possible to derive the transport equation for f by considering first the motion of another distribution function, the Liouville distribution function $F(\mathbf{x}_1, \mathbf{x}_2, \ldots \mathbf{x}_N; \mathbf{v}_1, \mathbf{v}_2, \ldots \mathbf{v}_N; t)$, which gives the joint probability of finding particle 1 at $\mathbf{x}_1$ with velocity $\mathbf{v}_1$, while particle 2 is at $\mathbf{x}_2$ with velocity $\mathbf{v}_2$, and particle N at $\mathbf{x}_N$ with velocity $\mathbf{v}_N$. The one particle distribution function f which gives the probability of finding a particle at x_1 may be obtained from F by integrating over all but one of the particle coordinates, thus

$$f(\mathbf{x}_1, \mathbf{v}_1, t) = \int \mathrm{d}^3x_2 \ldots \mathrm{d}^3x_N \, \mathrm{d}^3v_2 \ldots \mathrm{d}^3v_N \cdot F(\mathbf{x}_1 \ldots \mathbf{x}_N, \mathbf{v}_1 \ldots \mathbf{v}_N, t)$$

In particular, if all the particles move independently F may be factorized into the product of N one particle distribution functions

$$F(\mathbf{x}_1 \ldots \mathbf{x}_N, \mathbf{v}_1 \ldots \mathbf{v}_N, t) = f(\mathbf{x}_1, \mathbf{v}_1, t) f(\mathbf{x}_2, \mathbf{v}_2, t) f(\mathbf{x}_N, \mathbf{v}_N, t)$$

$$= f^N(\mathbf{x}, \mathbf{v}, t)$$

F, which represents the probability of finding a given complexion (complete set of coordinates $\mathbf{x}_1 \ldots \mathbf{x}_N, \mathbf{v}_1 \ldots \mathbf{v}_N$) for the total N-particle system satisfies Liouville's equation

$$\frac{\partial F}{\partial t} + (F, H) = 0 \tag{8.1.1}$$

(F, H) being the Poisson bracket of F with the Hamiltonian H of the complete system,

$$(F, H) = \sum_i \frac{\partial H}{\partial p_i}\frac{\partial F}{\partial q_i} - \frac{\partial H}{\partial q_i}\frac{\partial F}{\partial p_i} = \sum_i \dot{q}_i\frac{\partial F}{\partial q_i} + \dot{p}_i\frac{\partial F}{\partial p_i} = \sum_i \mathbf{v}_i \cdot \frac{\partial F}{\partial \mathbf{x}_i} + \mathbf{a}_i \cdot \frac{\partial F}{\partial \mathbf{v}_i}$$

where the $\mathbf{a}_i$ are the accelerations experienced by the ith particle. Clearly, if the initial probability is $F_0(\mathbf{x}, \ldots \mathbf{x}_N, \mathbf{v}, \ldots \mathbf{v}_N, 0)$, the change in F is due entirely to the motion of particles in their orbits, i.e.

$$F(\mathbf{x}_1, \ldots \mathbf{x}_N, \mathbf{v}_1, \ldots \mathbf{v}_N, t) - (F_0(\mathbf{x}_1{}^0 \ldots \mathbf{x}_N{}^0, \mathbf{v}_1{}^0 \ldots \mathbf{v}_N{}^0, 0) = 0$$

where

$$\mathbf{x}_1 = \mathbf{x}_1{}^0 + \int_0^t \mathbf{v}_1 \, dt, \ \mathbf{v}_1 = \mathbf{v}_1{}^0 + \int_0^t \mathbf{a}_1 \, dt$$

thus

$$\frac{\partial F}{\partial t} + \mathbf{v}_i \cdot \frac{\partial F}{\partial \mathbf{x}_i} + \mathbf{a}_i \cdot \frac{\partial F}{\partial \mathbf{v}_i} = 0$$

which is eq. (8.1.1). To get the transport equation for f we may integrate eq. (8.1.1) over all but one of the coordinates, and in doing this the only difficulty is produced by $\mathbf{a}_i$, since this quantity depends in general not only on the co-ordinate $\mathbf{x}_i$, but on the coordinates of the remaining particles. For the case of non-interacting particles, however, $\mathbf{a}_i$ depends only on $\mathbf{x}_i$ and $\mathbf{v}_i$, and eq. (8.1.1) may be integrated to yield the collisionless Boltzmann equation, or the Vlasov equation

$$\frac{\partial f}{\partial t} + \mathbf{v} \cdot \frac{\partial f}{\partial \mathbf{x}} + \mathbf{a} \cdot \frac{\partial f}{\partial \mathbf{v}} = 0 \tag{8.1.2}$$

where $\mathbf{a}$ is a given function of $\mathbf{x}, \mathbf{v}, t$. The same equations may be used to determine f even when $\mathbf{a}$ is a functional of f, e.g. when $\mathbf{a}$ depends on some moments of f, and in this latter form, will become the principal object of our study.

If particles interact through an intermolecular potential, $\phi(\mathbf{x}_i, \mathbf{x}_j)$, so that

$$\mathbf{a}(x_1) = -\sum_j \frac{1}{m_1}\frac{\partial}{\partial \mathbf{x}_1}\phi(\mathbf{x}_1, \mathbf{x}_j)$$

eq. (8.1.1) reduces on integration to

$$\frac{\partial f(1)}{\partial t} + \mathbf{v} \cdot \frac{\partial f(1)}{\partial \mathbf{x}_1} - \frac{1}{m_1}\int \frac{\partial \phi}{\partial \mathbf{x}_1}(\mathbf{x}_1, \mathbf{x}_2) \cdot \frac{\partial}{\partial \mathbf{v}_1}f_2(\mathbf{x}_1, \mathbf{x}_2, \mathbf{v}_1, \mathbf{v}_2) \, d^3x_2 \, d^3v_2 \tag{8.1.3}$$

where f_2 is the binary distribution, the joint probability of finding a particle at x_1, v_1, with another particle at x_2, v_2,

$$f_2(x_1, x_2, v_1, v_2, t) = \int d^3x_3 \ldots d^3x_N, d^3v_3 \ldots d^3v_N \times$$

$$\times F(x_1 \ldots x_N, v_1 \ldots v_N, t)$$

Thus eq. (8.1.3) determining the time development of f_1 requires a knowledge of f_2. Similarly to determine f_2 we must solve

$$\frac{\partial f_2(1, 2)}{\partial t} + v_1 \cdot \frac{\partial f_2(1, 2)}{\partial x_1} + v_2 \cdot \frac{\partial f_2(1, 2)}{\partial x_2} - \int \left[\frac{1}{m_1} \frac{\partial \phi(x_1, x_3)}{\partial x_1} \cdot \frac{\partial}{\partial v_1} + \right.$$

$$\left. + \frac{1}{m_2} \frac{\partial \phi(x_2, x_3)}{\partial x_2} \cdot \frac{\partial}{\partial v_2} \right] f_3(1, 2, 3) \cdot d^3x_3 \, d^3v_3 \qquad (8.1.4)$$

and an exact treatment closes only at eq. (8.1.1). Clearly, approximate methods must be involved if the reduced equations are to be closed, and many different procedures may be used. One useful method is the e^2/m limiting procedure. If we imagine the charges in a plasma to be subdivided so that $e \to 0$, $m \to 0$, while $e/m \to$ const, then no macroscopic phenomena are altered; however, the final term in eq. (8.1.3) $\simeq (1/m)(\partial \phi/\partial x) \simeq e^2/m \to$ $\to 0$, and in this limit Vlasov's equation, (8.1.2), is valid (ROSENBLUTH and ROSTOKER).

A second procedure is valid when the interparticle forces are of short range, so that at any instant a negligible fraction of particles are interacting. This means that almost always particles are uncorrelated, although impulsive scattering contributes to the rate of change of f. Indeed, if we average over a time long compared to the duration of a collision, the contribution to the rate of change of f produced by scattering $\partial f(v_1, x_1, t)/\partial t$ is the difference between the rate at which particles having velocities v_2 different from v_1 are scattered into d^3v_1 and the rate at which particles having velocities v_1 are scattered out of d^3v_1. The second term here is clearly

$$\int f(v_1) f(v_2) \sigma(v_1 - v_2, \theta) |v_1 - v_2| d\Omega \, d^3v_2$$

while the first may be written

$$\int f(\bar{v}_1) f(\bar{v}_2) \sigma(\bar{v}_1 - \bar{v}_2, \theta) |v_1 - v_2| d\Omega \, d^3v_2$$

and represents the sum of collisions reciprocal to the first, i.e. where the roles of final and initial velocities are interchanged. The $\bar{v}$ may be given explicitly in terms of the v's by noting that the change in velocity on collision may be written in terms of the initial and final velocities. In the initial state we introduce the centre of mass and relative velocities

$$V = \frac{m_1 v_1 + m_2 v_2}{m_1 + m_2}: \quad g = v_2 - v_1$$

and observe that conservation of energy and momentum require that after collision

$$\mathbf{V}_f = \frac{m_1\bar{\mathbf{v}}_1 + m_2\bar{\mathbf{v}}_2}{m_1 + m_2} = \mathbf{V}$$

while $\mathbf{g}_f = \bar{\mathbf{v}}_2 - \bar{\mathbf{v}}_1 = \mathbf{0}\mathbf{g}$, $\mathbf{0}$ being a rotation operator, a unitary tensor depending on the scattering angle (θ, ϕ), in fact $\mathbf{g}_f \cdot \mathbf{g} = g^2\cos\theta$.

$$\mathbf{g}_f - (\mathbf{g}_f \cdot \hat{\mathbf{g}})\hat{\mathbf{g}} = (g\sin\theta\cos\phi,\, g\sin\theta\sin\phi)$$

where θ and ϕ are the angle of scatter in the centre of mass system. Then $\bar{\mathbf{v}}_2 = \bar{\mathbf{v}}_1 + \mathbf{g}_f$; and

$$\frac{m_1\mathbf{v}_1 + m_2\mathbf{v}_2}{m_1 + m_2} = \mathbf{V} = \mathbf{V}_f = \frac{m_1\bar{\mathbf{v}}_1 + m_2\bar{\mathbf{v}}_2}{m_1 + m_2} = \frac{(m_1 + m_2)\bar{\mathbf{v}}_1 + m_2\mathbf{g}_f}{m_1 + m_2}$$

$$\bar{\mathbf{v}}_1 = \mathbf{V} - \frac{m_2}{m_1 + m_2}\mathbf{g}_f$$

while

$$\mathbf{v}_1 = \mathbf{V} - \frac{m_2}{m_1 + m_2}\mathbf{g}$$

thus

$$\bar{\mathbf{v}}_1 = \mathbf{v}_1 - \frac{m_2}{m_1 + m_2}(\mathbf{g}_f - \mathbf{g}) = \mathbf{v}_1 - \frac{m_2}{m_1 + m_2}\Delta\mathbf{g}$$

$$= \mathbf{v}_1 - \frac{m_2}{m_1 + m_2}(\mathbf{0} - \mathbf{1})\cdot\mathbf{g} \tag{8.1.5}$$

while

$$\bar{\mathbf{v}}_2 = \mathbf{v}_2 + \frac{m_1}{m_1 + m_2}(\mathbf{0} - \mathbf{1})\cdot\mathbf{g}$$

The Boltzmann equation may then be written

$$\left(\frac{\partial}{\partial t} + \mathbf{v}\cdot\frac{\partial}{\partial\mathbf{x}} + \mathbf{a}_{\text{ext}}\cdot\frac{\partial}{\partial\mathbf{v}}\right)f = Df = I(f,f) = \int d^3v_2 \int d\Omega\sigma(g,\theta)g\times$$

$$\times[f(\bar{\mathbf{v}}_1)f(\bar{\mathbf{v}}_2) - f(\mathbf{v}_1)f(\mathbf{v}_2)] \tag{8.1.6}$$

and forms the basis of the standard kinetic theory of diffuse gases.

A second method of treating eq. (8.1.3) is the use of the Fokker–Planck equation, which is appropriate for weakly interacting particles. To understand this equation suppose that during a time τ the probability of a system undergoing a transformation from a state characterized by x_1 to one characterized by x_2 is $\omega(x_1, x_2)$, a function only of these two states. Then, the probability F of finding the system in the state x at time t is

$$F(x, t) = \int dx' F(x', t-\tau)\omega(x', x)$$

$$= \int d\xi F(x-\xi, t-\tau)\omega(x-\xi, x)$$

If large transitions are scarce, i.e. if ω is a rapidly decreasing function of ξ the R.H.S. may be expanded; thus

$$\int d\xi F(x, t-\tau)\omega(x+\xi; x) -$$

$$\int d\xi \frac{\partial}{\partial x}[F(x, t-\tau)\omega]\,\xi + \tfrac{1}{2}\int d\xi \frac{\partial^2}{\partial x^2}[F(x, t-\tau)\omega]\,.\,\xi^2 + \ldots$$

$$= F(x, t-\tau) - \frac{\partial}{\partial x}F(x, t-\tau)\Delta + \frac{\partial^2}{\partial x^2}F(x, t-\tau)\tfrac{1}{2}\Delta^2 + \ldots$$

therefore

$$\frac{F(x,t)-F(x,t-\tau)}{\tau} = \frac{\partial F}{\partial t} = -\frac{\partial}{\partial x}\left(F(x, t)\,.\,\frac{\Delta}{\tau}\right) + \frac{\partial^2}{\partial x^2}\left[F(x, t)\tfrac{1}{2}\frac{\Delta^2}{\tau}\right] + \ldots$$

$$(8.1.7)$$

where $\int d\xi \omega(x+\xi, x) = 1$ since some transition must occur, and

$$\Delta = \int d\xi \xi \omega(x+\xi, x) = \text{mean value of the transition, and}$$

$$\Delta^2 = \text{mean square of the transition.}$$

In kinetic theory problems we are usually interested in the effects of a, hence the Fokker–Planck equation takes the form

$$\frac{Df}{Dt} = -\frac{\partial}{\partial v_i}f\left\langle\frac{\Delta v_i}{\tau}\right\rangle + \frac{\partial^2}{\partial v_i\partial v_j}\left\{f\tfrac{1}{2}\left\langle\frac{\Delta v_i\Delta v_j}{\tau}\right\rangle\right\} + \ldots \quad (8.1.8)$$

If the change in g on collision is small, the Boltzmann collision integral may be reduced to the Fokker Planck form. As an illustration of this, let us consider a reduction of that integral for collision between like Coulomb particles for which

$$\bar{v}_1 = v_1 - \tfrac{1}{2}\Delta g$$

$$\bar{v}_2 = v_2 + \tfrac{1}{2}\Delta g$$

and the cross section

$$\sigma = \left(\frac{e^2}{2m_r}\right)^2 (g\sin\theta/2)^{-4}$$

and the Boltzmann integral becomes (with $m_r = \frac{1}{2} \cdot m$)

$$I = \left(\frac{e^2}{m}\right)^2 \int d^3v^1 \int \sin\theta d\theta d\phi \frac{g}{g^4 \sin^4\theta/2}[f(\mathbf{v}^1+\tfrac{1}{2}\Delta\mathbf{g})f(\mathbf{v}-\tfrac{1}{2}\Delta\mathbf{g})-f(\mathbf{v}^1)f(\mathbf{v})]$$

Also if $\mathbf{m}$ and $\mathbf{n}$ are orthogonal unit vectors normal to $\mathbf{g}$

$$\Delta\mathbf{g} = 2g\sin\frac{\theta}{2}\left\{-\hat{\mathbf{g}}\sin\frac{\theta}{2}+\mathbf{m}\cos\frac{\theta}{2}\cos\phi+\mathbf{n}\cos\frac{\theta}{2}\sin\phi\right\}$$

(8.1.9)

Now we may expand the quantity in square brackets thus

$$f(\mathbf{v}^1+\tfrac{1}{2}\Delta\mathbf{g})f(\mathbf{v}-\tfrac{1}{2}\Delta\mathbf{g}) = f(\mathbf{v}^1)f(\mathbf{v})+\left[f\frac{\partial f^1}{\partial v_i^1}-f^1\frac{\partial f}{\partial v_i}\right]\tfrac{1}{2}\Delta g_i+$$

$$+\tfrac{1}{2}\left[f\frac{\partial^2 f^1}{\partial v_i^1\partial v_j^1}+f^1\frac{\partial^2 f}{\partial v_i\partial v_j}-2\frac{\partial f^1}{\partial v_i^1}\frac{\partial f}{\partial v_j}\right]\tfrac{1}{2}\Delta g_i\,\tfrac{1}{2}\Delta g_j.$$

When this expansion is substituted into I and 8.1.9 used, the integral over ϕ eliminates terms $\sim \cos\phi$, $\sin\phi$, $\cos\phi\sin\phi$ and

$$I = 8\pi\left(\frac{e^2}{m}\right)^2\int d^3v^1\int d\frac{\theta}{2}\cos\frac{\theta}{2}\left\{-\frac{g_i}{g^3\sin\theta/2}\cdot\left(f\frac{\partial f^1}{\partial v_i^1}-f^1\frac{\partial f}{\partial v_i}\right)+\right.$$

$$+\tfrac{1}{2}\left(f\frac{\partial^2 f^1}{\partial v_i^1\partial v_j^1}+f^1\frac{\partial^2 f}{\partial v_i\partial v_j}-2\frac{\partial f^1}{\partial v_i^1}\frac{\partial f}{\partial v_j}\right)\times$$

$$\left.\times\frac{1}{g}\left(\frac{g_ig_j}{g^2}\sin\frac{\theta}{2}+\tfrac{1}{2}(m_im_j+n_in_j)\right)\left(\frac{1}{\sin\theta/2}-\sin\frac{\theta}{2}\right)\right\}$$

Now

$$\int_0^{2\pi} d\frac{\theta}{2}\cos\frac{\theta}{2}\sin\frac{\theta}{2} = 0 \qquad \int d\frac{\theta}{2}\cos\frac{\theta}{2}\frac{1}{\sin(\theta/2)}$$

diverges, but if the range of integration is cut off at some maximum and minimum θ, where our approximations become invalid, it may be replaced by

$$\log\left(\frac{\sin(\theta/2)_{max}}{\sin(\theta/2)_{min}}\right) = \log\Lambda.$$

Further, the tensor $m_im_j+n_in_j$ merely projects out components normal to $\mathbf{g}$, hence may be written as

$$\delta_{ij}-\frac{g_ig_j}{g^2}.$$

We may now introduce a tensor

$$\omega_{ij} = \frac{1}{g}\left(\delta_{ij}-\frac{g_ig_j}{g^2}\right)$$

(8.1.10)

and on observing that

$$\frac{\partial \omega_{ji}}{\partial g_j} = -2\frac{g_i}{g^3}$$

write the integral as

$$I = 2\pi \left(\frac{e^2}{m}\right)^2 \log \Lambda \int d^2 v^1 \, 2\left(f\frac{\partial f^1}{\partial v_i^1} - f^1\frac{\partial f}{\partial v_i}\right)\frac{\partial}{\partial g_j}\omega_{ij} +$$

$$+ \frac{\partial}{\partial v_j}\left(f^1\frac{\partial f}{\partial v_i} - f\frac{\partial f^1}{\partial v_i^1}\right)\cdot \omega_{ij} +$$

$$+ \left(f\frac{\partial^2 f^1}{\partial v_i^1 \partial v_j^1} - \frac{\partial f^1}{\partial v_j^1}\frac{\partial f}{\partial v_i}\right)\omega_{ij}.$$

The last term may be integrated by parts and on observing that

$$\frac{\partial \omega_{ij}}{\partial g_j} = -\frac{\partial \omega_{ji}}{\partial v_j}$$

the entire integral may be written

$$I = 2\pi \left(\frac{e^2}{m}\right)^2 \log \Lambda \frac{\partial}{\partial v_j} \int d^3 v^1 \left(f^1\frac{\partial f}{\partial v_i} - f\frac{\partial f^1}{\partial v_j^1}\right)\omega_{ij} \qquad (8.1.11)$$

a form first given by LANDAU.

An alternative form for the Fokker–Planck equation may be derived by noting that in a specific configuration the one particle distribution, which has the form $\delta[x_i - X_i(t)]\,\delta[v_i - V_i(t)]$, where X and V are the actual trajectories of particles, satisfies an equation of the Liouville form

$$\frac{\partial f^1}{\partial t} + \mathbf{v}\cdot\frac{\partial f^1}{\partial \mathbf{x}} + \frac{e}{m}\mathbf{E}\cdot\frac{\partial f^1}{\partial \mathbf{v}} = 0$$

where now $\mathbf{E}$ is the actual field experienced by the particle, and is a rapidly fluctuating quantity. The Boltzmann distribution f is obtained by coarse graining f^1, i.e. averaging over a volume containing many particles, and over a time long enough to smooth the rapid fluctuations. The relevant equation has the form

$$\frac{\partial f}{\partial t} + \mathbf{v}\cdot\frac{\partial f}{\partial \mathbf{x}} + \frac{e}{m}\frac{\partial}{\partial \mathbf{v}}\cdot \langle \mathbf{E}.f^1\rangle = 0$$

The time averaging in the last term may be carried out by first splitting off the rapidly fluctuating part of $\mathbf{E}, \mathbf{E}^f$, from the smooth macrofield $\mathbf{E}_0$ obtaining

$$\mathbf{E}_0 \cdot \frac{\partial}{\partial \mathbf{v}}f + \frac{\partial}{\partial \mathbf{v}}\langle \mathbf{E}^f.f^1\rangle$$

In the second term note that

$$f^1(\mathbf{x}, \mathbf{v}, t) = \int f^1(\mathbf{x}_0, \mathbf{v}_0, 0)\, \delta(\mathbf{x} - \mathbf{x}_0 - \int \mathbf{v}\, dt)\, \delta(\mathbf{v} - \mathbf{v}_0 - \frac{e}{m}\int \mathbf{E}\, dt) \times$$

$$\times\, \theta(t)\, d^3x_0\, d^3v_0$$

where $\theta(t)$ is the step function, $= 0$ for $t < 0$, $= 1$ for $t > 0$, and the integrals within the δ functions follow particle trajectories. If now, the fluctuating fields are assumed small, the δ functions may be expanded, and

$$\delta(\mathbf{v} - \mathbf{v}_0 + e\int \mathbf{E}\, dt) = \delta(\mathbf{v} - \mathbf{v}_0 - \frac{e}{m}\int \mathbf{E}_0\, dt) -$$

$$- \frac{e}{m}\frac{\partial\delta}{\partial v_j}(\mathbf{v} - \mathbf{v}_0 - \frac{e}{m}\int \mathbf{E}_0\, dt)\int E_j{}^f\, dt$$

and

$$\left\langle \frac{1}{\tau}\int\limits_{t-\tau}^{t} E_i{}^f f^1 \right\rangle = \left\langle \frac{1}{\tau}\int\limits_{t-\tau}^{t} E^f f \right\rangle +$$

$$+ \left\langle \frac{e}{m}\frac{1}{\tau}\int\limits_{t-\tau}^{t} ds E_i{}^f(s)\frac{\partial}{\partial v_j}\int\limits_{0}^{\tau} E_j{}^f(s-s')\, ds' f(\mathbf{x}, \mathbf{v}, s) \right\rangle$$

Provided f is sensibly constant over τ, and $\langle E(t)E(t-s)\rangle \to 0$ for $s^1 > \tau'$ $\ll \tau$, then the Fokker–Planck equation takes the form

$$\frac{\partial f}{\partial t} + \mathbf{v}\cdot\frac{\partial f}{\partial \mathbf{x}} + \frac{e}{m}\mathbf{E}_0\cdot\frac{\partial f}{\partial \mathbf{v}} + \frac{\partial}{\partial v_i}\left(\left\langle \frac{e}{m}E_i\right\rangle f\right) +$$

$$+ \frac{\partial^2}{\partial v_i \partial v_j}\frac{e^2}{m^2}\left\langle \int E_i(t)E_j(t-s)\, ds \right\rangle f = 0 \qquad (8.1.12)$$

Regardless of which of eqs. (8.1.2), (8.1.6), (8.1.11) or (8.1.12) are used, provided only that the R.H.S. satisfies conservation of mass, energy and momentum the equations of hydrodynamics may be derived in the same way.

The equation of transport may be written in the general form

$$\frac{\partial f}{\partial t} + \mathbf{v}\cdot\frac{\partial f}{\partial \mathbf{x}} + \frac{\mathbf{F}}{m}\cdot\frac{\partial f}{\partial \mathbf{v}} = \frac{\partial f}{\partial t}\bigg|_{col}$$

and from this the equations of motion for the moments $\int f v^n\, d^3v$ may be formed. For the five moments m, $m\mathbf{v}$, $\frac{1}{2}mv^2$, the R.H.S. gives no contribution, since it represents the change in total mass, momentum, and kinetic energy produced by interaction between the particles, which is zero provided the potential energy of interaction is negligible. The first moment equation

$$\int m\left[\frac{\partial f}{\partial t}+\mathbf{v}\cdot\frac{\partial f}{\partial \mathbf{x}}+\frac{\mathbf{F}}{m}\cdot\frac{\partial f}{\partial \mathbf{v}}\right]d^3v-\int \frac{\partial f}{\partial t}\bigg|_{\text{col}}m\,d^3v$$

$$=\frac{\partial}{\partial t}\int mf+\frac{\partial}{\partial \mathbf{x}}\cdot\int m\mathbf{v}f+Ff\bigg|_{-\infty}^{\infty}$$

$$=\frac{\partial \rho}{\partial t}+\frac{\partial}{\partial \mathbf{x}}\cdot\rho\mathbf{V}=0 \tag{8.1.13}$$

where with f normalized to N,

$$\rho=\int mf\,d^3v \text{ is the mass density}$$

$$\mathbf{V}=(1/\rho)\int m\mathbf{v}f\,d^3v \text{ the mean velocity}$$

and where we have used the fact that $\mathbf{x}$, $\mathbf{v}$, t are independent variables, although ρ, $\mathbf{V}$ are functions of $\mathbf{x}$ and t, and have assumed that $\partial F_i/\partial v_i=0$. If, in fact F_i depends on v_i, then the reduction from Liouville's equation leads to $\partial(F_if)/\partial v_i$ and the result (8.1.13) holds for the altered transport equation.

For the moment with the component mv_j of the momentum

$$\frac{\partial}{\partial t}\int mv_jf+\frac{\partial}{\partial x_i}\int mv_iv_jf+\int v_jF_i\frac{\partial f}{\partial v_i}=0$$

The last term may be integrated by parts to $-\mathbf{F}n=-F$, the force per unit volume and the second term simplified by introducing $\mathbf{c}=\mathbf{v}-\mathbf{V}$, so that $\int \mathbf{c}f\,d^3v=0$, and

$$\frac{\partial}{\partial x_i}\int fmv_iv_j=\frac{\partial}{\partial x_i}(\rho V_iV_j)+\frac{\partial}{\partial x_i}\rho\langle c_ic_j\rangle=\frac{\partial}{\partial x_i}(\rho V_iV_j)+\frac{\partial}{\partial x_i}p_{ij}$$

hence on using eq. (8.1.13)

$$\rho\left(\frac{\partial V_j}{\partial t}+V_i\frac{\partial V_j}{\partial x_i}\right)+\frac{\partial}{\partial x_i}p_{ij}-\mathscr{F}_j=0$$

or

$$\rho\frac{DV}{Dt}+\nabla\cdot\mathbf{p}-\mathscr{F}=0 \tag{8.1.14}$$

Finally the energy equation,

$$\frac{\partial}{\partial t}\int \tfrac{1}{2}mv^2 f + \frac{\partial}{\partial x_i}\int v_i\tfrac{1}{2}mv^2 f + \int \tfrac{1}{2}v^2 F_j\frac{\partial f}{\partial v_j} = 0$$

$$\frac{\partial}{\partial t}(\tfrac{1}{2}\rho V^2 + n\langle\tfrac{1}{2}mc^2\rangle) + \frac{\partial}{\partial x_i}V_i(\tfrac{1}{2}\rho V^2 + \tfrac{1}{2}n\langle\tfrac{1}{2}mc^2\rangle) +$$

$$+\frac{\partial}{\partial x_i}\rho\langle c_i c_j\rangle Vj + \frac{\partial}{\partial x_i}\rho\tfrac{1}{2}\langle c_i c^2\rangle - Vj\mathscr{F}j = 0$$

or

$$\tfrac{1}{2}V^2\left[\frac{\partial\rho}{\partial t} + \frac{\partial\rho V_i}{\partial x_i}\right] + V_j\left[\rho\frac{DV_j}{Dt} + \frac{\partial p_{ij}}{\partial x_i} - \mathscr{F}_j\right] +$$

$$+\frac{\partial}{\partial t}n\langle\tfrac{1}{2}mc^2\rangle + \mathbf{V}\cdot\boldsymbol{\nabla} n\langle\tfrac{1}{2}mc^2\rangle + n\langle\tfrac{1}{2}mc^2\rangle\frac{\partial V_i}{\partial x_i} +$$

$$+p_{ij}\frac{\partial V_j}{\partial x_i} + \frac{\partial}{\partial x_i}n\langle c_i\tfrac{1}{2}mc^2\rangle = 0$$

or defining

$$C_v T = n\langle\tfrac{1}{2}mc^2\rangle \tag{8.1.15}$$

$$\frac{D}{Dt}C_v T + C_v T\,\mathrm{div}\,\mathbf{V} + p_{ij}\frac{\partial V_i}{\partial x_j} + \mathrm{div}\,\mathbf{q} = 0$$

$\mathbf{q} = \tfrac{1}{2}\rho\langle\mathbf{c}c^2\rangle$ being the heat flux vector. If the distribution function is symmetric in c, $\mathbf{p}$ is diagonal with components $\tfrac{1}{3}n\langle mc^2\rangle = \tfrac{2}{3}C_v T$ and eq. (8.1.15) becomes

$$\frac{D}{Dt}C_v T + \frac{5}{3}C_v T\,\mathrm{div}\,V = 0$$

or since

$$\frac{D}{Dt}\rho + \rho\,\mathrm{div}\,V = 0$$

$$\frac{1}{p}\frac{Dp}{Dt} - \frac{5}{3\rho}\frac{D\rho}{Dt} = 0$$

$$\frac{D}{Dt}(p\rho^{-5/3}) = 0 \tag{8.1.16}$$

the adiabatic equation of state for a monatomic gas.

When the dynamics of an ionized gas is considered these relations are considerably complicated by the presence of two distinct types of particles, electrons and ions, and the problem may be treated in either of two ways.

The two gases may be considered separately, in which case the term on the R.H.S. becomes

$$\frac{\partial f_+}{\partial t}\bigg|_c = \frac{\partial f_{++}}{\partial t}\bigg|_c + \frac{\partial f_{+-}}{\partial t}\bigg|_c \quad \text{and} \quad \frac{\partial f_-}{\partial t}\bigg|_c = \frac{\partial f_{--}}{\partial t}\bigg|_c + \frac{\partial f_{-+}}{\partial t}\bigg|_c$$

where the first terms represent the change produced by ion–ion (electron–electron) encounters and the second that by ion–electron interactions.

The conservation laws will then apply to the first term in each case, but not to the second which does not vanish but represents the interchange of momentum or energy between the ion and electron gases. If ionization processes occur, even number conservation does not hold, and a third distribution function for the neutrals must be added.

The two-fluid hydrodynamic equations have the form (8.1.13)–(8.1.15) except that the R.H.S. is modified, thus

$$\frac{\partial \rho_\pm}{\partial t} + \operatorname{div}(\rho_\pm \mathbf{V}_\pm) = 0 \tag{8.1.17}$$

$$\rho_\pm\left(\frac{\partial}{\partial t} + \mathbf{V}_\pm \cdot \boldsymbol{\nabla}\right)\mathbf{V}_\pm + \boldsymbol{\nabla} \cdot \mathbf{p}_\pm - (ne)_\pm(\mathbf{E} + \mathbf{V}_\pm \times \mathbf{B}) = (\Delta \mathbf{p})_{\pm\mp} \tag{8.1.18}$$

$$\left(\frac{\partial}{\partial t} + \mathbf{V}_\pm \cdot \boldsymbol{\nabla}\right)C_{v\pm}T_\pm + C_{v\pm}T_\pm \operatorname{div}\mathbf{V}_\pm + \mathbf{p}_\pm : \boldsymbol{\nabla}\mathbf{V}_\pm + \boldsymbol{\nabla}\cdot q_\pm = \Delta\mathscr{E}_{\pm\mp} \tag{8.1.19}$$

the terms on the R.H.S. representing the transfer of energy and momentum between the ions and electrons. From conservation of total energy and momentum $\Delta\mathbf{p}_{+-}+\Delta\mathbf{p}_{-+} = \Delta\mathscr{E}_{+-}+\Delta\mathscr{E}_{-+} = 0$.

From these two fluid equations, one fluid equation can be formed, for adding the equations for ions and electrons we obtain

$$\frac{\partial}{\partial t}\rho + \operatorname{div}\rho\mathbf{V} = 0 \tag{8.1.20}$$

where

$$\rho = \rho_+ + \rho_- , \qquad (\rho_+ + \rho_-)\mathbf{V} = \rho_+\mathbf{V}_+ + \rho_-\mathbf{V}_-$$

$$\rho\left(\frac{\partial V_j}{\partial t} + \mathbf{V}\cdot\boldsymbol{\nabla}V_j\right) + \frac{\partial}{\partial x_i}(p_{ij+} + p_{ij-} + \rho_+\Delta V_i\Delta V_{j+} + \rho_-\Delta V_i\Delta V_{j-}) -$$

$$- [(ne)_+ + (ne)_-](\mathbf{E} + \mathbf{V}\times\mathbf{B}) -$$

$$- (ne_+\Delta\mathbf{V}_+ + ne_-\Delta\mathbf{V}_-)\times\mathbf{B} = 0$$

where

$$\Delta\mathbf{V}_\pm = \mathbf{V}_\pm - \mathbf{V}$$

If random velocities are described with respect to $\mathbf{V}$, not $\mathbf{V}_\pm$, then the second bracket is $\partial p_{ij}/\partial x_i$, the gradient of the total pressure, while with the definitions of the charge Q and net current $\mathbf{j}$ already given, the momentum transfer equation becomes

$$\rho\frac{D\mathbf{V}}{Dt} + \mathbf{\nabla}\cdot\mathbf{p} - Q(\mathbf{E}+\mathbf{V}\times\mathbf{B}) - \mathbf{j}\times\mathbf{B} = 0 \qquad (8.1.21)$$

Removing the same mean drift velocity the moments with $\frac{1}{2}mv^2$ may be formed, and the energy conservation law yields

$$\frac{D}{Dt}C_vT + C_vT\,\mathrm{div}\,\mathbf{V} + \mathbf{p}:\mathbf{\nabla}\mathbf{V} + \mathbf{\nabla}\cdot\mathbf{q} - \mathbf{j}\cdot(\mathbf{E}+\mathbf{V}\times\mathbf{B}) = 0 \qquad (8.1.22)$$

2. THE DIELECTRIC PROPERTIES OF A HOT PLASMA IN THE ABSENCE OF A MAGNETIC FIELD

A simple and important problem which is easily tackled by means of the Vlasov equation is that of the dielectric properties of a *hot* plasma. In Chapter 2, a simple approach to this problem was presented in which all charged particles were considered as equivalent, and no account was taken of the initial velocity distribution. We shall now approach this problem formally, considering the effect of thermal motions but not that of inter-particle collisions, thus we expect the analysis to be valid at high frequencies.

To determine the dielectric behaviour of the plasma we must find the currents introduced by an applied electric field, which may be taken as harmonic in *space* and time, thus short wavelengths as well as high frequencies may be treated. The plasma is characterized by given distribution functions $f_0{}^+$, $f_0{}^-$, perturbed by a small electric field which may be represented by the real part of $\mathbf{E}_0\exp(i\omega t + i\mathbf{k}\cdot\mathbf{x})$, and produces a small perturbation f_1 on the initial distribution function, so that the problem may be linearized. Neglecting collisions, the equations to be solved are

$$\frac{\partial f_1}{\partial t} + \mathbf{v}\cdot\nabla f_1 + \frac{e}{m}\mathbf{E}\cdot\frac{\partial f_0}{\partial\mathbf{v}} = 0 \qquad (8.2.1)$$

There are two possible ways of solving this, the simplest and most direct being to observe that we may write $f_1(\mathbf{v},\mathbf{x},t) = f_1(\mathbf{v},\mathbf{k},\omega)\exp(i\mathbf{k}\cdot\mathbf{x}+i\omega t)$ and reduce eq. (8.2.1) to the algebraic form

$$i(\omega+\mathbf{k}\cdot\mathbf{v})f_1 = \frac{-e}{m}\mathbf{E}_0\cdot\frac{\partial f_0}{\partial\mathbf{v}}$$

whence

$$f_1 = \frac{-e}{m}\cdot\frac{\mathbf{E}_0\cdot(\partial f_0/\partial\mathbf{v})}{i(\omega+\mathbf{k}\cdot\mathbf{v})} \qquad (8.2.2)$$

More laboriously, but with more generality, one observes that the solution to

$$\frac{\partial G_1}{\partial t} + \mathbf{v}\cdot\mathbf{\nabla}G_1 + \mathbf{F}\cdot\frac{\partial}{\partial\mathbf{v}}G_1 = \delta(\mathbf{x}-\mathbf{x}_0)\delta(\mathbf{v}-\mathbf{v}_0)\delta(t-t_0)$$

is

$$G_1 = \delta[\mathbf{x} - \mathbf{X}(t; \mathbf{x}_0, \mathbf{v}_0)]\delta[\mathbf{v} - \mathbf{V}(t; \mathbf{x}_0, \mathbf{v}_0)]\theta(t - t_0) \qquad (8.2.3)$$

where

$$\mathbf{V} = \mathbf{v}_0 + \int_{t_0}^{t} dt' \mathbf{F}[\mathbf{X}(t'), t']$$

and

$$\mathbf{X} = \mathbf{x}_0 + \int_{t_0}^{t} dt' \mathbf{V}(t', \mathbf{x}_0, \mathbf{v}_0)$$

and

$$\theta(x) = \begin{cases} 1 & x > 0 \\ 0 & x \leqslant 0 \end{cases}$$

i.e. $\mathbf{X}, \mathbf{V}$ are the trajectories of particles moving in the acceleration field $\mathbf{F}$. Hence the solution to

$$\frac{\partial f_1}{\partial t} + \mathbf{v} \cdot \nabla f_1 + \mathbf{F} \cdot \frac{\partial}{\partial \mathbf{v}} f_1 = I(x, v, t)$$

is

$$f_1 = \int G(\mathbf{x}, \mathbf{v}, t; \mathbf{x}', \mathbf{v}', t') I(\mathbf{x}', \mathbf{v}', t') \, dt' \, d\mathbf{x}' \, d\mathbf{v}'$$

$$f_1 = \int I[\mathbf{X}(t'') \mathbf{V}(t''), t''] \, dt'' \qquad (8.2.4)$$

where the integrals are carried along the unperturbed trajectories passing through $\mathbf{x}, \mathbf{v}, t$. In the present context eq. (8.2.4) yields

$$f_1 = \frac{-e}{m} \int_{-\infty}^{0} \exp[i\omega(t+s)]\exp[i\mathbf{k} \cdot (\mathbf{x} + \mathbf{v}s)]\mathbf{E}_0 \cdot \frac{\partial f_0}{\partial \mathbf{v}}(\mathbf{v}) \, ds$$

$$= \frac{-e}{m} \frac{\mathbf{E}_0 \cdot (\partial f_0 / \partial \mathbf{v})}{i(\omega + \mathbf{k} \cdot \mathbf{v})} \exp[i(\omega t + \mathbf{k} \cdot \mathbf{x})]$$

which is eq. (8.2.2).

We shall require integrals of f_1 over $\mathbf{v}$ to form the currents and charges, hence the denominator in eq. (8.2.2) must be treated with some care. We may (a) consider an initial value problem in which f_1 is zero for $t < 0$ when the electric field is switched on, and use a Laplace transform solution, or (b) imagine that the electric field is switched on slowly at $t = -\infty$, and varies as $\exp(+\gamma s)$ for $s < 0$, or (c) consider an approximate representation of the effect of collisions by introducing on the R.H.S. of eq. (8.2.1) a term $-f_1/\tau$, representing the collisional relaxation of f_1 to f_0. Each one of these methods replaces the denominator in eq. (8.2.2) by $i(\omega + \mathbf{k} \cdot \mathbf{v}) + \epsilon$, $\epsilon = \gamma, 1/\tau$, and it is now possible to take the limit as $\gamma, (1/\tau) \to 0$ after all questionable integrals have been evaluated. For instance, the perturbed electron density

$$q = e \int f_1 \, d^3v = \frac{-e^2}{m} \lim_{\epsilon \to 0} \int \frac{\mathbf{E}_0 \cdot (\partial f_0/\partial \mathbf{v})}{i(\omega + \mathbf{k} \cdot \mathbf{v}) + \epsilon} \, d^3v$$

$$= -\frac{e^2}{m} \int \frac{\mathbf{E}_0 \cdot (\partial f_0/\partial \mathbf{v})}{[\omega + (\mathbf{k} \cdot \mathbf{v})]^2 + \epsilon^2} [-i(\omega + \mathbf{k} \cdot \mathbf{v}) + \epsilon] \, d^3v$$

$$= -\frac{e^2}{m} P \int \frac{\mathbf{E}_0 \cdot (\partial f_0/\partial \mathbf{v})}{i(\omega + \mathbf{k} \cdot \mathbf{v})} \, d^3v - \left\{ \lim_{\epsilon \to 0} \frac{e^2}{m} \cdot \int \mathbf{E}_0 \cdot \frac{\partial f_0}{\partial \mathbf{v}} \frac{\epsilon}{(\omega + \mathbf{k} \cdot \mathbf{v})^2 + \epsilon^2} \, d^3\mathbf{v} \right\}$$

But since

$$\lim_{\epsilon \to 0} \int \frac{g(v_\parallel)\epsilon \, dv_\parallel}{(\omega + kv_\parallel)^2 + \epsilon^2} = k^{-1} g(-\omega/k) \lim_{\epsilon \to 0} \int \frac{\epsilon \, dx}{x^2 + \epsilon^2} = (\pi/k) g(-\omega/k)$$

and

$$q_- = -\frac{e^2}{m} \left[P \int \frac{\mathbf{E}_0 \cdot (\partial f_0/\partial \mathbf{v}) \, d^3v}{i(\omega + \mathbf{k} \cdot \mathbf{v})} + \frac{\pi}{k} \int \mathbf{E}_0 \cdot (\partial f_0/\partial \mathbf{v}) \, d^2v_\perp \Big|_{\omega + k_\parallel v_\parallel = 0} \right] \tag{8.2.5}$$

This prescription for interpreting the singular integral,

$$\int_L \frac{1}{X} = P \int \frac{1}{X} + \pi i \delta(X) \tag{8.2.6}$$

is due to LANDAU.

The induced currents are

$$\mathbf{j} = \frac{-e^2}{m} \mathbf{E} \cdot \int_L \frac{(\partial f_0/\partial \mathbf{v}) \, \mathbf{v}}{i(\omega + \mathbf{k} \cdot \mathbf{v})} \, d^3v$$

where

$$\int_L \frac{1}{X} = P \int \frac{1}{X} + \pi i \delta(x)$$

is the Landau integral.

If f_0 is symmetric in the components of $\mathbf{v}$, e.g. a function of v^2, then

$$q = \frac{-e^2}{m}E_\parallel \int \frac{(\partial f_0/\partial v_\parallel)\,d^3v}{i(\omega+kv_\parallel)} \tag{8.2.7}$$

where

$$E_\parallel = \mathbf{E}.\hat{\mathbf{k}}, \quad v_\parallel = \mathbf{v}.\hat{\mathbf{k}}; \quad \hat{\mathbf{k}} = \mathbf{k}/|k|$$

$$j_\parallel = \frac{-e^2}{m}E_\parallel \int \frac{v_\parallel(\partial f_0/\partial v_\parallel)}{i(\omega+kv_\parallel)} \tag{8.2.8}$$

Note that these satisfy the equation of continuity

$$i\omega q + ik.j = \frac{-e^2}{m}E_\parallel \int \frac{i(\omega+kv_\parallel)}{i(\omega+kv_\parallel)}\frac{\partial f_0}{\partial v_\parallel}\,dv^3 = 0$$

If $\mathbf{v}_\perp = \mathbf{v}-v_\parallel\hat{\mathbf{k}} = (v_1, v_2, 0)$

$$j_{1,2} = \frac{-e^2}{m}E_{1,2}\int \frac{v_{1,2}(\partial f_0/\partial v_{1,2})\,d^3v}{i(\omega+kv_\parallel)} = \frac{-e^2}{m}E_{1,2}\int \frac{v_\perp(\partial f/\partial v_\perp)\,d^3v}{i(\omega+kv_\parallel)} \tag{8.2.9}$$

Hence, although $\mathbf{j}$ is not in general parallel to $\mathbf{E}$, the longitudinal and transverse parts are uncoupled, and for each part of the field the induced current is parallel to $\mathbf{E}$. If we normalize f_0 to unity, $f_0 = n\hat{f_0}$, and introduce $\omega_0^2 = 4\pi ne^2/m$, we may write the dielectric coefficients

$$\epsilon_\parallel = 1 + \frac{\omega_0^2}{\omega^2}\left[\int \frac{v_\parallel(\partial\hat{f_0}/\partial v_\parallel)}{1+kv_\parallel/\omega}\right]$$

$$= 1 - \frac{\omega_0^2}{\omega^2}\cdot\left[\left(\frac{\omega}{k}\right)^2\int \frac{\partial\hat{f_0}/\partial v_\parallel}{\omega/k+v_\parallel}\,d^3v\right]$$

$$\epsilon_\perp = 1 + \frac{\omega_0^2}{\omega^2}\left[\frac{\omega}{k}\int \frac{v_\perp\partial\hat{f_0}/\partial v_\perp}{\omega/k+v_\parallel}\,d^3v\right]$$

i.e.

$$\epsilon_\parallel = 1 - \frac{\omega_0^2}{\omega^2}\phi_1\left(\frac{\omega}{k}\right)$$

$$\epsilon_\perp = 1 - \frac{\omega_0^2}{\omega^2}\phi_2\left(\frac{\omega}{k}\right) \tag{8.2.10}$$

where

$$\phi_1(x) = x^2 \int_L \frac{\partial\hat{f}/\partial v_\parallel}{(x+v_\parallel)}\,d^3v \tag{8.2.11}$$

$$\phi_2(x) = x \int_L \frac{\hat{f_0}}{(x+v_\parallel)}\,d^3v$$

(integrating by parts).

For large x,

$$\phi_2(x) = \int \hat{f_0}\left(1 - \frac{v_\parallel}{x} + \frac{v_\parallel^2}{x^2} + \ldots\right) dx$$

$$= 1 + \frac{\langle v_\parallel^2 \rangle}{x^2} + \ldots = 1 + \tfrac{1}{3}\frac{\langle v^2 \rangle}{x^2} \qquad (8.2.12)$$

while

$$\phi_1(x) = x^2 \int \frac{\hat{f_0}}{(x + v_\parallel)^2}\, d^3v = \int \hat{f_0}\left(1 - 2\frac{v_\parallel}{x} + 3\left(\frac{v_\parallel}{x}\right)^2\right)$$

$$= 1 + \frac{3\langle v_\parallel^2 \rangle}{x^2} = 1 + \frac{\langle v^2 \rangle}{x^2}$$

If the phase velocity is high, i.e. ω/k large, then $\epsilon_\parallel \to \epsilon_\perp \to 1 - (\omega_0^2/\omega^2)$ which is the low-temperature result. Specifically, if $\hat{f_0}$ is Maxwellian

$$\hat{f_0}\, d^3v = \left(\frac{m}{2\pi kT}\right)^{3/2} \exp\left[-\frac{mv^2}{2kT}\right] d^3v = \pi^{-3/2}\exp\left(-\frac{v^2}{v_\theta^2}\right) d^3\left(\frac{v}{v_\theta}\right)$$

and

$$\phi_1\left(\frac{v_p}{v_\theta}\right) = \frac{-2}{\sqrt{\pi}}\frac{v_p^2}{v_\theta^2} \cdot \int \frac{v_\parallel/v_\theta \exp(-v_\parallel^2/v^2{}_\theta)}{v_p/v_\theta + v_\parallel/v_\theta}\, d\left(\frac{v_\parallel}{v_\theta}\right)$$

$$= 2\left(\frac{v_p^2}{v_\theta^2}\right) \times \left[\frac{1}{\sqrt{\pi}}\frac{v_p}{v_\theta} \cdot \int_{-\infty}^{\infty} \frac{\exp(-t^2)}{v_p/v_\theta + t} - 1\right]$$

while

$$\phi_2\left(\frac{v_p}{v_\theta}\right) = \frac{1}{\sqrt{\pi}}\left(\frac{v_p}{v_\theta}\right) \int_{-\infty}^{\infty} \frac{\exp(-t^2)}{t + v_p/v_\theta}\, dt$$

The integral

$$I(x) = P \int_{-\infty}^{\infty} \frac{\exp(-t^2)}{t + x}\, dt$$

may be transformed as follows.
Observe that

$$I(-x) = \int_{-\infty}^{\infty} \frac{\exp(-t^2)}{t - x}\, dt = +\int_{-\infty}^{\infty} \frac{\exp-(-t)^2}{-t - x}\, d(-t) = -I(x)$$

hence

$$2I(x) = I(x) - I(-x) - = -2x \int\limits_{-\infty}^{\infty} \frac{\exp(-t^2)}{t^2 - x^2}$$

$$= -2x \exp(-x^2) \int\limits_{-\infty}^{\infty} \frac{\exp[-(t^2 - x^2)]}{(t^2 - x^2)}$$

$$= 2x \exp(-x^2) \int\limits_{-\infty}^{\infty} dt \left\{ \int\limits_{0}^{1} d\lambda \exp[-\lambda(t^2 - x^2)] - \frac{1}{t^2 - x^2} \right\}$$

The second term,

$$P \int\limits_{-\infty}^{\infty} \frac{dt}{t^2 - x^2} = \frac{1}{2x} \log \frac{t - x}{t + x} \Bigg]_{-\infty}^{\infty} = 0$$

while

$$2x \exp(-x^2) \left\{ \int\limits_{-\infty}^{\infty} dt \int\limits_{0}^{1} d\lambda \exp[-\lambda(t^2 - x^2)] = \sqrt{\pi} \int\limits_{0}^{1} \frac{d\lambda}{\sqrt{\lambda}} \exp(\lambda x^2) \right.$$

$$\left. = \frac{2\sqrt{\pi}}{x} \int\limits_{0}^{x} \exp(t^2)\, dt \right\}$$

therefore

$$I(x) = 2\sqrt{\pi} \exp(-x^2) \int\limits_{0}^{x} \exp(t^2)\, dt \qquad\qquad (8.2.13)$$

a result which holds for any complex x.

We may now consider the transmission problem in the hot plasma. From Maxwell's equations in the form,

(a) $\nabla \times \mathbf{B} = \dfrac{4\pi}{c} \mathbf{j} + \dfrac{1}{c} \dfrac{\partial \mathbf{E}}{\partial t}$,   (b) $\nabla \cdot \mathbf{B} = 0$

(c) $\nabla \times \mathbf{E} = -\dfrac{1}{c} \dfrac{\partial \mathbf{B}}{\partial t}$,   (d) $\nabla \cdot \mathbf{E} = 4\pi q$,

13

we obtain, operating $\partial/\partial t$ on (a) and eliminating $\partial B/\partial t$ through (c)

$$-\nabla \times (\nabla \times \mathbf{E}) = \frac{4\pi}{c^2}\frac{\partial \mathbf{j}}{\partial t} + \frac{1}{c^2}\frac{\partial^2 \mathbf{E}}{\partial t^2}$$

and since $\nabla \times (\nabla \times \mathbf{E}) = \nabla \operatorname{div} \mathbf{E} - \nabla^2 \mathbf{E}$

$$\nabla^2 \mathbf{E} - \frac{1}{c^2}\frac{\partial^2}{\partial t^2}\mathbf{E} = \frac{4\pi}{c^2}\frac{\partial \mathbf{j}}{\partial t} + 4\pi \nabla q \tag{8.2.14}$$

For plane waves this becomes

$$\left[k^2 - \frac{\omega^2}{c^2}\right]\mathbf{E} = -i\left[\frac{4\pi}{c^2}\omega\mathbf{j} + 4\pi\mathbf{k}q\right]$$

To separate the longitudinal and transverse waves, we take the scalar and vector products with $\mathbf{k}$,

$$\left[k^2 - \frac{\omega^2}{c^2}\right]\mathbf{k}\cdot\mathbf{E} = -4\pi i\left[\frac{\omega}{c^2}\mathbf{k}\cdot\mathbf{j} + k^2 q\right]$$

$$\left[k^2 - \frac{\omega^2}{c^2}\right]\mathbf{k}\times\mathbf{E} = -4\pi i\frac{\omega}{c^2}\mathbf{k}\times\mathbf{j} = \frac{\omega^2}{c^2}\frac{4\pi}{i\omega}\mathbf{k}\times\mathbf{j}$$

The first equation may be transformed by making use of the equation of continuity for the current, $i\omega q + i\mathbf{k}\cdot\mathbf{j} = 0$
therefore

$$\frac{\omega}{c^2}\mathbf{k}\cdot\mathbf{j} + k^2 q = \frac{1}{\omega}\left[\frac{\omega^2}{c^2} - k^2\right]\mathbf{k}\cdot\mathbf{j}$$

and

$$\left[k^2 - \frac{\omega^2}{c^2}\right]\mathbf{k}\cdot\mathbf{E} = -\frac{4\pi}{i\omega}\mathbf{k}\cdot\mathbf{j}\left[k^2 - \frac{\omega^2}{c^2}\right]$$

and the equations for the longitudinal and transverse oscillations become

$$\left[k^2 - \frac{\omega^2}{c^2}\right]\epsilon_{\parallel}\mathbf{k}\cdot\mathbf{E} = 0 \tag{8.2.15}$$

$$\left[k^2 - \frac{\omega^2}{c^2}\epsilon_{\perp}\right]\mathbf{k}\times\mathbf{E} = 0 \tag{8.2.16}$$

For finite $\mathbf{k}$ and ω, both waves are damped since ϵ is complex, the imaginary part arising from the Landau definition of the singular integrals. For the transverse waves, we find the phase velocity $\omega/k = c/\sqrt{\epsilon_{\perp}}$; and if this is large, and f_0 has the properties given above,

$$\epsilon_{\perp} \to 1 - \frac{\omega_0^2}{\omega^2}, \qquad \frac{\omega}{k} = \frac{c}{\sqrt{[1-(\omega_0^2/\omega^2)]}} > c$$

and the plasma behaves as though cold. [Observe that the group velocity

$$\frac{d\omega}{dk} = \frac{d}{dk}\sqrt{(\omega_0^2 + c^2k^2)} = \frac{c^2k}{\sqrt{(\omega_0^2 + c^2k^2)}} = c\sqrt{[1 - (\omega_0^2/\omega^2)]} < c]$$

For longitudinal waves of long wavelength $k \ll k_D$, the Landau damping is negligible, and $\epsilon_\parallel = 1 - (\omega_0^2/\omega^2)$ vanishes at $\omega = \pm\,\omega_0$, thus reproducing the Langmuir oscillations of a cold plasma, the phase velocity being infinite and the group velocity zero. Finite values of these quantities may be approximated by expanding the integral in eq. (8.2.10), whereupon

$$\epsilon_\parallel \simeq 1 - \frac{\omega_0^2}{\omega^2}\left[1 + \frac{3}{2}\frac{v_\theta^2}{v_p^2}\right] + \dots$$

$$\omega^2 = \omega_0^2 + \frac{3}{2}v_\theta^2 k^2 + \dots$$

an approximate dispersion relation given by Bohm and Gross. It is sometimes important to consider the motion of the ions as well as of the electrons. The change produced by these is the addition of an extra current

$$\mathbf{j} = -\frac{e^2}{M}\mathbf{E}\cdot\int\frac{\mathbf{v}(\partial f_0^+/\partial\mathbf{v})}{i(\omega + \mathbf{k}\cdot\mathbf{v})}$$

hence the functions ϕ_1 and ϕ_2 are modified, becoming

$$\phi_1(x) = x^2\int\frac{(\partial\hat{f}_0^-/\partial v_\parallel) + (m/M)(\partial\hat{f}_0^+/\partial v_\parallel)}{x + v_\parallel}\,d^3v$$

$$\phi_2(x) = x^2\int\frac{\hat{f}_0^- + (m\hat{f}_0^+/M)}{x + v_\parallel}\,d^3v$$

Among the important consequences of the added term is the appearance of slightly damped waves at frequencies much below the plasma frequency; the ion plasma waves. Consider a longitudinal wave whose phase velocity is $\ll v_\theta^-$ and $\gg v_\theta^+$, and note that in $\epsilon_\parallel$ the Landau damping term is

$$\frac{\omega_0^2}{\omega^2}\frac{2}{\sqrt{\pi}}\frac{v_p^2}{v_\theta^2}\exp\ -\left(\frac{v_p^2}{v_\theta^2}\right)$$

while for small x

$$\phi_1(x) = x^2\left[\frac{1}{\sqrt{\pi}}x\int\frac{\exp(-t^2)}{t + x} - 1\right] = x^2[2x\exp(-x^2)\int_0^x\exp(t^2)\,dt - 1]$$

$$\simeq x^2(x^3 - 1) \simeq -x^2$$

and to order x^2

$$\epsilon_\parallel = 1 - \frac{\omega_0^2}{\omega^2}\left[-\frac{v_p^2}{v_\theta^2} + \frac{m}{M}\left(1 + \frac{v_\theta^{+2}}{v_p^2}\right)\right]$$

If $\omega \ll \omega_0$, waves exist with phase velocity

$$v_p = v_\theta^- \Big/ \sqrt{\left(\frac{m}{M}(1+T_+/T_-) - \frac{\omega^2}{\omega_0^2}\right)}$$

If the ion and electron temperatures are equal $v_\theta^+ = (m/M)^{\frac{1}{2}} v_\theta^-$ and if $\omega \ll (m/M)^{\frac{1}{2}} \omega_0 = \omega_0^+$ these are isothermal sound waves.

3. SCREENING AND THE FOKKER-PLANCK EQUATION FOR A PLASMA

The dielectric theory which we have developed is valid wherever collisions are negligible, hence particularly at high frequencies and short wavelengths. This suggests a possible approach to the interaction between charges in a plasma. Let us consider first the electric field produced by a point charge q at rest in a plasma. We have the dielectric coefficient in the form $\epsilon(k, \omega)$ and we may attempt to solve

$$\nabla \cdot (\epsilon \mathbf{E}) = 4\pi q$$

by considering the harmonic components separately. A point charge may be Fourier analysed as

$$q(k, \omega) = q\delta(\omega)$$

hence, the potential is determined by

$$k^2 \epsilon(k, \omega)\phi = 4\pi q \qquad (8.3.1)$$

$$\phi(k, \omega) = \frac{4\pi q}{k^2 \epsilon(k, \omega)} = \frac{4\pi q}{k^2[1 + (\omega_0^2/\omega^2)(\omega^2/k^2)(2/v_\theta^2)]} = \frac{4\pi q}{k^2 + k_D^2}$$

We may now obtain $\phi(\mathbf{r})$ by back transforming

$$\phi(\mathbf{r}) = \frac{4\pi q}{(2\pi)^3} \int d^3k \frac{\exp(i\mathbf{k}\cdot\mathbf{r})}{k^2 + k_D^2} = \frac{8\pi^2}{(2\pi)^3} q \int k^2\, dk \sin\theta\, d\theta \frac{\exp(ikr\cos\theta)}{k^2 + k_D^2}$$

$$= \frac{8\pi^2}{(2\pi)^3} q \cdot \int_0^\infty \frac{k\, dk}{ir} \frac{[\exp(ikr) - \exp(-ikr)]}{k^2 + k_D^2} = \frac{q}{i\pi r} \int_{-\infty}^\infty \frac{dk\, k \exp(ikr)}{(k^2 + k_D^2)}$$

On extending the integral into the upper half-plane, and observing that the residue at $k = ik_D$ is $= \frac{1}{2}\exp -k_D r$

$$\phi(r) = q\frac{\exp(-k_D r)}{r} \qquad (8.3.2)$$

which is the Debye shielded potential.

If the source, instead of being at rest, moves with the velocity $\mathbf{v}$, the harmonic components of q become

$$q(k, \omega) = 2\pi q\delta(\omega + \mathbf{k}\cdot\mathbf{v})$$

and the potential

$$\phi(k,\ \omega) = \frac{8\pi^2 q\delta(\omega + \mathbf{k}\cdot\mathbf{v})}{k^2\epsilon(\mathbf{k},\ \omega)} \tag{8.3.3}$$

The field here consists of two parts: the self field of the particle

$$\phi_{\text{self}} = \frac{8\pi^2 q\delta(\omega + \mathbf{k},\ \mathbf{v})}{k^2}$$

and the field due to the polarization induced in the plasma

$$\phi_{\text{ind}} = \frac{8\pi^2 q\delta(\omega + \mathbf{k}\cdot\mathbf{v})}{k^2}\left(\frac{1}{\epsilon} - 1\right)$$

Now, the induced electric field will act upon the particle and resist its motion; the induced electric field being

$$\tfrac{1}{2}(E_{\text{ind}} + E^*{}_{\text{ind}}) = -\tfrac{1}{2}8\pi^2 q\delta(\omega + \mathbf{k}\cdot\mathbf{v})\left\{\frac{i\mathbf{k}}{k^2}\left(\frac{1}{\epsilon} - 1\right) - \frac{i\mathbf{k}}{k^2}\left(\frac{1}{\epsilon^*} - 1\right)\right\}$$

$$= -8\pi^2 q\delta(\omega + \mathbf{k}\cdot\mathbf{v})\cdot\frac{\mathbf{k}}{k^2}\frac{\mathscr{I}(\epsilon)}{\epsilon\epsilon^*}$$

where $\mathscr{I}(\epsilon)$ is the imaginary part of ϵ. The force on the particle is then $qE(0)$,

$$F_r = -\frac{8\pi^2 q^2}{(2\pi)^4}\int d^3k\ d\omega\cdot\delta(\omega + \mathbf{k}\cdot\mathbf{v})\frac{k}{k^2}\frac{\mathscr{I}(\epsilon)}{\epsilon\epsilon^*}\cdot\frac{\mathbf{v}}{|v|}$$

$\mathscr{I}(\epsilon)$, however, is just the Landau damping term, which in terms of the distribution function for the electrons is

$$-\int 2\pi\frac{\omega_0^2}{\omega^2}\frac{\omega^2}{k^2}\cdot\frac{1}{|k|}\frac{\widehat{\partial f_0}}{\partial v_\parallel{}'}\delta(\omega + \mathbf{k}\cdot\mathbf{v})\ d^3v$$

$$F_r = \frac{1}{\pi}q^2\omega_0^2\int d^3k\ d\omega\cdot\int d^3v'\cdot\frac{\mathbf{k}\cdot\mathbf{v}}{|v|}\frac{\hat{\mathbf{k}}}{|k|}\cdot\frac{\partial f_0(v')}{\partial v'}\frac{\delta(\omega + \mathbf{k}\cdot\mathbf{v})}{|k^2\epsilon|^2}\delta(\omega + \mathbf{k}\cdot\mathbf{v}')$$

$$= \frac{1}{\pi}q^2\omega_0^2\int d^3k\ d\omega\cdot\int d^3g\frac{\mathbf{k}\cdot\mathbf{v}}{v}\frac{\hat{\mathbf{k}}}{k}\cdot\frac{\partial f_0(\mathbf{v}+\mathbf{g})}{\partial v'}\cdot\frac{\delta(\mathbf{k}\cdot\mathbf{g})}{|k^2\epsilon|^2}\delta(\omega + \mathbf{k}\cdot\mathbf{v}) \tag{8.3.5}$$

If now, we write $k^2\epsilon = k^2 - k_D^2 X + ik_D^2 Y$ where X and Y are functions of (ω/kv_θ) so that carrying out the integration over ω these become X, $Y(v\cos\theta/v_\theta)$, the integration over the magnitude of k becomes

$$\int dk\frac{k^3}{(k^2 - k_D^2 X)^2 + (k_D^2 Y)^2} = \tfrac{1}{2}\int_0^\infty\frac{dk^2\cdot k^2}{(k^2 - k_D^2 X)^2 + (k_D^2 Y)^2}$$

$$= \tfrac{1}{2}\log[(k^2 - k_D^2 X)^2 + k_D^2 Y^2]\ \Big|_0^\infty + \frac{X}{|Y|}\tan^{-1}\frac{(k^2 - k_D^2 X)}{k_D^2|Y|}\ \Big|_0^\infty \tag{8.3.6}$$

At the upper limit this diverges, which is scarcely surprising since there the linearizing approximation upon which the original theory was based becomes invalid, and a finite upper limit k_{max} (determined, for example, by the size of the body bearing the charge q) must be used. Then the integral becomes

$$2\left[\log\frac{k_{max}}{k_D} + \tfrac{1}{2}\log\left[\frac{1-\left(\dfrac{k_D{}^2}{k_{max}}\right)^2 X^2 + \left(\dfrac{k_D{}^2}{k_{max}{}^2}\right)^2 Y^2}{X^2 + Y^2}\right] + \frac{X}{|Y|}\left(\frac{\pi}{2} + \tan^{-1}\frac{X}{|Y|}\right)\right]$$

and provided k_{max} is large, and $(k^2 - k_D{}^2 X)^2 + k_D{}^4 Y^2 \neq 0$ in the range integration, this is approximately

$$\int \frac{k^3\, dk}{(k^2 - k_D{}^2 X)^2 + k_D{}^4 Y^2} \simeq 2\log\frac{k_{max}}{k_D} \tag{8.3.7}$$

and the force on the charge becomes

$$F_r = 8\frac{n \cdot e^2}{m_-}q^2 \int d\Omega \int d^3g \left(\frac{\hat{\mathbf{k}}\cdot\mathbf{v}}{v}\right)^2 \frac{\partial f_0}{\partial \mathbf{v}}(\mathbf{v}+\mathbf{g})\cdot\delta(\hat{\mathbf{k}}\cdot\mathbf{g})\cdot\log\left(\frac{k_{max}}{k_D}\right) \tag{8.3.8}$$

A second important property of the field due to a moving point charge arises from the asymptotic form of $k^2\epsilon$, which for large phase velocities tends not to $k^2 + k_D{}^2$, but to $k^2[(1-(\omega_0{}^2/\omega^2)][(1+\langle v^2\rangle(k^2/\omega^2)+\ldots]$, hence the singularity in the integral moves from the imaginary axis on to the real axis, after the ω integration the denominator becoming

$$\sim k^2 - k_D{}^2\frac{v_\theta{}^2}{v^2\cos\theta} \text{ if } v^2 \gg v_\theta{}^2$$

over most of the range of θ, the field appears not exponentially screened but as a propagated oscillating wave train, in fact, a wake.

We may now consider the consequences of the dielectric coefficient for the calculation of the interaction of the particles in the plasma. The standard method of approach to this problem requires the use of chains of equations typified by eq. (8.1.3), in which the particle correlations are calculated explicitly; a process which demands the cutting of the chain at some point although for the case of the plasma, the cut-off procedure can be justified by considering e/m as a small parameter.

Particle correlations are used, however, only to determine the electric fields and we shall content ourselves with calculating only the latter quantity. The spirit of the calculation is this: In the absence of correlations the Coulomb potential at a point $\mathbf{r}_i$ is

$$\phi_c = \sum_j \frac{e_i e_j}{|\mathbf{r}_i - \mathbf{r}_j|}$$

where $\mathbf{r}_i$ and $\mathbf{r}_j$ are uncorrelated, and this is the quantity whose divergence leads to the difficulty in defining collision integrals in a plasma. We shall replace it by

$$\phi_M = \sum_{j,k} \frac{e_i e_j}{|\mathbf{r}_i - (\mathbf{r}_j + \delta \mathbf{r}_{jk})|}$$

where $\delta \mathbf{r}_{jk}$ is the perturbation produced in the position of the particle at $\mathbf{r}_j$ by its interaction with the kth particle, a perturbation which is calculated to first order in ϕ_M not, of course, ϕ_c which is divergent. This calculation, however, is merely making allowance for the polarizability of the plasma. Since we anticipate little effect for separations $\ll \lambda_D$ and since $\lambda_D n^{-1/3}$ is large, many particles are required before correlation effects become important and the continuum approximation to the dielectric coefficient given by Vlasov's solution provides an adequate representation of the polarization. If we use the Fokker–Planck solution in the form eq. (8.1.12) we must calculate the auto-correlation of the internal fluctuating field

$$\left\langle \int E_i(t) . E_j(t-s) \, ds \right\rangle$$

along the path of a particle moving with velocity $\mathbf{v}$. This may be written in terms of the harmonic components of the field, for if

$$E(\mathbf{x}, t) = \Sigma E(\mathbf{k}, \omega) \exp(i\mathbf{k}.\mathbf{x} + i\omega t)$$

and

$$E[x(t-s), (t-s)] = \Sigma E(\mathbf{k}'\omega') \exp[i\mathbf{k}' . (\mathbf{x} - \mathbf{v}s)] \exp[i\omega'(t-s)]$$

and the required integral

$$\left\langle \int_0^\infty E_i(t) E_j(t-s) \, ds \right\rangle$$

$$= \frac{\mathscr{R}}{(2\pi)^8} \left\langle \int_0^\infty ds \int d^3k \int d\omega \int d^3k' \int d\omega' . E_i(k, \omega) E_j(k', \omega') \times \right.$$

$$\left. \times \exp[i\mathbf{k}.\mathbf{x} + i\omega t] \exp[i\mathbf{k}' . (\mathbf{x} - \mathbf{v}s)] \exp[i\omega'(t-s)] \right\rangle$$

$$= \frac{1}{(2\pi)^2} \mathscr{R} \int \left\langle E_i(\mathbf{k}.\omega) E_j(\mathbf{k}.\omega) \right\rangle \delta(\omega + \mathbf{k}.\mathbf{v}) \, d^3k \, d\omega$$

$\mathscr{R}f$ being the real part of f.

To calculate the harmonic components of the fluctuating field, eq. (8.3.3) may be used, where the charge density q is calculated as for uncorrelated particles, at positions x_i, thus

$$q(\mathbf{x}, t) = \Sigma e_i \delta[\mathbf{x} - \mathbf{x}_i(t)] = \Sigma e_i \delta[\mathbf{x} - (\mathbf{x}_i + \mathbf{v}_i t)]$$

and

$$q(k, \omega) = \Sigma e_i \exp(i\mathbf{k}.\mathbf{x}_i) \delta(\omega + \mathbf{k}.\mathbf{v}_i)$$

The energy spectrum of the electric field is then (neglecting the ions)

$$\langle E_\alpha E_\beta(\mathbf{k}, \omega) \rangle = \sum_{ij} \int \frac{k_\alpha k_\beta{}'}{k^2 \epsilon(k, \omega) k'^2 \epsilon(k' \omega')} \times$$

$$\delta(\omega + \mathbf{k} . \mathbf{v}_i) \delta(\omega' + \mathbf{k}' . \mathbf{v}) \exp(i\mathbf{k} . \mathbf{x}_i) \exp(i\mathbf{k}' . \mathbf{x}_j) . \mathrm{d}^3 k' \, \mathrm{d}\omega'$$

In this sum, the particle positions are uncorrelated, hence we may use the random phase approximation to reduce the double sum to a single one and on observing that $\Sigma g(v_i) = \int f(v) g(v) \, \mathrm{d}^3 v$, obtain for the fields

$$\langle E_i E_j(k . \omega) \rangle = \int e^2 \frac{k_i k_j}{|k^2 \epsilon(k, \omega)|^2} . f(v) \delta(\omega + \mathbf{k} . \mathbf{v}), \mathrm{d}^3 v \qquad (8.3.10)$$

hence the relevant correlation function becomes

$$\left\langle \int E_i(t) E_j(t-s) \right\rangle = \int e^2 \frac{k_i k_j}{|k^2 \epsilon(k\omega)|^2} f(v') \delta(\omega + \mathbf{k} . \mathbf{v}') \times$$

$$\times \delta(\omega + \mathbf{k} . \mathbf{v}) \, \mathrm{d}^3 v' \, \mathrm{d}^3 k \, \mathrm{d}\omega$$

From this, the Fokker–Planck diffusion coefficient obtains the form

$$D_{ij} = \frac{e^2}{m^2} \left\langle \int E_i(t) E_j(t-s) \, \mathrm{d}s \right\rangle = \frac{1}{2\pi m^2} \frac{e^4}{} \int \frac{k_i k_j}{(k^2 - k_D^2 X)^2 + k_D^4 Y^2} \times$$

$$\times f(\mathbf{v} + \mathbf{g}) \delta(\mathbf{k} . \mathbf{g}) \delta(\omega + \mathbf{k} . \mathbf{v}) \, \mathrm{d}^3 g \, \mathrm{d}^3 k \, \mathrm{d}\omega \qquad (8.3.11)$$

which may be written,

$$\frac{1}{2\pi} \frac{e^4}{m^2} \int \mathrm{d}^3 g \int \mathrm{d}\Omega \hat{k}_i \hat{k}_j \delta(\hat{\mathbf{k}} . \mathbf{g}) f(\mathbf{v} + \mathbf{g}) . \int \frac{\mathrm{d}k \, k^2}{(k^2 - k_D^2 X)^2 + k_D^4 Y^2}$$

or, using the dominant approximation, eq. (8.3.7), where now k_{max} is determined not by the size of the charge, but by the point at which local correlations between colliding particles become important, a point which is correctly treated by the Boltzmann collision term and is $k_{max} = 1/b_{min} = m_r g^2/e^2$

$$D_{ij} = \frac{2}{\pi} \frac{e^4}{m^2} \int \mathrm{d}^3 g \int \mathrm{d}\Omega \hat{k}_i \hat{k}_j \delta(\hat{\mathbf{k}} . \mathbf{g}) f(\mathbf{v} + \mathbf{g}) . \log \Lambda \qquad (8.3.12)$$

where

$$\log \Lambda = \log \frac{k_{max}}{k_D} \simeq \log \left(\frac{kT}{e^2 n^{1/3}} \right)^{3/2}$$

By comparison with eq. (8.1.10) it is clear that the integral over Ω reduces to $\delta_{ij} - (g_i g_j/g^2)$, hence, the electron–electron diffusion term in the Fokker–Planck equation becomes

$$\frac{\partial}{\partial v_i v_j} (D_{ij} f) = \frac{e^4}{m^2} \frac{\partial^2}{\partial v_i \partial v_j} \int \mathrm{d}^3 g^{-1} \left[\delta_{ij} - \frac{g_i g_j}{g^2} \right] f(\mathbf{v} + \mathbf{g}) . f(\mathbf{v}) \log \Lambda \quad (8.3.13)$$

which has exactly the form of the same term in Landau's expansion of the Boltzmann integral. This suggests what is borne out by a calculation of the remaining coefficients. In the dominant approximation—i.e. to order $\log \Lambda$— Landau's approximation to the interaction term takes into account the effect of long range correlations, even although the Debye screened field is a poor representation of the field of a single charge. Care is needed in calculating the drag, for an electron in the plasma experiences in addition to the drag F_r, eq. (8.3.5), an equal drag due to the fluctuating field in the plasma.

For a Maxwellian distribution we find for the term arising from interaction between electrons

$$D_{ij}(v) = D_{\perp}(\delta_{ij} - \hat{v}_i \hat{v}_j) + D_{\parallel} \hat{v}_i \hat{v}_j$$

or

$$D_{\parallel} = \frac{8\pi n e^4}{m^2 v} \log \Lambda \, G(v/v_\theta) \tag{8.3.14}$$

$$D_{\perp} = \frac{8\pi n e^4}{m^2 v} \log \Lambda H(v/v_\theta)$$

while D_i is in the direction $-v$, i.e. $-D\hat{\mathbf{v}}$ where

$$D = \frac{8\pi n e^4}{m(kT)} \log \Lambda \, G(v/v_\theta) \tag{8.3.15}$$

and where the functions G and H are

$$\left.\begin{array}{c} G(x) = \dfrac{2}{\sqrt{\pi}} \left\{ \displaystyle\int_0^x dt \exp(-t^2) - x \exp(-x^2) \right\} \bigg/ 2x^2 \\[2em] H = (2/\sqrt{\pi}) \displaystyle\int_0^x \exp(-t^2)\, dt - G \end{array}\right\} \tag{8.3.16}$$

4. ELECTROSTATIC INSTABILITIES

If the dielectric coefficient vanishes for a finite value of ω and $\mathbf{k}$, the method given above for calculating the Fokker–Planck coefficients may break down, the integrals being undefined. However, if so the the plasma is unstable, and the internal fields may reach values limited only by non-linear phenomena which we have not yet calculated. To understand this process, as in the magnetohydrodynamic problem we must first investigate the free propagation of electrostatic oscillations through the system. Since we have already calculated the charge q induced by a field $E(k, \omega)$ the equation of motion for longitudinal oscillations is

$$-\nabla^2\phi = k^2\phi = +4\pi q_{\text{ind}} = \frac{4\pi e^2}{m} \int \frac{\mathbf{k}.(\partial f_0/\partial \mathbf{v})}{(\omega+\mathbf{k}.\mathbf{v})} \, d^3v\phi$$

from which follows the dispersion relation

$$k^2 - \sum \frac{4\pi e^2}{m} \int \frac{\mathbf{k}.(\partial f_0/\partial \mathbf{v})}{(\omega+\mathbf{k}.\mathbf{v})} = 0 \qquad (8.4.1)$$

where the sum Σ extends over the possible types of particle in the system. Introducing $g = \Sigma(4\pi ne^2/m) \int f_0 \, d^2v_\perp$, the dispersion relation becomes

$$k^2 = \int dv_\parallel \frac{\partial g/\partial v_\parallel}{[(\omega/k)+v_\parallel]} = Z(\omega/k)$$

where the Landau prescription must be used to define the integral in the lower half plane, and on the real axis. In studying stability we are interested in the behaviour of the complex solutions $\omega(k)$ as a function of real k. For small k, $Z(\omega/k) \to (\omega_p/\omega)^2 k^2 + i\pi(\partial/\partial v)g(-\omega/k)$, and since the last term is small $\omega \simeq \pm \omega_p$. Since, further, $g \to 0$ as $v^2 \to 0$, $v.(\partial g/\partial v) > 0$, the last term always introduces damping. If therefore instability is to occur, $\omega(k)$ must cross the real axis, i.e. there must exist some real $(\mathbf{k}, \omega)$ for which $k^2\epsilon(\mathbf{k}, \omega) = 0$. If g has a single maximum no instability is possible, for the zero can occur only at this maximum, since $i\pi(\partial/\partial v)g(-\omega/k)$ must vanish. With no loss in generality the velocity zero may be taken at the maximum and the real part of the integral becomes $\int(1/v)(\partial g/\partial v) \, dv$, which is negative definite since $v = 0$ is the sole maximum in g. If the system has more than one maximum an instability is possible, but need not appear, since the principal part must also be positive.

The simplest and most typical instability occurs when the distribution function represents two well defined interpenetrating beams, whereupon the dispersion relation takes the form

$$1 - \frac{\omega_1^2}{(\omega+kv_1)^2} - \frac{\omega_2^2}{(\omega+kv_2)^2} = 0 \qquad (8.4.2)$$

where ω_1 and ω_2 are the plasma frequencies of the two streams. As k increases, this quartic has at first four real roots $\omega = 0, 0, \omega = \pm \sqrt{(\omega_1^2+\omega_2^2)}$, but finally two of these become complex and conjugate, one having the form $\omega = \omega_r - i\gamma$. The disturbance corresponding to this root grows as $\exp(i\omega_r t + \gamma t)$, and corresponds to an instability. If $\omega_2^2 \simeq \lambda\omega_1^2$ where λ is small, this occurs for $(\mathbf{k}.\mathbf{v})^2 = [\omega_1^2/(1+\lambda^{1/3})]$. For larger values of k the perturbations are unstable. If the two beams are identical, moving with a relative velocity $2u$ the dispersion relation becomes

$$1 - \omega_p^2 \left[\frac{1}{(\omega-ku)^2} + \frac{1}{(\omega+ku)^2} \right] = 0 \qquad (8.4.3)$$

with roots

$$\omega^2 = \omega_p{}^2\left\{1+\left(\frac{k\cdot u}{\omega_p}\right)^2 \pm \sqrt{\left[1+4\left(\frac{k\cdot u}{\omega_p}\right)^2\right]}\right\}$$

which becomes negative for $(k\cdot u)^2 < 2\omega_p{}^2$.

Two identical beams with a spread in velocities may be represented by the distribution function

$$f = \frac{v_\theta}{2\pi}\left[\frac{1}{(v-u)^2+v_\theta{}^2}+\frac{1}{(v+u)^2+v_\theta{}^2}\right] \qquad (8.4.4)$$

for which simple function the dispersion relation becomes

$$1-\omega_p{}^2\left[\frac{1}{(\omega-ikv_\theta-ku)^2}+\frac{1}{(\omega-ikv_\theta+ku)^2}\right]=0$$

and the roots are

$$\omega = ikv_\theta \pm \omega_p\left\{1+\left(\frac{ku}{\omega_p}\right)^2 \pm \sqrt{\left[1+4\left(\frac{ku}{\omega_p}\right)^2\right]}\right\}^{\frac{1}{2}}$$

For instability ω must be negative and imaginary, and this is possible only if

$$k^2(u^2+v_\theta{}^2)^2 < 2\omega_p{}^2(u^2-v_\theta{}^2) \qquad (8.4.5)$$

Thus an instability criterion is obtained, the two beams can be unstable only if

$$u > v_\theta$$

This is a somewhat artificial example, for although v_θ may be identified with the velocity spread in the beam, the energy spread with the distribution (8.4.4) is infinite. Similar analysis may be carried out for Maxwellian distribution functions, but these depend on the properties of the functions ϕ_1 and ϕ_2 (8.2.15) and must be studied numerically. It has been shown that for two interpenetrating Maxwellian distributions of ions and electrons the condition on the drift velocity u for the appearance of instability is

$$u > 0{\cdot}9v_\theta$$

where $\frac{1}{2}m_-(v_\theta)^2 = kT$. (cf. BUNEMANN)

The two-stream instability has been intensively studied, and has been demonstrated experimentally by KARCHENKO and his associates. An electron beam of energy 80 kV and current up to 1 A focused by a magnetic field was passed through a tube of length 10–20 cm, 6·5 cm dia., containing an intense plasma excited by r.–f. Beyond the plasma there was a tuned resonator, followed by an electrostatic analyser, so that both the magnitude of the fluctuating field and the energy in this beam could be measured.

With the beam on, an r.-f. voltage was produced. This was analysed in frequency, and was shown to have a maximum above the plasma frequency as determined from a Langmuir double probe. The detailed theoretical prediction is:

$$\frac{\Delta\omega}{\omega} = \frac{1}{2^{4/3}}\left(\frac{\omega_b}{\omega_p}\right)^{1/3}$$

ω_p and ω_b being the plasma frequencies of the plasma and the beam. Agreement was not exact, the probe density (measured on axis) being twice that estimated from the radio frequency noise produced by the beam. The energy loss by the beam was spectacularly increased; in a plasma with density $n \sim 2 \times 10^{16}$ cm^{-3} it lost 40 eV/cm, or 10^8 times that predicted by Coulomb scattering; and 10^3 times that expected from scattering by neutrals.

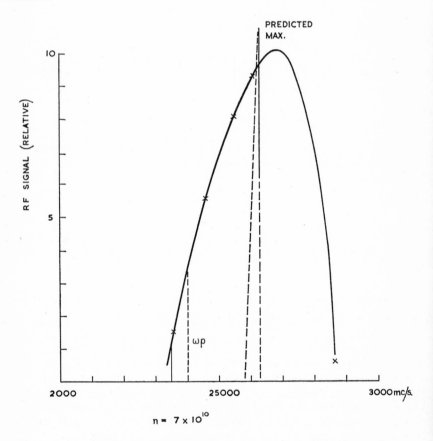

FIG. 8.1. Two stream instability. Measured r.f. noise produced by electron beam after passing through plasma. (Karchenko et al., Proc. 4th Int. Conf. on Ion. Phen. in Gases, 1960.)

5. EQUILIBRIUM IN A MAGNETIC FIELD.
SOME EXACT SOLUTIONS

In this section we shall begin the discussion of the properties of a diffuse plasma in a magnetic field, our aim being ultimately to derive equations of a magnetohydrodynamic type, with however a more realistic basis than was available for the equations of hydrodynamics. This involves, in general, obtaining approximate solutions to a suitable transport equation, but before proceeding to a discussion of that question, we will describe some **exact** self-consistent solutions to the Vlasov equation.

Such exact solutions can be found if the system under consideration has a high enough symmetry, their discovery depending upon the existence of exact constants of motion for the particles. These are most easily presented by writing the equations of motion in Hamiltonian form, where the Hamiltonian H is in terms of the vector and scalar potentials, $\mathbf{A}$ and ϕ,

$$H = \frac{1}{2m}(p_i - eA_i)^2 + e\phi \tag{8.5.1}$$

where p_i is the canonical momentum, not $m\dot{x}$, for from $\dot{x}_i = \partial H/\partial p_i$

$$\dot{x}_i = \frac{1}{m}(p_i - eA_i) \quad \text{therefore} \quad p_i = m\dot{x}_i + eA_i$$

where electromagnetic units of charge have been introduced.

Our problem is that of finding a self-consistent solution to the Vlasov–Maxwell set of equations

$$\frac{\partial f_i}{\partial t} + (H_i, f_i) = 0 \tag{8.5.2}$$

$$\nabla^2 \mathbf{A} - \frac{1}{c^2}\frac{\partial^2 \mathbf{A}}{\partial t^2} = -4\pi\mathbf{j} = -4\pi \sum e_i \int f_i \mathbf{v} \, \mathrm{d}^3 v \tag{8.5.3}$$

$$\nabla^2 \phi - \frac{1}{c^2}\frac{\partial^2 \phi}{\partial t^2} = -4\pi q = -4\pi \sum e_i \int f_i \, \mathrm{d}^3 v \tag{8.5.4}$$

and in particular in finding steady solutions, in which $\partial/\partial t = 0$. Under such circumstances the total energy of each particle is a constant, i.e. H is a constant. If, further, H is independent of one of the coordinates q_0, then the canonical momentum conjugate to that coordinate is also a constant of the motion for $\dot{p}_j = -\partial H/\partial q_j = 0$.

Finally, if the distribution function f is a function only of constants of motion, then $(H, f) = 0$ and the Vlasov equation is satisfied. Having f, usually as a function of the potentials $\mathbf{A}$ and ϕ, it is possible to form the moments and obtain equations determining $\mathbf{A}$ and ϕ. Rather than using the full Poisson equation to determine ϕ, it is often more realistic to use the hypothesis of charge neutrality

$$\int f_+ \, \mathrm{d}^3 v = \int f_- \, \mathrm{d}^3 v$$

and calculate ϕ from this condition.

As a simple application of this technique, consider a cylindrically symmetric system in which the current flows along the cylindrical axis OZ. Then the only component of the vector potential to survive is A_z, and two suitable constants of motion are H and p_z. Consider a distribution in the form

$$f = C \exp[-\beta'(H - Wp_z)] = C \exp\{-\beta'[\tfrac{1}{2}mv_\perp^2 + \tfrac{1}{2}mv_z^2 + e\phi - W(mv_z + eA_z)]\}$$

$$= C \exp\left\{-\beta\left[\tfrac{1}{2}v_\perp^2 + \tfrac{1}{2}v_z^2 + \frac{e\phi}{m} - W\left(v_z + \frac{e}{m}A_z\right)\right]\right\} \qquad (8.5.6)$$

The constant C is determined by setting $n = n_0$ at $\mathbf{A} = 0$, $\phi = 0$ then

$$n_0 = C \int \exp[-\beta\tfrac{1}{2}(v_\perp^2 + v_z^2 - 2Wv_z)] \, \mathrm{d}^3 v$$

$$= C \int \exp(-\beta\tfrac{1}{2}v_x^2) \, \mathrm{d}v_x \cdot \int \exp(-\beta\tfrac{1}{2}v_y^2) \, \mathrm{d}v_y \times$$

$$\times \int \exp[-\beta\tfrac{1}{2}(v_z^2 - 2Wv_z + W^2)] \exp(\beta W^2/2) \, \mathrm{d}v_z$$

$$= C \exp(\tfrac{1}{2}\beta W^2) \cdot (2\pi/\beta)^{3/2}$$

therefore

$$C = n_0 \, (\beta/2\pi)^{3/2} \exp[-\tfrac{1}{2}\beta W^2] \qquad (8.5.7)$$

and the density

$$n = n_0 \exp\left[-\beta\frac{e_-}{m_-}(\phi - WA_z)\right]$$

The drift velocity

$$n \langle v_z \rangle = n \left(\frac{\beta}{2\pi}\right)^{3/2} \exp[-\tfrac{1}{2}\beta W^2] \int v_z \exp[-\beta\{\tfrac{1}{2}(v_x^2 + v_y^2 + v_z^2) - Wv_z\}] \, \mathrm{d}^3 v$$

$$= n \left(\frac{\beta}{2\pi}\right)^{1/2} \int \exp-\left[\frac{\beta}{2}(v_z - W)^2\right] v_z \, \mathrm{d}v_z = nW \qquad (8.5.8)$$

The ions may be taken as at rest $W_+ = 0$, and their density becomes

$$n_+ = n_0 \exp\left[-\beta_+\frac{e_+}{m_+}\phi\right]$$

The potential ϕ may be determined by insisting that

$$n_+ = n_-$$

i.e.

$$\beta_+ \frac{e_+}{m_+} \phi = \beta_- \frac{e_-}{m_-}[\phi - WA_z]$$

$$\phi = \frac{WA_z}{1-(\beta_+/\beta_-)(e_+/e_-)(m_-/m_+)} = \frac{WA_z}{1+(\beta_+/\beta_-)(m_-/m_+)}$$

and

$$n = n_0 \exp - \beta_- \frac{e_-}{m_-}\left[\frac{-\beta_+}{\beta_-}\frac{m_-}{m_+}\frac{WA_z}{1+(\beta_+/\beta_-)(m_-/m_+)}\right]$$

$$= n_0 \exp -\left\{\frac{\beta_-\beta_+}{m_+\beta_-+m_-\beta_+}eWA_z\right\} = n_0 \exp(-\alpha A_z) \qquad (8.5.9)$$

Finally, Maxwell's equation determining A_z becomes

$$\frac{1}{r}\frac{\partial}{\partial r}r\frac{\partial A_z}{\partial r} = -4\pi j_z = 4\pi n_0 eW \exp(-\alpha A_z)$$

On introducing $y = \exp(-\alpha A_z)$; $x^2 = 4\pi n_0 eW\alpha r^2$

$$\frac{1}{x}\frac{d}{dx}\frac{x}{y}\frac{dy}{dx}+y = 0$$

With $A(0) = 0$, $y(0) = 1$, $y'(0) = 0$, this yields

$$y = \frac{1}{(1+x^2/8)^2}$$

finally with $\beta_- = m_-/kT_-$, $\beta_+ = m_+/kT_+$

$$n = n_0\bigg/\left[1+\frac{\pi}{2}\frac{n_0 e^2}{m}\frac{mW^2r^2}{k(T_++T_-)}\right]^2 \qquad (8.5.10)$$

a solution first given by BENNETT.

6. THE APPROXIMATION PROCEDURE FOR SOLVING THE TRANSPORT EQUATIONS

Although special exact solutions such as those presented in Section 8.5 are of great importance, they can usually be discovered only for systems of a high degree of symmetry, and for the study of the gross dynamics of a plasma are inadequate. Much more useful would be approximate solutions of the type used in classical kinetic theory where there exist two disparate scales of length and time, the macroscopic scales associated with hydro-dynamic phenomena and the microscopic scales associated with the motions of individual molecules. We shall consider, very briefly, three procedures that have been used in obtaining approximate solutions to the transport equation, and pay particular attention to the last of the three which is valid when the mean free path is large on the *macroscopic* scale.

The first of these methods is the classical procedure of HILBERT for finding the normal solutions to Boltzmann's equation, which forms the basis for most developments of the kinetic theory of gases. It is applicable when the mean free path l and the mean free time between collisions τ are the only microscopic lengths in the problem, thus may be applied to a dense plasma in a weak magnetic field, although the density must still be low enough for the Boltzmann equation to be applicable, i.e. $n\lambda_D{}^3 \gg 1$. To develop this procedure, we write

$$\frac{\partial f}{\partial t} + v \cdot \frac{\partial f}{\partial x} + F \frac{\partial f}{\partial v} = Df = \mathscr{I}(f, f) \qquad (8.6.1)$$

the R.H.S. being the non-linear collision term. We now introduce the macroscopic and microscopic scales, by introducing a macroscopic length L and time T, which are measures of the scales of hydrodynamic changes. It proves convenient to relate these by the mean thermal speed v_0 of the particles $L/T = v_0$. The L.H.S. then may be written, by measuring times and lengths in terms of L and T,

$$Lx' = x, \quad Tt' = t, \quad v_0 v' = v$$

$$Df = \frac{1}{T} \frac{\partial f}{\partial t'} + \frac{v_0}{L} v' \cdot \frac{\partial f}{\partial x'} + \frac{F}{v_0} \cdot \frac{\partial f}{\partial v'} = \frac{1}{T} D'f \qquad (8.6.2)$$

where F/v_0 is taken as $\sim 1/T$, i.e. the acceleration is not strong enough to produce changes on less than the macroscopic scales.

The R.H.S. of eq. (8.6.1) has the form

$$\mathscr{I}(f, f) = \int dv_1 \int d\Omega \, \sigma(\theta, \mathbf{v} - \mathbf{v}_1) |\mathbf{v} - \mathbf{v}_1| [f(\bar{\mathbf{v}}) f(\bar{\mathbf{v}}_1) - f(\mathbf{v}) f(\mathbf{v}_1)]$$

If we write $f(v_1) = n_0 \hat{f}(v_1)$, $\sigma(\theta, v - v_1) = \sigma_0 \sigma'(\theta, v - v_1)$ this takes the dimensionless form

$$n\sigma_0 v_0 \mathscr{I}'(f, f) = \frac{1}{\tau} \mathscr{I}'(f, f) \qquad (8.6.3)$$

and eq. (8.6.1) may be written in a form suitable for expansion, as

$$\mathscr{I}'(f, f) = \frac{\tau}{T} D'f \qquad (8.6.4)$$

where $\tau/T = \epsilon$ representing the ratio between the microscopic and macroscopic scales, is small. To solve we write f as a series in ϵ, $f = f_0 + \epsilon f_1 + \epsilon^2 f_2 + \ldots$. Introduce this into eq. (8.6.4) and equate the coefficients of the separate powers of ϵ thus,

$$\mathscr{I}(f_0, f_0) = 0 \qquad (8.6.5)$$

$$\mathscr{I}(f_0, f_1) = Df_0 \qquad (8.6.6)$$

The solution to the first of these is the Maxwellian distribution of the velocities with temperature, mean velocity and density arbitrary functions of position and time (since $\mathscr{I}$ involve only the random velocities), thus

$$f_0 = n(x, t)\left[\frac{m}{2\pi kT(x, t)}\right]^{3/2} \exp\left\{-\tfrac{1}{2}m\frac{[\mathbf{v} - \mathbf{V}(x, t)]^2}{kT(x, t)}\right\} \qquad (8.6.7)$$

If we write $f_1 = f_0\psi(v)$ the function ψ satisfies

$$\int K(\mathbf{v}, \mathbf{v}')\psi(\mathbf{v}')\,\mathrm{d}^3v' = Df_0 \qquad (8.6.8)$$

where the kernel K has been shown to be symmetric in $\mathbf{v}$ and $\mathbf{v}'$, and the L.H.S. represents the rate of change in ψ produced by collisions. Non-trivial solutions to an equation of the form (8.6.8) are possible only if the R.H.S. satisfies certain integral constraints; it must be orthogonal to any solution $h(\mathbf{v})$ of the associated homogeneous equation, for if

$$\int K(\mathbf{v}, \mathbf{v}')f(\mathbf{v}')\,\mathrm{d}^3v' = \mathscr{I}(\mathbf{v})$$

and

$$\int K(\mathbf{v}, \mathbf{v}')h(\mathbf{v}')\,\mathrm{d}^3v' = 0$$

then

$$\int \mathrm{d}^3vh(\mathbf{v})\int K(\mathbf{v}, \mathbf{v}')f(\mathbf{v}')\,\mathrm{d}^3v' = \int \mathrm{d}^3v'f(\mathbf{v}')\int K(\mathbf{v}, \mathbf{v}')h(\mathbf{v})\,\mathrm{d}^3v$$

$$= 0 = \int \mathscr{I}(\mathbf{v})h(\mathbf{v})\,\mathrm{d}^3v \qquad (8.6.9)$$

where the symmetry of K has been used. The homogeneous solutions associated with eq. (8.6.8) are, however, just those quantities which remain invariant on collision, n, the particle number, $m\mathbf{v}$, the momentum and $\tfrac{1}{2}mv^2$, the energy. Thus the five constraints $\int Df_0(m, m\mathbf{v}, \tfrac{1}{2}mv)^2\mathrm{d}^3v = 0$ which serve to determine the lowest approximation to the five functions n, $\mathbf{V}$, $T(x, t)$, are exactly the hydrodynamic equations for adiabatic flow, cf. Section 8.1.

At each stage in the approximation procedure, similar constraints are obtained, although from f_1 on, the distribution function is no longer isotropic in v, and instead of the adiabatic flow equations, in first order the Navier–Stokes equations are produced. Note that this expansion procedure produces magnetohydrodynamic phenomena only in first order, thus the electric current appears in the same order as viscosity and heat conductions, so that the equations of idealized magnetohydrodynamics are never produced.

A modification of the Hilbert procedure introduced by CHAPMAN and COWLING overcomes this difficulty. In this method of analysis, the centre of mass motion $\mathbf{V}$ of the gas is split off, and instead of $\mathbf{v}$ the independent variable $\mathbf{c} = \mathbf{v} - \mathbf{V}$ is introduced. This modifies the L.H.S. of the Boltzmann equation, for in its initial form, the partial derivation with respect to space and time are taken at constant $\mathbf{v}$, and to change variables we need, e.g.

$$\left.\frac{\partial f}{\partial t}\right|_v = \left.\frac{\partial f}{\partial t}\right|_c + \frac{\partial f}{\partial \mathbf{c}} \cdot \frac{\partial \mathbf{c}}{\partial t} = \frac{\partial f}{\partial t} - \frac{\partial \mathbf{V}}{\partial t} \cdot \frac{\partial f}{\partial \mathbf{c}}$$

therefore the L.H.S. becomes (for an ionized gas) in e.m.u.

$$Df = \frac{\partial f_\pm}{\partial t} + (\mathbf{V} + \mathbf{c}) \cdot \frac{\partial f_\pm}{\partial \mathbf{x}} - \left[\frac{\partial \mathbf{V}}{\partial t} + \left(\mathbf{V} + \mathbf{c}\right) \cdot \frac{\partial}{\partial \mathbf{x}} \mathbf{V}\right] \cdot \frac{\partial f_\pm}{\partial \mathbf{c}} +$$

$$+ \left\{\left(\frac{e}{m}\right)_\pm (\mathbf{E} + \mathbf{V} \times \mathbf{B}) + \left(\frac{e}{m}\right)_\pm (\mathbf{c} \times \mathbf{B})\right\} \frac{\partial f_\pm}{\partial \mathbf{c}} \qquad (8.6.10)$$

The Chapman and Cowling procedure is obtained by insisting that the last term in Df, namely $(e/m)(\mathbf{c} \times \mathbf{B}).\partial f/\partial \mathbf{c}$, a term which is of order Ωf, where Ω is the gyrofrequency of the particles, should be considered as of the same order as f/τ, the collision term, thus the gyromotion of the ions is considered as a microscopic, not a macroscopic motion, and $\Omega \tau$ is considered, for the purpose of expansion, as of order unity. Its actual numerical value, however, is irrelevant, provided only that the macroscopic periods characterized by T are much greater than the microscopic periods, i.e. both ΩT and $T/\tau \gg 1$.

When the expansion procedure is carried out the equations obtained are of the form

$$\Omega \mathbf{c} \times \mathbf{b} \cdot \frac{\partial f_0}{\partial \mathbf{c}} = \mathscr{I}(f_0, f_0)$$

which again is satisfied by the Maxwellian distribution

$$n(x, t) \left[\frac{m}{2\pi k T(x, t)}\right]^{3/2} \exp\left[-\frac{1}{2} \frac{mc^2}{kT}\right]$$

with $c^2 = |\mathbf{v} - \mathbf{V}(x, t)|^2$, since

$$\mathbf{c} \times \mathbf{b} \cdot \frac{\partial f(c^2)}{\partial \mathbf{c}} = 0$$

In first order, the equation which holds is

$$\int K'(\mathbf{v}', \mathbf{v}) \psi_1(\mathbf{v}') = f_0 \Omega \mathbf{c} \times \mathbf{b} \frac{\partial \psi_1}{\partial \mathbf{c}} + D' f_0 \qquad (8.6.11)$$

where $D' = D - (e/m)\mathbf{c} \times \mathbf{B}.(\partial/\partial \mathbf{c})$. Once again, the moments of the L.H.S. with the collision invariants must vanish, and these imply that the hydrodynamic moments of the R.H.S. must also vanish. Now however, the R.H.S. does *not* contain only the function f_0, hence the zero-order hydrodynamic equations do *not* determine explicit approximations to the spatially dependent functions, n, $\mathbf{V}$, T; instead, these quantities depend on the first-order distribution function f_1.

This function, however, contributes only to the momentum equation since

$$\int \tfrac{1}{2} c^2 \mathbf{c} \times \mathbf{b} \cdot \frac{\partial f}{\partial \mathbf{c}} = - \int f \mathbf{c} \cdot \mathbf{c} \times \mathbf{b} = 0$$

on integrating by parts; the second integrand vanishing for any f. To the momentum term its contribution is

$$\sum e \int \mathbf{cc} \times \mathbf{B} \cdot \frac{\partial f}{\partial \mathbf{c}} = - \sum e \int \mathbf{c} \times \mathbf{B} f = -\mathbf{j} \times \mathbf{B}$$

It follows that the zero-order constraint on the Chapman–Cowling procedure gives not adiabatic hydrodynamics, but idealized magnetohydrodynamics.

The final method we shall consider is one which will occupy our attention for the rest of this work. It is a method which is at once more general and less specific than the other two, in that it does not demand that the approximation procedure begin from a state of thermal equilibrium, as is required by these. On the other hand, it is somewhat unsatisfactory in that the zero-order solution is only very slightly constrained. This procedure begins with the ordering $\Omega \gg 1/T \gg 1/\tau$, thus is adapted to the study of those dynamical phenomena which occur in times short compared with the collision period. A comparison of typical periods is given in Table 1, Chapter 7, which reveals that this condition is certainly satisfied for diffuse hot plasmas, especially those of interest in thermonuclear research, and it is indeed this interest which has done most to stimulate the development of the theory to which we now turn.

It might be thought that the vast scale of astrophysical phenomena precluded the application of the collisionless theory, but this is by no means clear. If $\Omega \tau \gg 1$ it is quite possible that observable gross phenomena may represent the combined effect of many small motions for which $T < \tau$. In particular the characteristics of plasma turbulence may be profoundly affected by such processes. Again, the dynamical properties of diffuse interstellar matter, particularly the nature of its oscillations, can be discussed largely without considering collisions.

To discuss the approximate procedure and the nature of the solutions, we consider the collisionless Boltzmann equation in the form suggested by eq. (8.6.10). We write first the raw Vlasov equation, which for both positive ions and electrons has the form

$$\frac{\partial f}{\partial t} + \mathbf{v} \cdot \frac{\partial f}{\partial \mathbf{x}} + \frac{e}{m}[\mathbf{E} + \mathbf{v} \times \mathbf{B}] \cdot \frac{\partial f}{\partial \mathbf{v}} = 0$$

and introduce the electric drift $\mathbf{V}$ such that

$$[\mathbf{E}_\perp + \mathbf{V} \times \mathbf{B}] = 0 \qquad\qquad (8.6.12)$$

where $\mathbf{E}_\perp = \mathbf{E} - (\mathbf{E} \cdot \mathbf{b})\mathbf{b}$ is the component of $\mathbf{E}$ normal to the magnetic field $\mathbf{B}$.

The component of $\mathbf{V}$ in the direction of $\mathbf{B}$ is as yet unspecified, and for convenience, we will now define this quantity as the mean value of the velocity in the direction of the field, i.e.

$$\mathbf{V} \cdot \mathbf{b} = \int (\mathbf{b} \cdot \mathbf{v}) f \, d^3 v$$

Writing $\mathbf{c} = \mathbf{v} - \mathbf{V}$ reduces the Vlasov equation to a form resembling eq. (8.6.10),

$$\frac{\partial f}{\partial t} + (\mathbf{V} + \mathbf{c}) \cdot \frac{\partial f}{\partial \mathbf{x}} - \left[\frac{\partial \mathbf{V}}{\partial t} + (\mathbf{V} + \mathbf{c}) \cdot \frac{\partial \mathbf{V}}{\partial \mathbf{x}} \right] \cdot \frac{\partial f}{\partial \mathbf{c}}$$

$$+ \frac{e}{m} E_\parallel \frac{\partial f}{\partial c_\parallel} + \frac{e}{m} \mathbf{c} \times \mathbf{B} \cdot \frac{\partial f}{\partial \mathbf{c}} = 0 \qquad (8.6.13)$$

If eq. (8.6.13) is normalized as was eq. (8.6.2), where now the assumption of small acceleration is not made, it is clear that the first three terms are of order $(1/T)$, T being the macroscopic period, while the last term is of order Ω, the gyrofrequency. The magnitude of the fourth term is not specified, but we now make the, admittedly restrictive, assumption that $E_\parallel$ is so small that this term, too, is of order $(1/T)$. Our approximation procedure will then be obtained by insisting that $1/\Omega T$ be small.

Further to simplify eq. (8.6.13), we use a specific, in general, non-Cartesian representation of the components of the "random velocity" $\mathbf{c}$. Instead of the projections on a fixed Cartesian frame, we introduce the component parallel to the magnetic field $c_\parallel = \mathbf{c} \cdot \mathbf{b}$, and the two-vector normal to the field

$$\mathbf{c}_\perp = \mathbf{c} - c_\parallel \mathbf{b} \qquad (8.6.14)$$

Just as the introduction of the drift velocity complicated the form of the $\partial f / \partial t$, so does this transformation, for in eq. (8.6.13) the derivatives with respect to space and time are taken with the components of $\mathbf{c}$ on a rigid frame held fixed. On translating to $c_\parallel$, $\mathbf{c}_\perp$ we must allow for the variation of the axes of reference through the variation of the field direction $\mathbf{b}$ thus

$$\left. \frac{\partial f}{\partial t} \right|_{c_i} = \left. \frac{\partial f}{\partial t} \right|_{c_\parallel, c_\perp} + \frac{\partial f}{\partial c_\parallel} \left. \frac{\partial c_\parallel}{\partial t} \right|_{c_i} + \frac{\partial f}{\partial \mathbf{c}_\perp} \cdot \left. \frac{\partial \mathbf{c}_\perp}{\partial t} \right|_{c_i}$$

$$= \left. \frac{\partial f}{\partial t} \right|_{c_\parallel, c_\perp} + \frac{\partial f}{\partial c_\parallel} \frac{\partial \mathbf{b}}{\partial t} \cdot \mathbf{c} - c_\parallel \frac{\partial f}{\partial \mathbf{c}_\perp} \cdot \frac{\partial \mathbf{b}}{\partial t} - \frac{\partial f}{\partial \mathbf{c}_\perp} \cdot \mathbf{b} \left[\mathbf{c} \cdot \frac{\partial \mathbf{b}}{\partial t} \right]$$

$$(8.6.15)$$

In this expression the last term vanishes, $(\partial f / \partial \mathbf{c}_\perp) \cdot \mathbf{b} = 0$, while since

$$\mathbf{b} \cdot \frac{\partial \mathbf{b}}{\partial t} = \frac{1}{2} \frac{\partial}{\partial t}(b^2) = 0, \qquad \mathbf{c} \cdot \frac{\partial \mathbf{b}}{\partial t} = \mathbf{c}_\perp \cdot \frac{\partial \mathbf{b}}{\partial t}$$

If, finally, a polar representation of $\mathbf{c}_\perp$ is introduced $\mathbf{c}_\perp = (c_x, c_y)$ $= (c_\perp \cos \phi, c_\perp \sin \phi)$, the dominant term is greatly simplified. Indeed, using $c_\perp = \sqrt{(c_x^2 + c_y^2)}$, $\phi = \tan^{-1}(c_y/c_x)$;

$$\mathbf{c} \times \mathbf{B} \cdot \frac{\partial f}{\partial \mathbf{c}} = B\left(c_y \frac{\partial f}{\partial c_x} - c_x \frac{\partial f}{\partial c_y}\right)$$

$$= Bc_\perp\left[\left(\sin\phi\frac{\partial c_\perp}{\partial c_x} - \cos\phi\frac{\partial c_\perp}{\partial c_y}\right)\frac{\partial f}{\partial c_\perp} + \left(\sin\phi\frac{\partial \phi}{\partial c_x} - \cos\phi\frac{\partial \phi}{\partial c_y}\right)\frac{\partial f}{\partial \phi}\right] = -B\frac{\partial f}{\partial \phi}$$

whereupon eq. (8.1.13) becomes

$$\frac{\partial f}{\partial \phi} = \frac{1}{\Omega}\mathscr{D}f \tag{8.6.16}$$

with $\Omega = eB/m$, the gyrofrequency, and

$$\mathscr{D} = \frac{e}{m}E_{\parallel}\frac{\partial}{\partial c_{\parallel}} + D' + \mathbf{c}_\perp \cdot D'\mathbf{b}\frac{\partial}{\partial c_{\parallel}} - (D'\mathbf{V} + c_{\parallel}D'\mathbf{b}) \cdot \frac{\partial}{\partial \mathbf{c}_\perp} - D'\mathbf{V}_{\parallel}\frac{\partial}{\partial c_{\parallel}} \tag{8.6.17}$$

with

$$D' = \frac{\partial}{\partial t} + (\mathbf{V}+\mathbf{c}) \cdot \frac{\partial}{\partial \mathbf{x}}$$

Once the form (8.6.16) has been obtained, the solution procedure follows fairly simply. Formally we write

$$\frac{\partial f}{\partial \phi} = \epsilon\frac{1}{\Omega}\mathscr{D}f$$

and by expanding f as a series in ϵ and equating coefficients of separate terms, obtain the set

$$\frac{\partial f_0}{\partial \phi} = 0$$

$$\frac{\partial f_1}{\partial \phi} = \frac{1}{\Omega}\mathscr{D}f_0 \tag{8.6.18}$$

$$\frac{\partial f_n}{\partial \phi} = \frac{1}{\Omega}\mathscr{D}f_{n-1}$$

and the chain of solutions

$$f_0 = f_0(c_{\parallel}, c_\perp^2, x, t)$$

$$f_1 = \int \frac{1}{\Omega}\mathscr{D}f_0 \, d\phi + h_1(c_{\parallel}, c_\perp^2) = f_1^t + h_1 \tag{8.6.19}$$

$$f_n = \int \frac{1}{\Omega}\mathscr{D}f_{n-1} \, d\phi + h_n(c_{\parallel}, c_\perp^2)$$

However, it must now be observed that the solution must be periodic in ϕ, thus added constraints are required, since the aperiodic parts of the integrands in eq. (8.6.19) must vanish, i.e.

$$\frac{1}{2\pi} \int_0^{2\pi} \mathscr{D} f_n \, \mathrm{d}\phi = 0 = \langle \mathscr{D} f_n \rangle$$

and partial differential equations are obtained for the homogeneous solutions f_0 and h_t. For example, if $(\mathscr{D} f_n) = \mathscr{D} f_n - \langle \mathscr{D} f_n \rangle$ is the periodic part of $\mathscr{D} f_n$, then

$$\langle \mathscr{D} h_{n+1} \rangle = - \langle \mathscr{D} (1/\Omega) \int (\mathscr{D} f_n) \, \mathrm{d}\phi \rangle \qquad (8.6.20)$$

is an inhomogeneous equation determining h_{n+1}, hence f_{n+1} in terms of f_n.

To evaluate the form of the constraining equation, we must express $\mathscr{D} f(c_\perp^2, c_\parallel, x_1 t)$ in terms of the phase ϕ. Thus using $\partial f / \partial \mathbf{c}_\perp = 2(\partial f / \partial c_\perp^2) \mathbf{c}_\perp$

$$\mathscr{D} f(c_\parallel, c_\perp^2) = \frac{e}{m} E_\parallel \frac{\partial f}{\partial c_\parallel} + \frac{\partial f}{\partial t} + \mathbf{V} \cdot \frac{\partial f}{\partial \mathbf{x}} + c_\parallel \frac{\partial f}{\partial x_\parallel} +$$

$$+ \mathbf{c}_\perp \cdot \frac{\partial f}{\partial \mathbf{x}_\perp} + \mathbf{c}_\perp \cdot \left[\frac{\partial \mathbf{b}}{\partial t} + \mathbf{V} \cdot \frac{\partial \mathbf{b}}{\partial \mathbf{x}} + c_\parallel \frac{\partial \mathbf{b}}{\partial x_\parallel} + \mathbf{c}_\perp \cdot \frac{\partial \mathbf{b}}{\partial \mathbf{x}_\perp} \right] \cdot \frac{\partial f}{\partial c_\parallel} -$$

$$- \left[\frac{\partial}{\partial t} \mathbf{V} + \mathbf{V} \cdot \frac{\partial}{\partial \mathbf{x}} \mathbf{V} + c_\parallel \frac{\partial \mathbf{V}}{\partial x_\parallel} + \mathbf{c}_\perp \cdot \frac{\partial \mathbf{V}}{\partial \mathbf{x}_\perp} \right] \cdot \frac{\partial f}{\partial \mathbf{c}} -$$

$$- c_\parallel \left[\frac{\partial \mathbf{b}}{\partial t} + \mathbf{V} \cdot \frac{\partial}{\partial \mathbf{x}} \mathbf{b} + c_\parallel \frac{\partial \mathbf{b}}{\partial x_\parallel} + \mathbf{c}_\perp \cdot \frac{\partial \mathbf{b}}{\partial \mathbf{x}_\perp} \right] \cdot 2 \mathbf{c}_\perp \frac{\partial f}{\partial c_\perp^2}$$

To form the phase average of this, observe that

$$\frac{1}{2\pi} \int \mathbf{c}_\perp \, \mathrm{d}\phi = \frac{1}{2\pi} \int_0^{2\pi} c_\perp (\cos \phi, \sin \phi) \, \mathrm{d}\phi = 0$$

$$\frac{1}{2\pi} \int c_x c_y = \frac{1}{2\pi} \int c_\perp^2 \cos \phi \sin \phi \, \mathrm{d}\phi = 0$$

$$\frac{1}{2\pi} \int c_x^2 = \frac{1}{2\pi} \int c_y^2 = \frac{1}{2\pi} \int c_\perp^2 \cos^2 \phi \, \mathrm{d}\phi = \tfrac{1}{2} c_\perp^2$$

Hence

$$\langle \mathscr{D}f \rangle = \frac{e}{m}E_{\parallel}\frac{\partial f}{\partial c_{\parallel}} + \frac{\partial f}{\partial t} + \mathbf{V}\cdot\frac{\partial f}{\partial \mathbf{x}} + c_{\parallel}\frac{\partial f}{\partial x_{\parallel}} + \tfrac{1}{2}c_{\perp}^{2}\,\mathrm{div}\,\mathbf{b}\,\frac{\partial f}{\partial c_{\parallel}} -$$

$$-c_{\perp}^{2}(\mathrm{div}\,\mathbf{V})_{\perp}\cdot\frac{\partial f}{\partial c_{\perp}^{2}} - \left[\frac{D\mathbf{V}}{Dt}_{\parallel} + c_{\parallel}\frac{\partial \mathbf{V}_{\parallel}}{\partial x_{\parallel}}\right]_{\parallel}\cdot\frac{\partial f}{\partial c_{\parallel}}$$

$$-c_{\parallel}c_{\perp}^{2}\,\mathrm{div}\,\mathbf{b}\frac{\partial f}{\partial c_{\perp}^{2}}$$

Now, introducing $D/Dt = \partial/\partial t + \mathbf{V}\cdot\mathbf{\nabla}$ and using $\mathrm{div}\,\mathbf{b} = -(1/B)(\partial B/\partial x_{\parallel})$, a relation proved in Chapter 7,

$$\langle \mathscr{D}f \rangle = \frac{Df}{Dt} + c_{\parallel}\frac{\partial f}{\partial x_{\parallel}} + \frac{e}{m}E_{\parallel}\frac{\partial f}{\partial c_{\parallel}} + \frac{1}{B}\frac{\partial B}{\partial x_{\parallel}}c_{\parallel}c_{\perp}^{2}\left[\frac{\partial f}{\partial c_{\perp}^{2}} - \frac{\partial f}{\partial c_{\parallel}^{2}}\right] -$$

$$-c_{\perp}^{2}(\mathrm{div}\,\mathbf{V})_{\perp}\frac{\partial f}{\partial c_{\perp}^{2}} - \left[\frac{D\mathbf{V}}{Dt}_{\parallel} + c_{\parallel}(\mathrm{div}\,\mathbf{V})_{\parallel}\right]\frac{\partial f}{\partial c_{\parallel}} \qquad (8.6.21)$$

To understand the significance of this equation, we first seek stationary solutions to the homogeneous equation, in which $\partial/\partial t$ and $\mathbf{V} = 0$, whereupon eq. (8.6.21) becomes

$$c_{\parallel}\left\{\frac{\partial f}{\partial x_{\parallel}} + 2\frac{e}{m}E_{\parallel}\frac{\partial f}{\partial c_{\parallel}^{2}} + \frac{1}{B}\frac{\partial B}{\partial x_{\parallel}}c_{\perp}^{2}\left[\frac{\partial f}{\partial c_{\perp}^{2}} - \frac{\partial f}{\partial c_{\parallel}^{2}}\right]\right\} = 0 \qquad (8.6.22)$$

Consider now f as a function of the "longitudinal energy"

$$\mathscr{E} = c_{\perp}^{2} + c_{\parallel}^{2} - \frac{2e}{m}\int E_{\parallel}\,dx_{\parallel}$$

and the magnetic moment $\mu = c_{\perp}^{2}/B$, so that

$$\mathscr{E} = B\mu + c_{\parallel}^{2} - \frac{2e}{m}\int E_{\parallel}\,dx_{\parallel}$$

Then

$$\frac{\partial}{\partial x_{\parallel}}f(\mathscr{E},\mu)\bigg|_{c_{\parallel},c_{\perp}} = -\frac{2e}{m}E_{\parallel}\frac{\partial f}{\partial\mathscr{E}} - \frac{c_{\perp}^{2}}{B^{2}}\frac{\partial B}{\partial x_{\parallel}}\frac{\partial f}{\partial\mu}$$

and

$$\frac{\partial f}{\partial c_{\perp}^{2}}\bigg|_{x,c_{\parallel}} = \frac{1}{B}\frac{\partial f}{\partial\mu} + \frac{\partial f}{\partial\mathscr{E}}$$

$$\frac{\partial f}{\partial c_{\parallel}^{2}}\bigg|_{x,c_{\perp}} = \frac{\partial f}{\partial\mathscr{E}}$$

hence,

$$\langle \mathscr{D}f \rangle = \left[\frac{-2e}{m}E_\parallel + \frac{2e}{m}E_\parallel + \frac{1}{B}\frac{\partial B}{\partial x_\perp}c_\perp^2(1-1) \right]\frac{\partial f}{\partial \mathscr{E}} +$$

$$+ \left[\frac{-c_\perp^2}{B^2}\frac{\partial B}{\partial x_\parallel} + \frac{c_\perp^2}{B^2}\frac{\partial B}{\partial x_\parallel} \right]\frac{\partial f}{\partial \mu} = 0$$

and $f(,\mathscr{E}\ \mu)$ is a solution to the homogeneous equation. $\mathscr{E}$ and μ, however are just the zero-order adiabatic invariants of the motion. Further observe that as far as the spatial dependence is concerned, the dependence of f on $x_\parallel$ is included in $\mathscr{E}$, and $f = f(\mathscr{E}, \mu, \mathbf{x}_\perp)$, where $\mathbf{x}_\perp$ must be defined as $\mathbf{x}_\perp = \int \mathbf{b} \times d\mathbf{x}$, and is the coordinate of a flux line.

7. THE MAGNETOHYDRODYNAMIC EQUATIONS

From the zero order constraint certain of the magnetohydrodynamic equations may be deduced. If we form the moments of $\langle \mathscr{D}f_0 \rangle = 0$ with m we obtain

$$\frac{D\rho}{Dt} + \rho[(\mathrm{div}\ \mathbf{V})_\perp + (\mathrm{div}\ \mathbf{V})_\parallel] = 0$$

or

$$\frac{D\rho}{Dt} + \rho\ \mathrm{div}\ \mathbf{V} = 0$$

hence $\mathbf{V}$ represents the drift velocity of each component. Since ρ must be the same for positives and negatives from quasi-neutrality, it follows that $\mathbf{V}$ must also be the same, hence $\mathbf{V}$ is the zero-order approximation to the fluid velocity of the plasma. It follows that to zero order the plasma behaves as a perfect conductor since

$$\mathbf{E} + \mathbf{V} \times \mathbf{B} = 0$$

If we form the moment with $mc_\parallel$, there results

$$\rho\left(\frac{DV}{Dt}\right)_\parallel + \frac{\partial}{\partial x_\parallel}\rho\langle c_\parallel^2 \rangle + \frac{1}{B}\frac{\partial B}{\partial x_\parallel}[\tfrac{1}{2}\rho\langle c_\perp^2 \rangle - \rho\langle c_\parallel^2 \rangle] - qE_\parallel = 0$$

where $\langle c_\parallel^2 \rangle$, $\langle c_\perp^2 \rangle$ are the mean square velocity components, thus

$$\rho\langle c_\parallel^2 \rangle = m\int fc_\parallel^2\ d^3c = p_\parallel$$

while $p_{xx} = \rho\langle c_x^2 \rangle = \int fc_\perp^2 \cos^2\phi\ d^3c = \tfrac{1}{2}\rho\langle c_\perp^2 \rangle = p_\perp$, and q is the charge, $q = ne$. Hence, for each fluid

$$\rho\left(\frac{DV}{Dt}\right)_\parallel + \frac{\partial p_\parallel}{\partial x_\parallel} + \frac{1}{B}\frac{\partial B}{\partial x_\parallel}[p_\perp - p_\parallel] - q.E_\parallel = 0 \qquad (8.7.1)$$

or adding and using quasi-neutrality $q_+ + q_- = 0$, we obtain the magneto-hydrodynamic equation

$$\rho \left(\frac{DV}{Dt} \right)_{\parallel} + \frac{\partial p_{\parallel}}{\partial x_{\parallel}} + \frac{1}{B} \frac{\partial B}{\partial x_{\parallel}} [p_{\perp} - p_{\parallel}] = 0$$

Introducing the pressure tensor

$$p_{ij} = p_{\perp} \delta_{ij} + b_i b_j (p_{\perp} - p_{\parallel}) \qquad (8.7.2)$$

enables this to be written

$$\mathbf{b} \cdot \left[\rho \left(\frac{DV}{Dt} \right) + \nabla \cdot \mathbf{p} \right] = 0 \qquad (8.7.3)$$

Since the components of $c_{\perp}$ are periodic in the phase ϕ these moments with $\langle Df_0 \rangle$ must vanish. We may, however, form the moments with $\frac{1}{2} c_{\perp}^2$, thus obtaining an equation of state for the transverse pressure

$$p_{\perp} = \rho \langle c_{\perp}^2 \cos^2 \phi \rangle = \rho \langle \tfrac{1}{2} c_{\perp}^2 \rangle$$

$$\frac{Dp_{\perp}}{Dt} + \frac{\partial}{\partial x_{\parallel}} q_{\parallel}^{\perp} - \frac{2}{B} \frac{\partial B}{\partial x_{\parallel}} q_{\parallel}^{\perp} + p_{\perp}[2(\operatorname{div} \mathbf{V})_{\perp} + (\operatorname{div} \mathbf{V})_{\parallel}] = 0 \qquad (8.7.4)$$

or

$$\frac{Dp_{\perp}}{Dt} + p_{\perp}[2 \operatorname{div} \mathbf{V} - \mathbf{b} \cdot (\mathbf{b} \cdot \nabla \mathbf{V})] + \nabla \cdot (\mathbf{b} q_{\parallel}^{\perp}) - q_{\parallel}^{\perp} \frac{1}{B} \frac{\partial B}{\partial x_{\parallel}} = 0$$

where $q_{\parallel}^{\perp} = \int f \frac{1}{2} m c_{\perp}^2 c_{\parallel}$ is the flux of transverse energy along the field lines. The moments with $m c_{\parallel}^2$ are equally easily formed and there results

$$\frac{Dp_{\parallel}}{Dt} + \frac{\partial}{\partial x_{\parallel}} q_{\parallel}^{\parallel} + \frac{1}{B} \frac{\partial B}{\partial x_{\parallel}} [2 q_{\parallel}^{\perp} - q_{\parallel}^{\parallel}] + p_{\parallel}[(\operatorname{div} \mathbf{V})_{\perp} + 3(\operatorname{div} \mathbf{V})_{\parallel}] = 0$$

$$(8.7.5)$$

or

$$\frac{D}{Dt} p_{\parallel} + p_{\parallel}[(\operatorname{div} \mathbf{V})_{\perp} + 3(\operatorname{div} \mathbf{V})_{\parallel}] + \nabla \cdot q_{\parallel}^{\parallel} \mathbf{b} + \frac{2}{B} \frac{\partial B}{\partial x_{\parallel}} q_{\parallel}^{\perp} = 0$$

As might be expected, forming the moments of an undetermined function does not actually determine anything; and it will be observed, that even if $\mathbf{V}_{\perp}$ is given, the set (8.7.1)–(8.7.5) is indeterminate.

If for some reason, the fluxes of $c_{\perp}^2$, $c_{\parallel}^2$ along the field lines vanish, i.e. if $q_{\parallel}^{\parallel}$, $q_{\parallel}^{\perp} = 0$ then the equations of state become,

$$\frac{D}{Dt} p_{\perp} + p_{\perp}[2(\operatorname{div} \mathbf{V})_{\perp} + (\operatorname{div} \mathbf{V})_{\parallel}] = 0$$

$$\frac{D}{Dt} p_{\parallel} + p_{\parallel}[(\operatorname{div} \mathbf{V})_{\perp} + 3(\operatorname{div} \mathbf{V})_{\parallel}] = 0 \qquad (8.7.6)$$

which are the double adiabatic equations.

To complete the equations of motion, we need an equation specifying the time development of $\mathbf{V}_\perp$, but as we know already, this requires the presence of the term $\mathbf{j} \times \mathbf{B}$, which is of order $(eB/m) \int fmc_\perp$, i.e. of order ΩT compared to the accelerations, and for consistency this must be determined from the first order approximation to f. Since it is of the form $\int fc_\perp \cos \phi$, it requires only the inhomogeneous part of f_1; which we can easily obtain by integrating $\int \mathcal{D}f_0 \, d\phi$, and preserving the periodic part, i.e.

$$f_1 = \frac{1}{\Omega} \int d\phi \mathcal{D}f_0 - \langle \mathcal{D}f_0 \rangle = \int d\phi (\mathcal{D}f_0)$$

$$= \frac{1}{\Omega} \int d\phi \mathbf{c}_\perp \cdot \{\boldsymbol{\nabla} - \boldsymbol{\nabla}\mathbf{V} \cdot \mathbf{b}\partial/\partial c_\parallel - 2D'\mathbf{V}\partial/\partial c_\perp{}^2 + 2c_\parallel D'\mathbf{b}(\partial/\partial c_\parallel{}^2 - \partial/\partial c_\perp{}^2) +$$

$$+ 2c_\parallel \boldsymbol{\nabla}\mathbf{b} \cdot \mathbf{c}_\perp (\partial/\partial c_\parallel{}^2 - \partial/\partial c_\perp{}^2) - 2\boldsymbol{\nabla}\mathbf{V} \cdot \mathbf{c}_\perp \partial/\partial c_\perp{}^2\}f_0$$

$$= \frac{1}{\Omega} \mathbf{c} \cdot \mathbf{b}x\{\boldsymbol{\nabla} - \boldsymbol{\nabla}\mathbf{V} \cdot \mathbf{b}\partial/\partial c_\parallel - 2D'\mathbf{V}\partial/\partial c_\perp{}^2 + 2c_\parallel D'\mathbf{b}(\partial/\partial c_\parallel{}^2 - \partial/\partial c_\perp{}^2)\}f_0 +$$

$$+ \frac{1}{\Omega}cxcy\{(\partial bx/\partial x - \partial by/\partial y)c_\parallel(\partial/\partial c_\parallel{}^2 - \partial/\partial c_\perp{}^2) - (\partial Vx/\partial x - \partial Vy/\partial y)\partial/\partial c_\perp{}^2\}f_0 +$$

$$+ \frac{1}{\Omega}(cy^2 - cx^2)\{(\partial bx/\partial y + \partial by/\partial x)c_\parallel(\partial/\partial c_\parallel{}^2 - \partial/\partial c_\perp{}^2) -$$

$$- (\partial Vx/\partial y + \partial Vy/\partial x)\partial/\partial c_\parallel{}^2\}f_0 \tag{8.7.7}$$

On forming the moment of this with c_x, c_y there results

$$\rho \langle \mathbf{C} \rangle = \frac{1}{\Omega}\mathbf{b} \times \{\boldsymbol{\nabla}p_\perp + \mathbf{b} \cdot \boldsymbol{\nabla}\mathbf{b}(p_\parallel - p_\perp) - (\partial/\partial t + \mathbf{V} \cdot \boldsymbol{\nabla})\mathbf{V}\} \tag{8.7.8}$$

If we multiply this by e/m and add the equations for ions and electrons there results

$$\rho\left(\frac{D\mathbf{V}}{Dt}\right)_\perp = -\boldsymbol{\nabla}_\perp p_\perp + \frac{n}{R}(p_\perp - p_\parallel) + \mathbf{j} \times \mathbf{B}$$

or, $\mathbf{n}$ being the principal normal to the field line,

$$\rho\left(\frac{D\mathbf{V}}{Dt}\right)_{\perp} = -(\boldsymbol{\nabla}\cdot\mathbf{p})_{\perp}+\mathbf{j}\times\mathbf{B} \qquad (8.7.9)$$

so that the full magnetohydrodynamic equation becomes

$$\rho\frac{D\mathbf{V}}{Dt} = -\boldsymbol{\nabla}\cdot\mathbf{p}+\mathbf{j}\times\mathbf{B} \qquad (8.7.10)$$

where $\mathbf{j} = \{ne\langle\mathbf{c}_{\perp}\rangle\}_{+}+\{ne\langle\mathbf{c}_{\perp}\rangle\}_{-}$ and the pressures are the summed pressures of positives and negatives.

From the small Larmor radius solution to the Vlasov equation we have thus produced an unclosed magnetohydrodynamic set of equations, which in the absence of heat conduction reduces to the double adiabatic set. This, although gratifying, is scarcely surprising, for having observed that the zero order distribution function depends only on $c_{\perp}{}^2$, the form of the pressure tensor follows, while the observation that the drift velocity consists of the electric drift $\mathbf{V}_E+$ quantities that vanish with the Larmor radius, insures that $\mathbf{E}+\mathbf{V}\times\mathbf{B}=0$, the perfect conductivity law holds in lowest order.

It is possible to proceed with this development, but since the equations are not necessarily closed, it has proved more fruitful to develop a theory of equilibrium, and to frame dynamic studies as a perturbation theory about equilibrium.

8. EQUILIBRIUM THEORY

In zero order we may write equations for the equilibrium of the plasma, and in fact, using the moment equations these become just

$$0 = -\boldsymbol{\nabla}\cdot\mathbf{p}+\mathbf{j}\times\mathbf{B} \qquad (8.8.1)$$

and we first note that if $\mathbf{p}$ is isotropic, i.e. $p_{\parallel} = p_{\perp}$, this reduces to the familiar magnetohydrostatic equation. Even in this case, however, added information may be obtained by examining the equilibrium in more detail.

In the absence of electric fields, for example, there is a mean drift induced in first order which from eq. (8.7.8) is

$$\rho\mathbf{V}_1 = \mathbf{b}\times\left[\frac{1}{\Omega_+}\boldsymbol{\nabla}p_++\frac{1}{\Omega_-}\boldsymbol{\nabla}p_-\right] \qquad (8.8.2)$$

To restore the system to rest, a first order electric field $\mathbf{E}_1$ is required such that $\mathbf{E}_1-\mathbf{V}_1\times\mathbf{B}=0$, i.e. $-(\rho\mathbf{E}_1/B)=(1/\Omega_+)\boldsymbol{\nabla}_{\perp}p_++(1/\Omega)\boldsymbol{\nabla}_{\perp}p_-$, or if $m_+ = M \gg m_-$

$$-ne\mathbf{E}_1 = \boldsymbol{\nabla}_{\perp}p_+ - \frac{m}{M}\boldsymbol{\nabla}_{\perp}p_- \qquad (8.8.3)$$

hence, the ions are effectively contained not directly by the magnetic field, but by the polarization field $\mathbf{E}_1$, which drags the electrons out against the Lorentz force $ne_-\mathbf{v}_- \times \mathbf{B}$, and we reproduce the simple model of confinement presented by classical discharge theory (cf. Chapter 3).

Of possibly greater interest are the configurations of equilibrium possible when $p_\parallel \neq p_\perp$. Equation (8.8.1) then takes on the form

$$\frac{\partial p}{\partial x_\parallel} + \frac{1}{B}\frac{\partial B}{\partial x_\parallel}[p_\perp - p_\parallel] = 0 \qquad (8.8.4)$$

and

$$\mathbf{V}_\perp \cdot p_\perp + \frac{n}{R}(p_\parallel - p_\perp) = \mathbf{j} \times \mathbf{B} \qquad (8.8.5)$$

and from eq. (8.8.4) it is clear that forces now exist which act along the magnetic lines, and a gradient in pressure along the field lines is possible. This is, however, just the macroscopic representation of the confinement of a plasma in a magnetic mirror, a process which was discussed from the individual orbit view point in Chapter 7. From that discussion it is clear that the distribution function for particles trapped in a mirror must be empty in a cone extending about the field line with an angle θ_0 such that $\sin^2\theta_0(x) = B(x)/B_{max}$, and that the rate of loss of particles is proportional to the frequency with which the particles are scattered into that cone. Using the Fokker–Planck equation, this process may be expressed as a diffusion in velocity space, where however, since the diffusion coefficients depend upon the form of the distribution function (cf. eq. (8.1.11)) the problem is non-linear. It has been solved numerically and it is discovered, as might be expected, that electrons are lost much more rapidly than ions (electron collision frequency $\sqrt{[m_+/m_-]} \times$ ion collision frequency). As a result, a polarization field appears along the lines of force accelerating ions out of the system.

In view of the anisotropy of the pressure tensor, it is not obvious that confining systems need to be composed of magnetic surfaces. Indeed from eq. (8.8.4) it is clear that for a sufficiently anisotropic distribution, flux lines may leave the plasma. In spite of this, however, magnetic surfaces are still required. Instead of considering the pressure, let us consider the zero order distribution function $f_0(\mathscr{E}, \mu, \mathbf{x}_\perp)$. This may be written $f^0(\mathscr{E}, \mu, \mathbf{x})$ with the added constraint

$$(\mathbf{B} \cdot \mathbf{V})\Big|_{\mathscr{E}} f_0 = 0 \qquad (8.8.6)$$

Clearly $f_0 = $ const. defines a surface, while the constraint indicates that the coordinate of a field line lies on this surface, hence the magnetic field lines lie on surfaces. Further, as the constraint indicates that f_0 is constant on a magnetic line, the magnetic lines lie wholly within the plasma. This is only possible, however, provided that everywhere on the field line $|c_\parallel| > 0$, i.e. provided

$$\mathscr{E} - \mu B(x) - \frac{2e}{m}\phi(x) > 0 \qquad (8.8.7)$$

Where the quantity vanishes, f_0 also vanishes, but discontinuously, and its vanishing corresponds to the trapping of particles.

As a result possible plasma containment requires:

(1) Magnetic field lines lie in surfaces;
(2) If on a magnetic surface there are untrapped particles, that surface lies wholly within the plasma; while if all particles are trapped the surface may leave the plasma in a direction of increasing B. This permits trapping of plasma in either magnetic mirrors or cusps, both configurations in which the field leaves the plasma.;
(3) Since the surface of the plasma is also a magnetic surface the magnetic surfaces must be nested. (This may be violated if the field contains singular points.)

9. PERTURBATION THEORY

The perturbation theory begins from an equilibrium in which $\mathbf{V}$ vanishes, and considers $\mathbf{V}$ as the perturbation. We may write eq. (8.6.21) as

$$
\frac{\partial f}{\partial t} + c_{\|}\frac{\partial f}{\partial x_{\|}} + \frac{e}{m}E_{\|}\frac{\partial f}{\partial c_{\|}} + \frac{1}{B}\frac{\partial B}{\partial x_{\|}}c_{\|}c_{\perp}{}^2\left[\frac{\partial f}{\partial c_{\perp}{}^2} - \frac{\partial f}{\partial c_{\|}{}^2}\right]
$$

$$
+ \mathbf{V}\cdot\frac{\partial f}{\partial \mathbf{x}} - c_{\perp}{}^2(\operatorname{div}\mathbf{V})_{\perp}\frac{\partial f}{\partial c_{\perp}{}^2} - c_{\|}(\operatorname{div}\mathbf{V})_{\|}\frac{\partial f}{\partial c_{\|}}
$$

$$
- \left(\frac{\partial \mathbf{V}}{\partial t}\right)_{\|}\frac{\partial f}{\partial c_{\|}} = 0
$$

Since the unperturbed distribution is $f_0(\mathbf{x}_{\perp}, \mathscr{E}, \mu)$, it is preferable to express the derivative on a fixed flux tube and write

$$
\frac{\partial f(x_{\|}, \mathbf{x}_{\perp}, \mathscr{E}, \mu)}{\partial t} + c_{\|}\frac{\partial f(x_{\|}, \mathbf{x}_{\perp}, \mathscr{E}, \mu)}{\partial x_{\|}} = (\operatorname{div}\mathbf{V}_{\perp})c_{\perp}{}^2\frac{\partial f}{\partial c_{\perp}{}^2} + c_{\|}(\operatorname{div}\mathbf{V})_{\|}\frac{\partial f}{\partial c_{\|}}
$$

$$(8.9.1)$$

This can now be solved by observing that the L.H.S. represents the motion of particles along the field lines, hence the procedure adopted in solving Vlasov's equation is applicable. Since the linearized form of eq. (8.9.1) becomes

$$
\frac{\partial f^1}{\partial t} + c_{\|}\frac{\partial f^1}{\partial x_{\|}} = (\operatorname{div}\mathbf{V})_{\perp}c_{\perp}{}^2\frac{\partial f_0}{\partial c_{\perp}{}^2} + c_{\|}(\operatorname{div}\mathbf{V})_{\|}\frac{\partial f_0}{\partial c_{\|}}
$$

the solution, on a given flux tube, becomes

$$
f^1 = \int \mathrm{d}t'\left[(\operatorname{div}\mathbf{V})_{\perp}c_{\perp}{}^2\frac{\partial f_0}{\partial c_{\perp}{}^2} + c_{\|}(\operatorname{div}\mathbf{V})_{\|}\frac{\partial f_0}{\partial c_{\|}}\right]
$$

the trajectory integral extending along a fixed flux tube. Since $\mathbf{V}$, the electric drift gives the rate of displacement of the magnetic flux tubes, we may, by analogy with eq. (5.5.7) introduce the displacement $\boldsymbol{\xi}$ of the lines of force, whereupon the R.H.S. becomes

$$\int dt'(\operatorname{div}\dot{\boldsymbol{\xi}})_{\perp} c_{\perp}{}^2 \frac{\partial f_0}{\partial c_{\perp}{}^2} + c_{\parallel}(\operatorname{div}\dot{\boldsymbol{\xi}})_{\parallel}\frac{\partial f_0}{\partial c_{\parallel}}$$

while if we need f^1 not on a fixed flux tube, but at a fixed point, we must re-introduce the terms concealed in eq. (8.9.1), i.e.

$$f^1(x_{\perp}, \mathscr{E}, \mu) = -\, \boldsymbol{\xi}\cdot\nabla f^0 + \dot{\boldsymbol{\xi}}\cdot\hat{\mathbf{b}}\frac{\partial f^0}{\partial c_{\parallel}}$$

$$+ \int dt'\left\{\left[\operatorname{div}\frac{\partial\boldsymbol{\xi}}{\partial t}(x', t')\right]_{\perp} c_{\perp}{}^2\frac{\partial f_0}{\partial c_{\perp}{}^2} + \left(\operatorname{div}\frac{\partial\boldsymbol{\xi}}{\partial t}\right)_{\parallel} c_{\parallel}\frac{\partial f_0}{\partial c_{\parallel}}\right\} \qquad (8.9.2)$$

The significance of $(\operatorname{div}\partial\boldsymbol{\xi}/\partial t)_{\parallel}$, $(\operatorname{div}\partial\boldsymbol{\xi}/\partial t)_{\perp}$ may be made more explicit, thus

$$\left(\operatorname{div}\frac{\partial\boldsymbol{\xi}}{\partial t}\right)_{\parallel} = \mathbf{b}\cdot(\mathbf{b}\cdot\nabla)\frac{\partial\boldsymbol{\xi}}{\partial t} \quad\text{and}\quad \left(\operatorname{div}\frac{\partial\boldsymbol{\xi}}{\partial t}\right)_{\perp} = \left(\operatorname{div}\frac{\partial\boldsymbol{\xi}}{\partial t}\right) - \left(\operatorname{div}\frac{\partial\boldsymbol{\xi}}{\partial t}\right)_{\parallel}$$

At this stage, we can short-circuit a deal of analysis by observing that f^1 is required only to give us the perturbation in the pressure, the statement that to zero order in the Larmor radius the plasma behaves as a perfect conductor leaving this the only undetermined quantity in the equation of motion for the perturbation.

However, since the trajectory integrals depend on the velocities, the moments cannot be evaluated until some scheme is found for dealing with these. A further complication arises from the presence of the longitudinal field $E_{\parallel}$, which in general will be perturbed by $E_{\parallel}'$ on a displacement of the plasma, hence to the R.H.S. must be added a term $-(e/m)\cdot\int dt' E_{\parallel}'\partial f_0/\partial c_{\parallel}$, which requires knowledge of $E_{\parallel}'$. A suitable scheme for obtaining this is insistence on quasi-neutrality, i.e. by requiring

$$n_{+}' = \int f_{+}'\, \mathrm{d}^3 c = n_{-}' = \int f_{-}'\, \mathrm{d}^3 c \qquad (8.9.3)$$

however, this greatly elaborates the analysis, and in some of our examples will be omitted. Caution must be exercised in using this, for as we have seen, if the ion temperature $\ll$ electron temperatures, low-frequency longitudinal oscillations can propagate, and quasi-neutrality does not hold.

10. LOW-FREQUENCY OSCILLATIONS OF A UNIFORM MAGNETIZED PLASMA

Since the treatment of the trajectory integrals depends to some extent on the nature of the problem, we shall, as an illustration of the method, consider the oscillation of a spatially uniform plasma in a uniform magnetic field. We shall, however, have f_0 as a function of $\mathscr{E}$ and μ or equivalently (for the problem) of $c_\parallel^2$ and $c_\perp^2$.

We may now introduce oscillation in the form $\boldsymbol{\xi}(x, t) = \boldsymbol{\xi} \exp(i\mathbf{k} . \mathbf{x} + i\omega t)$ whereupon the trajectory integrals in eq. (8.9.2) become $1/[i(\omega + k_\parallel c_\parallel)]$ with the usual Landau definition. The perturbed distribution function becomes

$$f^1 = -\boldsymbol{\xi} . \boldsymbol{\nabla} f_0 + i\omega \xi_\parallel \frac{\partial f_0}{\partial c_\parallel} + \frac{i\omega}{i(\omega + k_\parallel c_\parallel)}\left[(\operatorname{div}\boldsymbol{\xi})_\perp c_\perp^2 \frac{\partial f_0}{\partial c_\perp^2} + (\operatorname{div}\boldsymbol{\xi})_\parallel c_\parallel \frac{\partial f_0}{\partial c_\parallel}\right]$$

$$(8.10.1)$$

If the variation of the unperturbed field in a wavelength is small, eq. (8.10.1) holds approximately. If in addition f_0 is a rapidly decreasing function of $c_\parallel^2$ and if the phase velocity $\omega/k_\parallel \gg \sqrt{\langle c_\parallel^2 \rangle}$, then the trajectory integrals may be approximated [cf. eq. (8.2.12)] as

$$\int \frac{1}{i(\omega + k_\parallel c_\parallel)} g(c_\parallel, c_\perp) \, \mathrm{d}^3 c \simeq \frac{1}{i\omega} \int g(c_\parallel, c_\perp) \, \mathrm{d}^3 c \qquad (8.10.2)$$

and the perturbed distribution becomes, for large enough ω,

$$f^1 \simeq -\boldsymbol{\xi} . \boldsymbol{\nabla} f_0 + (\operatorname{div}\boldsymbol{\xi})_\perp c_\perp^2 \frac{\partial f_0}{\partial c_\perp^2} + (\operatorname{div}\boldsymbol{\xi})_\parallel c_\parallel \frac{\partial f^0}{\partial c_\parallel} + i\omega \xi_\parallel \frac{\partial f^0}{\partial c_\parallel} \qquad (8.10.3)$$

We need this quantity only to calculate the perturbed pressure;

$$p_\perp^1 = -(\boldsymbol{\xi} . \boldsymbol{\nabla})p_\perp^0 - p_\perp^0[2(\operatorname{div}\boldsymbol{\xi})_\perp + (\operatorname{div}\boldsymbol{\xi})_\parallel]$$
$$p_\parallel^1 = -(\boldsymbol{\xi} . \boldsymbol{\nabla})p_\parallel^0 - p_\parallel^0[(\operatorname{div}\boldsymbol{\xi})_\perp + 3(\operatorname{div}\boldsymbol{\xi})_\parallel]$$

$$(8.10.4)$$

hence the pressure is given by the double adiabatic relations [cf. eq. (8.7.6)]. The equations of motion for the displacement $\boldsymbol{\xi}$ became

$$-\omega^2 \rho_0 \boldsymbol{\xi} = -\nabla p^1 + (\mathbf{j}^1 \times \mathbf{B}_0) \qquad (8.10.5)$$

where $\mathbf{j}^1 = 1/4\pi \operatorname{curl} \mathbf{B}^1$, and

$$\mathbf{p}^1 = p_\perp^1 \delta_{ij} + b_i^0 b_j^0 (p_\parallel^1 - p_\perp^1) + (p_\parallel^0 - p_\perp^0)[\delta b_i b_j^0 + b_i^0 \delta b_j^0] \qquad (8.10.6)$$

Since the plasma, to this order, behaves as a perfect conductor, the perturbed magnetic field becomes

$$\mathbf{B}^1 = -\boldsymbol{\xi} . \boldsymbol{\nabla} \mathbf{B}_0 - \mathbf{B}_0(\operatorname{div}\boldsymbol{\xi}) + (\mathbf{B}_0 . \boldsymbol{\nabla})\boldsymbol{\xi}_\perp \qquad (8.10.7)$$

The perturbation in the unit vector $\delta \mathbf{b}$ must be normal to $\mathbf{b}_0$ and for this case

$$\delta \mathbf{b} = (\mathbf{b}_0 . \boldsymbol{\nabla} . \boldsymbol{\xi})_\perp \qquad (8.10.8)$$

$\mathbf{j}^1 \times \mathbf{B}_0$ is evaluated exactly as in the magnetohydrodynamic case, and the components of the equation of motion become (cf. LÜST)

$$[\rho_0 \omega^2 - 3p_\parallel k_\parallel^2]\xi_\parallel = p_\perp k_\parallel (\mathbf{k}_\perp . \boldsymbol{\xi}_\perp) \qquad (8.10.9)$$

while

$$\left\{\rho_0\omega^2+k_\parallel^2\left[p_\parallel-p_\perp-\frac{B^2}{4\pi}\right]\right\}\xi_\perp$$

$$=\mathbf{k}_\perp\left[2(\mathbf{k}_\perp\cdot\boldsymbol{\xi}_\perp)\left(p_\perp+\frac{B^2}{8\pi}\right)+k_\parallel p_\perp\xi_\parallel\right] \tag{8.10.10}$$

If we introduce the parallel and perpendicular "sound velocities" $c_\parallel^2 = p_\parallel/\rho$, $c_\perp^2 = p_\perp/\rho$, the Alfvén speed $c_A^2 = B^2/4\pi\rho$, the phase velocity $V = \omega/k$, the direction of propagation θ, such that $k_\parallel = k\cos\theta$, and eliminate the $\boldsymbol{\xi}$, there results the quadratic dispersion relation

$$(V^2-3c_\parallel^2\cos^2\theta)[V^2-(c_A^2+c_\perp^2-c_\parallel^2)\cos^2\theta-(2c_\perp^2+c_A^2)\sin^2\theta]-$$

$$-c_\perp^4\sin^2\theta\cos^2\theta = 0 \tag{8.10.11}$$

If either $\sin^2\theta$ or $\cos^2\theta = 0$ this equation may be factored.

For parallel propagation, either $V^2 = 3c_\parallel^2$—which are sound waves— or $V^2 = (c_A^2+c_\perp^2-c_\parallel^2)$—which are Alfvén waves, modified by the effect of anisotropy in the pressure tensor. V^2 may be negative, hence instabilities may occur if

$$c_\parallel^2 > c_\perp^2+c_A^2 \tag{8.10.12}$$

There are the "fire hose" instabilities, which have their origin in the centrifugal acceleration $c_\parallel^2/R$ experienced by a stream of particles moving with velocity $c_\parallel$ on a trajectory with radius of curvature R.

For perpendicular propagation $V^2 = 2c_\perp^2+c_A^2$, which is the magnetosonic wave. At arbitrary angles, the full quadratic equation must be solved. If we write $V^4+bV^2+c=0$, $V^2=[-b\pm\sqrt{(b^2-4c)}]/2$, and since $b<0$, V^2 is negative if $c < 0$; i.e.

$$c_\perp^4\sin^2\theta > 3c_\parallel^2[c_A^2+c_\perp^2+c_\perp^2\sin^2\theta-c_\parallel^2\cos^2\theta] \tag{8.10.13}$$

This is most easily satisfied if $\sin^2\theta \simeq 1$, $(c_\perp^4/3c_\parallel^2) > (c_A^2+2c_\perp^2)$ or

$$p_\perp\cdot\frac{1}{6}\frac{p_\perp}{p_\parallel} > \frac{B^2}{8\pi}+p_\perp \tag{8.10.14}$$

Since at this point $V = 0$, we cannot expect this result to hold exactly, a condition for the double adiabatic approximation to be valid being $V^2/\cos^2\theta \gg c_\parallel^2$. This second instability is the mirror instability, and arises from the mirror force $(\frac{1}{2}mc_\perp^2/B)(\partial B/\partial x_\parallel)$, matter flowing into those parts of the wave where the field is weak, increasing $p_\perp$, and forcing the field lines further apart, thus further weakening the field. If the phase velocity is reduced, the most important phenomenon to occur is the appearance of an imaginary part in the Landau prescription for the integrals—and the transmitted waves are unaltered. Since the Landau term does not appear for growing waves the double-adiabatic instabilities remain.

For problems in which the system is finite and the frequency or instability growth rate small, the approximation to the trajectory integrals used in this section become invalid, and a different scheme is appropriate.

The anisotropy-instabilities, in particular the mirror-instability $p_\perp > p_\parallel$, has been demonstrated by Post. He used the high compression mirror in which a hot confined plasma could be produced by compressing radially with a magnetic field. If the plasma density is low, few collisions will occur, the compression is double adiabatic and $p_\perp$ becomes $> p_\parallel$; on the other hand, if the density is increased, the distribution will be rendered isotropic by collisions and $p_\perp \simeq p_\parallel$. In the first case instability is expected for large

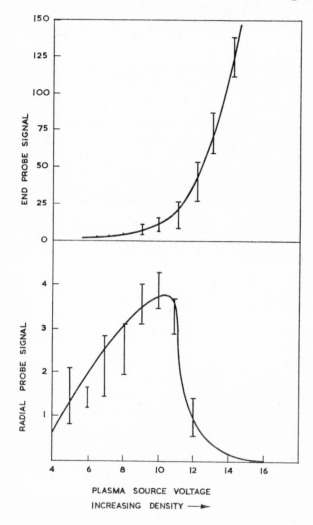

FIG. 8.2. Velocity space instability in a magnetic mirror. Radial and end probes measure rate of escape of electrons across field and through end. Plasma density increases with source voltage. At high densities, collisions keep $p_\parallel \simeq p_\perp$, plasma is stable and electrons are lost through ends. At low densities $p_\perp \gg p_\parallel$ and instabilities permit loss across field. (Post, *Phys. Rev. Letters* **6**, 25, 1961.)

enough ratios of $p_\perp/p_\parallel$. To detect instabilities electrons escaping across the mirror fields were detected by one scintillator, while those escaping along the field through the mirrors were detected by a second. The measured signals were plotted as a function of density, and the radial probe showed a signal first increasing with density then suddenly decreasing, as the condition for stability was satisfied. By measuring the energy of the escaping plasma, the plasma transverse pressure could be measured, and the axial variation of plasma density could be compared with that predicted theoretically to obtain an estimate of the isotropy. From these measurements the critical plasma pressure for the appearance of instability was estimated and found $1 \sim 4$ times that predicted by a detailed theory due to NEWCOMB.

11. STABILITY THEORY

A second important application of the perturbation theory is to the analysis of the stability of magnetically contained plasmas. Here, the growth rate of the instability is usually small, indeed, we are often interested in the problem of marginal instability, where the growth rate tends to zero. If we consider finite systems, the orbits are either periodic or nearly so, any particle may be assumed to pass close to its initial position before the perturbation grows significantly and the trajectory integral is determined by geometrical rather than kinematic considerations. (ROSENBLUTH AND ROSTOKER).

In these situations it is usual to Laplace transform the perturbation, writing it as $\xi(t) \sim \xi(p) \exp(pt)$, and the approximation we will use can be understood by considering the integral

$$\int_{-\infty}^{t} dt \exp(pt) \sin \omega t = \frac{[p \sin \omega t - \omega \cos \omega t]}{\omega^2 + p^2} \exp(pt)$$

$$\int_{t-(2\pi/\omega)}^{t} dt \exp(pt) \sin \omega t = \frac{[p \sin \omega t - \omega \cos \omega t]}{\omega^2 + p^2} \exp(pt)[1 - \exp(-2\pi p/\omega)]$$

hence

$$\int_{-\infty}^{t} dt \exp(pt) \sin \omega t = \frac{1}{1 - \exp(-2\pi p/\omega)} \int_{t-(2\pi/\omega)}^{t} dt \exp(pt) \sin \omega t$$

Since any periodic function $f(t)$ with period τ may be Fourier-analysed, this result holding for each component, we may write

$$\int_{-\infty}^{t} f(t) = \frac{1}{1 - \exp(-p\tau)} \oint f(t) \exp(pt) \, dt$$

where the integral extends over a single period. This may be approximated as

$$p \int_{-\infty}^{t} f(t) = \frac{1}{\tau} \oint f(t) \exp(pt)\, dt \tag{8.11.1}$$

If the periodicity is determined by the periodicity of the field line,

$$\tau(c_{\parallel}) = \oint dx/c_{\parallel}$$

where the periodicity is that of the field line. On the other hand, the periodicity may arise because particles are trapped between regions of high field, and

$$\tau = 2 \int_{x_1}^{x_2} \frac{dx_{\parallel}}{\sqrt{[\mathscr{E} - \mu B(x) - \phi(x)]}} \tag{8.11.2}$$

where $\phi = (-2e/m) \int E_{\parallel}\, dx_{\parallel}$ and the values of x_1, x_2 are determined by the vanishing of the denominator. The perturbed distribution function then becomes, using

$$c_{\parallel} \frac{\partial f_0}{\partial c_{\parallel}} = 2c_{\parallel}^2 \frac{\partial f_0}{\partial c_{\parallel}^2} = +2[\mathscr{E} - B\mu - \phi]\frac{\partial f_0}{\partial \mathscr{E}}$$

$$c_{\perp}^2 \frac{\partial f_0}{\partial c_{\perp}^2} = \mu \left[B\frac{\partial f_0}{\partial \mathscr{E}} + \frac{\partial f_0}{\partial \mu} \right]$$

$$f_1 = -\boldsymbol{\xi} \cdot \nabla f_0 + \frac{1}{\tau} \oint \frac{dx_{\parallel}'}{\sqrt{[\mathscr{E} - \mu B(x') - \phi(x')]}} \times$$

$$\times \left\{ (\operatorname{div} \boldsymbol{\xi})\mu \left[B\frac{\partial f_0}{\partial \mathscr{E}} + \frac{\partial f_0}{\partial \mu} \right] + 2(\operatorname{div} \boldsymbol{\xi})_{\parallel} \left[\left(\mathscr{E} - \frac{3}{2}B\mu - \phi \right)\frac{\partial f_0}{\partial \mathscr{E}} - \frac{1}{2}\mu\frac{\partial f_0}{\partial \mu} \right] \right\} \tag{8.11.3}$$

If the unperturbed distribution function is isotropic and the parallel component of the electron field negligible this simplifies to

$$f_1 = -\boldsymbol{\xi} \cdot \nabla f_0 + \frac{1}{\tau} \int \frac{dx_{\parallel}'}{\sqrt{(\mathscr{E} - B\mu)}} \left\{ (\operatorname{div} \boldsymbol{\xi})\mu B + (2\operatorname{div} \boldsymbol{\xi})_{\parallel} \left[\mathscr{E} - \frac{3}{2}B\mu \right] \right\}\frac{\partial f_0}{\partial \mathscr{E}}$$

The velocity may be removed from the integral for if $\mu/\mathscr{E} = (1/B)\sin^2\theta = \alpha$ where $c_{\parallel} = c\cos\theta$,

$$f_1 = -\boldsymbol{\xi} \cdot \boldsymbol{\nabla} f_0 + \cfrac{\mathscr{E}\, \partial f_0/\partial \mathscr{E}}{2 \displaystyle\int_{x_1}^{x_2} \cfrac{\mathrm{d}x'}{\sqrt{(1-B\alpha)}}} \times$$

$$\times \int \frac{\mathrm{d}x_\parallel{}'}{\sqrt{(1-B\alpha)}} \left\{ \mathrm{div}\, \boldsymbol{\xi} B\alpha + 2(\mathrm{div}\, \boldsymbol{\xi})_\parallel \left[1 - \frac{3}{2} B\alpha \right] \right\}$$

$$= -\boldsymbol{\xi} \cdot \boldsymbol{\nabla} f_0 + \mathscr{E} \frac{\partial f_0}{\partial \mathscr{E}} \frac{J(\mathbf{x}, \alpha, \boldsymbol{\xi})}{K(\mathbf{x}, \alpha)} = -\boldsymbol{\xi} \cdot \boldsymbol{\nabla} f_0 + f_1' \qquad (8.11.4)$$

We may now form the components of the perturbed pressure tensor

$$p' = p_0', p_\parallel', p_\perp'$$

where $p_0' = -\boldsymbol{\xi} \cdot \boldsymbol{\nabla} p_0$,

$$p_0 = \int c_x^2 f_0 \,\mathrm{d}^3 c$$

$$= \tfrac{1}{3}\pi \int \mathrm{d}\mathscr{E}(\mathscr{E})^{3/2} \sin\theta\, \mathrm{d}\theta f_0$$

$$= \tfrac{1}{3}\pi B \int \mathrm{d}\mathscr{E} \frac{\mathrm{d}\alpha}{2} \frac{(\mathscr{E})^{3/2} f_0}{\sqrt{(1-B\alpha)}} = \frac{\pi}{3} \int \mathrm{d}\mathscr{E}(\mathscr{E})^{3/2} f_0$$

and

$$p_\parallel' = \int f_1' \mathscr{E} \cos^2\theta\, \mathrm{d}\mathscr{E} \sqrt{\mathscr{E}}\, \mathrm{d}\Omega$$

$$= \frac{\pi}{2} B \int \mathrm{d}\mathscr{E}\, \mathrm{d}\alpha \frac{\sqrt{\mathscr{E}}}{\sqrt{(1-B\alpha)}} [1 - B\alpha] \mathscr{E}^2 \frac{\partial f_0}{\partial \mathscr{E}} \frac{J}{K}$$

$$= -\frac{5}{4}\pi B \int \mathrm{d}\mathscr{E} \cdot \mathscr{E}^{3/2} \cdot f_0 \int \mathrm{d}\alpha \frac{J}{K}\sqrt{(1-B\alpha)}$$

$$= -\frac{15}{2} p_0 B \int \mathrm{d}\alpha \frac{J}{K}\sqrt{(1-B\alpha)} \qquad (8.11.5)$$

$$p_\perp' = \frac{1}{2} \int f_1' \mathscr{E} \sin^2\theta \sqrt{\mathscr{E}}\, \mathrm{d}\mathscr{E}\, \mathrm{d}\Omega$$

$$= -\frac{15}{4} p_0 B^2 \int \mathrm{d}\alpha \frac{J}{K} \frac{\alpha}{\sqrt{(1-B\alpha)}} \qquad (8.11.6)$$

These quantities may now be substituted in the magnetohydrodynamic equations for the perturbation $\boldsymbol{\xi}$,

$$p^2\rho_0\boldsymbol{\xi} = \left\{\frac{1}{4\pi}[(\text{curl }\mathbf{B}_0)\times\mathbf{Q}+(\text{curl }\mathbf{Q})\times\mathbf{B}_0]+\boldsymbol{\nabla}\cdot(\boldsymbol{\xi}\cdot\boldsymbol{\nabla})p_0\right\}-$$

$$-\boldsymbol{\nabla}p_\perp'-\mathbf{b}^0[\mathbf{b}^0\cdot\boldsymbol{\nabla}(p_\perp'-p_\parallel')]-$$

$$-(p_\perp'-p_\parallel')(\mathbf{b}^0\text{ div }\mathbf{b}^0+\mathbf{b}^0\cdot\boldsymbol{\nabla}\mathbf{b}^0) \tag{8.11.7}$$

where $Q = \boldsymbol{\nabla}\times(\boldsymbol{\xi}\times\mathbf{B}_0)$ and $\mathbf{B}_0 = B_0\mathbf{b}_0$. This integro-differential equation has an extremely awkward form; however, it may be used as the starting point for the derivation of a variational principle such as was given in Chapter 6, Section 3. To do this we take the scalar product of eq. (8.11.7) with $\boldsymbol{\xi}$ and integrate. Then

$$\delta W = p^2\int\rho_0\boldsymbol{\xi}\cdot\boldsymbol{\xi} = \int\mathrm{d}v\boldsymbol{\xi}\cdot\{\tfrac{1}{4}\pi[(\text{curl }\mathbf{B}_0)\times\mathbf{Q}+(\text{curl }\mathbf{Q})\times\mathbf{B}_0]+\boldsymbol{\nabla}\cdot(\boldsymbol{\xi}\cdot\boldsymbol{\nabla})p_0\}$$

$$+\int\mathrm{d}v\boldsymbol{\xi}\cdot\boldsymbol{\nabla}[p_\perp'+(p_\parallel'-p_\perp')\mathbf{b}\cdot\mathbf{b}] \tag{8.11.8}$$

The first term here is common to this expression and the magnetohydro-dynamic energy δW, and only the last term is new. This may be trans-formed by an integration by parts to

$$\delta W_1 = -\int\mathrm{d}v[p_\perp'(\text{div }\boldsymbol{\xi})+(p_\parallel'-p_\perp')(\text{div }\boldsymbol{\xi})_\parallel] \tag{8.11.9}$$

and we must now use the expressions for eq. (8.11.5) and (8.11.6).

The integrals may be simplified if the volume is split into flux tubes, as was done in Chapter 6, Section 2 in the discussion of interchange instabilities, and

$$\mathrm{d}^3x = \int\mathrm{d}\phi(\mathbf{x}_\perp)\int\frac{\mathrm{d}x_\parallel}{B}$$

whereupon

$$\delta W_1 = +\frac{15}{2}\int\mathrm{d}\phi p_0\int\frac{\mathrm{d}x_\parallel}{B}B\int\mathrm{d}\alpha\frac{J(\mathbf{x},\alpha,\boldsymbol{\xi})}{K(x,\mathbf{x})}\times$$

$$\times\left\{\frac{1}{2}\frac{B\alpha}{\sqrt{(1-B\alpha)}}\text{ div }\boldsymbol{\xi}+\left[\sqrt{(1-B\alpha)}-\frac{1}{2}\frac{B\alpha}{\sqrt{(1-B\alpha)}}\right](\text{div }\boldsymbol{\xi})_\parallel\right\}$$

$$=\frac{15}{2}\int\mathrm{d}\phi p_0\int\mathrm{d}x_\parallel\int\mathrm{d}\alpha\frac{J(\mathbf{x},\alpha,\boldsymbol{\xi})}{K}\left[\frac{\tfrac{1}{2}B\alpha\text{ div }\boldsymbol{\xi}+(1-\tfrac{3}{2}B\alpha)(\text{div }\boldsymbol{\xi})_\parallel}{\sqrt{(1-B\alpha)}}\right]$$

and observing that the function $J(\alpha)$ is specified by $x_\perp$ we may interchange the order of the $\mathrm{d}\alpha$ and $\mathrm{d}x_\parallel$ integrals, whereupon the inner integral becomes

$$\int\frac{\mathrm{d}x_\parallel}{\sqrt{(1-B\alpha)}}[\tfrac{1}{2}B\alpha\text{ div }\boldsymbol{\xi}+(1-\tfrac{3}{2}B\alpha)(\text{div }\boldsymbol{\xi})_\parallel] = J(\mathbf{x},\alpha)$$

hence

$$\delta W_1 = +\frac{15}{2} \int \mathrm{d}\phi p_0 \int \mathrm{d}\alpha \frac{J^2(\phi, \alpha, \xi)}{K(\phi, \alpha)} \tag{8.11.10}$$

Using this form an important result has been established by ROSENBLUTH and ROSTOKER; and, using more direct methods, by OBERMAN and KRUSKAL. This makes use of the Schwartz inequality

$$\int f^2 \, \mathrm{d}x \int g^2 \, \mathrm{d}x \geqslant [\int fg \, \mathrm{d}x]^2$$

If this is applied to

$$\int \left(\frac{J}{\sqrt{K}}\right)^2 \mathrm{d}\alpha \cdot \int (\sqrt{K})^2 \, \mathrm{d}\alpha \geqslant \left[\int J \mathrm{d}\alpha\right]^2$$

$$\int \frac{J^2}{K} \, \mathrm{d}\alpha \geqslant \frac{[\int J \, \mathrm{d}\alpha]^2}{\int K \, \mathrm{d}\alpha}$$

But

$$\int J \, \mathrm{d}\alpha = \tfrac{2}{3} \int \frac{1}{B} (\mathrm{div}\,\xi) \, \mathrm{d}x_\parallel$$

$$\int K \, \mathrm{d}\alpha = \frac{2}{B}$$

and

$$\delta W_1 \geqslant +\frac{15}{2} \cdot \frac{1}{3} \int \mathrm{d}\tau p_0 \langle \mathrm{div}\,\xi \rangle^2 = +\frac{5}{2} \int \mathrm{d}\tau p_0 \langle \mathrm{div}\,\xi \rangle^2$$

where

$$\langle \mathrm{div}\,\xi \rangle = \int (\mathrm{div}\,\xi) \frac{\mathrm{d}x_\parallel}{B} \left(\int \frac{\mathrm{d}x_\parallel}{B} \right)^{-1}$$

This, however, is just the contribution of the perturbed pressure to the magnetohydrodynamic energy, and we may assert,

$$\delta W_p \geqslant \delta W_H \tag{8.11.11}$$

hence, if a plasma with an initially isotropic distribution is magnetohydrodynamically stable, it is stable in the kinetic picture.

On the other hand, we may use the Schwartz inequality in the other direction, and obtain an upper bound for δW_p.

We may write

$$\frac{J^2}{K} \leqslant \int \frac{\{[1 - \tfrac{3}{2} B'\alpha](\mathrm{div}\,\xi)_\parallel + \tfrac{1}{2} B'\alpha \,\mathrm{div}\,\xi\}^2}{\sqrt{(1 - \alpha B')}} \, \mathrm{d}x_\parallel$$

The $d\alpha$ integrations may now be carried through, and there results

$$\frac{1}{15} \int \frac{dx_\parallel}{B} [6(\operatorname{div} \boldsymbol{\xi})_\parallel{}^2 - 4(\operatorname{div} \boldsymbol{\xi})(\operatorname{div} \boldsymbol{\xi})_\parallel + 4(\operatorname{div} \boldsymbol{\xi})^2]$$

hence

$$\delta W_p \leqslant \int d^3 x p_0 [2(\operatorname{div} \boldsymbol{\xi})^2 - 2(\operatorname{div} \boldsymbol{\xi})_\parallel \operatorname{div} \boldsymbol{\xi} + 3(\operatorname{div} \boldsymbol{\xi})_\parallel{}^2]$$

The integrands may be written

$$p_0[2(\operatorname{div} \boldsymbol{\xi}_\perp)^2 + 2(\operatorname{div} \boldsymbol{\xi})_\parallel (\operatorname{div} \boldsymbol{\xi})_\perp + 3(\operatorname{div} \boldsymbol{\xi})_\parallel{}^2]$$
$$= p_0[2 \operatorname{div} \boldsymbol{\xi}_\perp + (\operatorname{div} \boldsymbol{\xi})_\parallel](\operatorname{div} \boldsymbol{\xi}_\perp) + p_0[\operatorname{div} \boldsymbol{\xi}_\perp + 3 \operatorname{div} \boldsymbol{\xi}_\parallel](\operatorname{div} \boldsymbol{\xi})_\parallel$$

and on a partial integration, as

$$- \int d^3 x \left\{ \boldsymbol{\xi}_\perp \cdot \nabla_\perp p_0[2 \operatorname{div} \boldsymbol{\xi}_\perp + (\operatorname{div} \boldsymbol{\xi})_\parallel] + \xi_\parallel \frac{\partial}{\partial x_\parallel} p_0[\operatorname{div} \boldsymbol{\xi}_\parallel + 3(\operatorname{div} \boldsymbol{\xi})_\perp] \right\}$$

This, however, is exactly the form taken by the pressure contribution to the energy integral formed with the double adiabatic equation of state, δW_D, hence

$$\delta W_p \leqslant \delta W_D \tag{8.11.12}$$

The important consequence of this theorem is if a plasma has an isotropic velocity distribution when unperturbed, then, if it is stable using the magnetohydrodynamic equations with scalar pressures, it is stable in the small Larmor radius limit. If it is unstable using the double adiabatic equations, it is unstable in the small Larmor radius limit.

With this result we will conclude our formal excursion into the kinetic theory of plasma. But by way of a conclusion, I will mention some further developments of the theory.

12. FURTHER DEVELOPMENTS OF THE KINETIC THEORY

The small Larmor radius expansion permits the deduction of double adiabatic hydrodynamics in appropriate limits, and one's first question may be, by the analogy with the kinetic theory of ionized gases, to ask what is the next approximation to magnetohydrodynamic phenomena, i.e. the small Larmor radius analogues of the Navier–Stokes equation. Such a programme may be carried out at the cost of a great deal of algebra, however, some results are quite readily obtained. The first order contributions to the off-diagonal components of the pressure tensor, and to the components of the heat flux vector across the lines of force may be calculated just from the inhomogeneous part of f^1 which we have already determined. Forming $\langle c_\parallel c_\perp \cos \phi \rangle$, $\langle c_\parallel c_\perp \sin \phi \rangle$ and $\langle c_\perp{}^2 \cos \phi \sin \phi \rangle$ we obtain

$$p_{xz} = -\frac{p_\perp}{\Omega}\left(\frac{\partial V_y}{\partial z} + \frac{\partial V_z}{\partial y}\right)$$

$$p_{yz} = \frac{p_\perp}{\Omega}\left(\frac{\partial V_x}{\partial z} + \frac{\partial V_z}{\partial x}\right)$$

$$p_{xy} = p_{yx} = \frac{1}{2}\frac{p_\perp}{\Omega}\left(\frac{\partial V_x}{\partial x} - \frac{\partial V_y}{\partial y}\right)$$

(8.12.1)

Since $\Omega_+ \ll \Omega_-$ it is the ions which contribute most effectively to this. The heat transfer vector requires terms

$$\mathbf{q}_\perp{}^\perp = \langle n\tfrac{1}{2}mc_\perp{}^2\mathbf{c}_\perp\rangle, \qquad \mathbf{q}_\perp{}^\| = \langle n\tfrac{1}{2}mc_\|{}^2\mathbf{c}_\perp\rangle$$

For the ions and electrons separately we obtain

$$\mathbf{q}_\perp{}^\perp = \frac{1}{\Omega}\left\{\mathbf{b}\times\boldsymbol{\nabla}\rho\langle\tfrac{1}{4}c_\perp{}^4\rangle + 2p_\perp\mathbf{b}\times\frac{D\mathbf{V}}{Dt} + \frac{\mathbf{b}\times\mathbf{n}}{R}\rho[\langle c_\|{}^2c_\perp{}^2\rangle - \langle\tfrac{1}{4}c_\perp{}^4\rangle]\right\}$$

or on eliminating $D\mathbf{V}/Dt$ by means of the equations of motion.

$$q_\perp{}^\perp = \frac{1}{eB}\left\{\mathbf{b}\times\boldsymbol{\nabla}[\tfrac{1}{4}nm^2\langle c_\perp{}^4\rangle] - \frac{m^2}{m_T}\langle c_\perp{}^2\rangle\left[\mathbf{b}\times\left(\boldsymbol{\nabla}p_\perp + \frac{\mathbf{n}}{R}p_\|\right)\right] - \frac{\mathbf{j}m^2}{\rho m_T}\langle c_\perp{}^2\rangle\right.$$

$$\left. + \frac{\mathbf{b}\times\mathbf{n}}{R}nm^2[\langle c_\|{}^2c_\perp{}^2\rangle - \tfrac{1}{4}\langle c_\perp{}^4\rangle]\right\}$$

(8.12.2)

$$q_\perp{}^\| = \frac{1}{eB}\left\{\mathbf{b}\times\boldsymbol{\nabla}\frac{n}{2}m^2\langle c_\|{}^2c_\perp{}^2\rangle - \frac{m^2}{m_T}\langle c_\perp{}^2\rangle\left[\mathbf{b}\times\left(\boldsymbol{\nabla}p_\perp + \frac{\mathbf{n}}{R}p_\|\right)\right]\right.$$

$$\left. + \frac{\mathbf{b}\times\mathbf{n}}{R}nm^2[\langle c_\|{}^4\rangle - \tfrac{3}{2}\langle c_\|{}^2c_\perp{}^2\rangle] - \frac{\mathbf{j}}{\rho}\frac{m^2}{m_T}\langle c_\perp{}^2\rangle\right\}$$

(8.12.3)

where $m_T = m_+ + m_-$ while m, e and the moments must be evaluated for each component separately. Note that the heat transport depends on the fourth moments of c with respect to the zero-order distribution function f_0, and those quantities are not determined by the collisionless equation, a respect in which its generality is a little too great. If, however, we take f_0 as Maxwellian in $c_\|{}^2$ and $c_\perp{}^2$, i.e.

$$f_0 \sim \exp\left[-\frac{\tfrac{1}{2}mc_\perp{}^2}{kT_\perp} - \frac{\tfrac{1}{2}mc_\|{}^2}{kT_\|}\right]$$

$$q_-{}^\perp = -\frac{2nkT_\perp{}^-}{eB}\mathbf{b}\times\boldsymbol{\nabla}(kT_\perp{}^-) - \frac{2kT_\perp{}^-}{eB}\left\{\mathbf{b}\times\left[\boldsymbol{\nabla}p_\perp{}^- + \frac{\mathbf{n}}{R}(p_\|{}^- - p_\perp{}^-)\right]\right\}$$

(8.12.4)

$$q_+{}^\perp = \frac{2nkT_\perp{}^+}{eB}\mathbf{b}\times\boldsymbol{\nabla}(kT_\perp{}^+) - \frac{2kT_\perp{}^+}{eB}\cdot\mathbf{b}\times\left[\boldsymbol{\nabla}p_\perp + \frac{\mathbf{n}}{R}nk(T_\|{}^+ - T_\|{}^- - T_\perp{}^+)\right] - \mathbf{j}\frac{kT_\perp{}^+}{e}$$

If the distributions are identical functions of the energy

$$q_{\parallel,\perp} = \frac{p^+{}_{\parallel,\perp}}{\Omega_+} \mathbf{b} \times \frac{D\mathbf{V}}{Dt} \tag{8.12.5}$$

and for a stationary system, vanishes in this approximation.

In first order an important change occurs in the relations defining $\mathbf{j}$. In zero order no such definition was required, since the zero order drift velocity $\mathbf{V}_0$ satisfied

$$\mathbf{E} + \mathbf{V}_0 \times \mathbf{B} = 0 \tag{8.12.6}$$

In first order, however, we must add to the drift velocity of positives and negatives separately, the first order drift

$$\rho \mathbf{v}^1 = \frac{1}{\Omega}\left\{ \mathbf{b} \times \left[\boldsymbol{\nabla} p_\perp + \rho \frac{D\mathbf{V}_0}{Dt} + p_\parallel \frac{\mathbf{n}}{R} \right] \right\} \tag{8.12.7}$$

Since, in particular, $1/\Omega$ is not the same for each class of particle, it is clear that the drift velocity of the gas as a whole differs from the drift velocity of the individual components. In fact, using the zero-order equations of motion

$$\rho \mathbf{v}_1 = \frac{1}{\Omega_+}\left\{ \mathbf{b} \times [\mathbf{j} \times \mathbf{B} - \boldsymbol{\nabla} \cdot p_-] - \frac{m_-}{m_+} \mathbf{b} \times [\mathbf{j} \times \mathbf{B} - \boldsymbol{\nabla} \cdot p_+] \right\}$$

and when this is added to the drift velocity $\mathbf{V}_0$ to form the drift velocity correct to first order, $\mathbf{V}_0 + \mathbf{V}_1 = \mathbf{U}$,

$$\mathbf{E} + \mathbf{U} \times \mathbf{B} + \frac{1}{ne}[\boldsymbol{\nabla} \cdot p_- - \mathbf{j} \times \mathbf{B}] = 0 \tag{8.12.8}$$

and the plasma no longer appears ohmic in this order.

(a) *Collisional Effects*

Provided the plasma remains stable, and the density is not too low (i.e. if $nmc^2/B^2 > 1$), the arguments in Section 8.3 justify the use of the Boltzmann representation of particle interaction even although the concept of independent binary encounters has a somewhat unusual significance.

An alternative form of magnetohydrodynamics may be derived by retaining the effect of collisions, but considering these as a perturbation about the small Larmor radius theory. The difficulty in carrying out such a programme lies in the incomplete specification of f_0; however, this approach is most useful in the study of the slow motions of a stable plasma produced by finite transport processes, and in such situations, the collision frequency τ^{-1} usually much greater than the characteristic hydrodynamic frequencies T^{-1}, although less than the gyrofrequency Ω, and it is reasonable to assume a zero-order distribution of the Maxwellian form,

$$f_0 = n(x, t)\left(\frac{m}{2\pi kT}\right)^{3/2} \exp\left[-\frac{\frac{1}{2}m[\mathbf{v} - \mathbf{U}(x, t)]^2}{kT(x, t)} \right]$$

With such a starting point, however, the Chapman and Cowling expansion procedure should be valid. If we insert this expression in the equation

$$\Omega \mathbf{c} \times \mathbf{b} . \frac{\partial f_0}{\partial \mathbf{c}} = \mathscr{I}(f_0, f_0)$$

it is satisfied, for since $f_0(c^2)$ when $\mathbf{c} = \mathbf{v} - \mathbf{U}$, the L.S. vanishes, while $\mathscr{I}(f_0, f_0)$ vanishes for a Maxwell distribution. Writing the full B.E. in the Chapman and Cowling form, i.e.

$$\epsilon D'f = -\Omega \mathbf{c} \times \mathbf{b} . \frac{\partial f}{\partial \mathbf{c}} + \mathscr{I}(f, f) \tag{8.12.9}$$

and

$$f = f_0(1 + \epsilon \phi + \ldots)$$

we obtain a first order equation for ϕ in the form (for electrons and ions),

$$f_0 \left\{ 2[W_i W_j - \frac{1}{3}\delta_{ij} W^2] \frac{\partial U_i}{\partial x_j} - [\frac{5}{2} - W^2]\mathbf{c} . \nabla \log T + \frac{n_T}{n_{+,-}} \mathbf{c} . \mathbf{d} \right\}$$

$$= f_0 \frac{m}{2kT} \frac{\mathbf{c}}{m} \left\{ \sum_{+,-} e_{+,-} \int d^3 v f_0 \phi_+ - \mathbf{c} \times \mathbf{B} \right\} - f^0 \left(\frac{e}{m} \right) \mathbf{W} \times \mathbf{B} . \frac{\partial \phi}{\partial \mathbf{W}}$$

$$+ \sum_{+,-} \int d^3 \mathbf{v}_1 \, d\Omega \sigma g f_0(\mathbf{v}) f_0(\mathbf{v}_1)[\phi(\mathbf{v}') + \phi_{+,-}(\mathbf{v}_1') - \phi(\mathbf{v}) - \phi_{+,-}(\mathbf{v}_1)]$$

where

$$\mathbf{d}_+ = \mathbf{d}_- = \nabla \frac{n_+}{n} + \frac{n_+ n_-(m_+ - m_-)}{p\rho} \nabla p - \frac{n_+ n_-}{p\rho}[e^+ m_- - e_- m_+][\mathbf{E} + \mathbf{U} \times \mathbf{B}]$$

and

$$\mathbf{W} = \sqrt{\left(\frac{m}{2kT} \right)} \mathbf{c}$$

In deriving this equation the zero-order magnetohydrodynamic equations have been used (adiabatic, perfect conductivity, scalar pressure), the last two terms on the right representing the R.H.S. of eq. (9.12.8), while the first sum is simply the term arising from $\mathbf{j} \times \mathbf{B}$ when $(\partial f_0/\partial \mathbf{c}) . \mathbf{c} . (D\mathbf{U}/Dt)$ has been relieved of its time derivative.

To solve eq. (8.12.9) the unknown function ϕ is written as

$$\phi = B_{ij} \frac{\partial U_i}{\partial X_j} + A_i \frac{\partial}{\partial x_i} \log T + E_i . \mathbf{d}_i$$

and the tensor $\mathbf{B}$ and vectors $\mathbf{A}$ and $\mathbf{E}$ represented in terms of the available vectors and tensors, e.g.

$$\mathbf{A} = \mathscr{A}^{\mathrm{I}}(w^2)\mathbf{W} + \mathscr{A}^{\mathrm{II}}(w^2)(\mathbf{B} \times \mathbf{W}) + \mathscr{A}^{\mathrm{III}}(w^2)\mathbf{B}(\mathbf{B} . \mathbf{W})$$

since $\mathbf{B}$ does not have the same vector character as $\nabla \log T$. With these substitutions there remains the problem of finding the scalars $\mathscr{A}^{\mathrm{I}} \ldots$, etc.

For this purpose, these quantities are expanded in a set of polynomials $S_n{}^m$, orthogonal with respect to f_0, i.e. The Sonine polynomials

$$\int \exp(-x^2)x^{2n+1}S_n{}^m S_n{}^{m'}(x^2) = \delta m, m' . \frac{1}{2} \frac{(n+m)!}{m!}$$

Thus $\mathscr{A} = a_0 S^0{}_{3/2} + a_1 S^1{}_{3/2} + \ldots$, and algebraic equations are derived for the coefficients a_i, either by terminating the series, or employing some variational procedure. The moments of hydrodynamic interest require a knowledge only of the lowest coefficients.

When moments are finally formed, the transport coefficients have a rather elaborate form, thus MARSHALL has found for the electric current

$$\mathbf{j} = \sigma^{\mathrm{I}}(\mathbf{D} \cdot \mathbf{b})\mathbf{b} + \sigma^{\mathrm{II}}(\mathbf{D} - \mathbf{D}_\| \mathbf{b}) + \sigma^{\mathrm{III}}\mathbf{b} \times \mathbf{D} +$$
$$+ \phi^{\mathrm{I}}(\mathbf{b} \cdot \nabla T)\mathbf{b} + \phi^{\mathrm{II}}[\nabla - \mathbf{b} \cdot (\mathbf{b} \cdot \nabla)]T + \phi^{\mathrm{III}}\mathbf{b} \times \nabla T \quad (8.12.10)$$

where

$$\mathbf{D} = \mathbf{E} + \mathbf{U} \times \mathbf{B} + \frac{1}{ne}\nabla p - \frac{m}{e}(\mathbf{X}_- - \mathbf{X}_+)$$

$\mathbf{X}$ being the non-electric force; while

$$\mathbf{q} = -\lambda^{\mathrm{I}}(\nabla T)_\| - \lambda^{\mathrm{II}}(\nabla T)_\perp - \lambda^{\mathrm{III}}\mathbf{b} \times \nabla T +$$
$$+ \psi^{\mathrm{I}}\mathbf{j}_\| + \psi^{\mathrm{II}}\mathbf{j}_\perp + \psi^{\mathrm{III}}\mathbf{b} \times \mathbf{j} \quad (8.12.11)$$

where

$$\nabla_\| = \mathbf{b}(\mathbf{b} \cdot \nabla)$$

and

$$\nabla_\perp = \nabla - \nabla_\|$$

Finally, the pressure tensor is expressed in terms of a divergenceless symmetric tensor formed from the velocity gradients

$$S_{ij} = \frac{1}{2}\left(\frac{\partial V_i}{\partial x_j} + \frac{\partial V_j}{\partial x_i}\right) - \frac{1}{3}\delta_{ij} \operatorname{div} \mathbf{V} \quad (8.12.12)$$

If the magnetic field is along OX, we obtain

$$p_{xx} = p - 2\mu S_{xx} \quad (8.12.13$$

$$p_{yy} = p - \frac{2\mu}{1 + \frac{16}{9}\Omega_+^2 \tau_+^2}\{S_{yy} + \frac{8}{9}(\Omega_+\tau_+)^2(S_{yy} + S_{zz}) + \frac{4}{3}(\Omega_+\tau_+)S_{yz}\}$$

$$p_{zz} = p - \frac{2\mu}{1 + \frac{16}{9}\Omega_+^2 \tau_+^2}\{S_{zz} + \frac{8}{9}(\Omega_+\tau_+)^2(S_{yy} + S_{zz}) - \frac{4}{3}(\Omega_+\tau)S_{yz}\}$$

$$p_{xy} = p_{yx} = -\frac{2\mu}{1+\frac{4}{9}\Omega_+^2\tau_+^2}\{S_{xy}+\tfrac{2}{3}\omega_+\tau_+S_{xz}\}$$

$$p_{xz} = p_{zx} = -\frac{2\mu}{1+\frac{4}{9}\Omega_+^2\tau_+^2}\{S_{xz}-\tfrac{2}{3}\omega_+\tau_+S_{xy}\}$$

$$p_{yz} = p_{zy} = \frac{2\mu}{1+\frac{4}{9}\Omega_+^2\tau_+^2}\{S_{yx}-\tfrac{2}{3}\omega_+\tau_+(S_{yy}-S_{zz})\}$$

The coefficients become, with the collision frequencies,

$$\frac{1}{\tau_-} = \frac{\sqrt{(2\pi)}}{3\sqrt{m_-}}\frac{ne^4}{(kT)^{3/2}}\log\Lambda, \qquad \tau_+ = \frac{5}{2\sqrt{2}}\sqrt{\left(\frac{m_+}{m_-}\right)}\tau_-$$

and further definition

$$\sigma_0 = \frac{ne^2}{m_-}\tau_- \qquad\qquad \phi_0 = \frac{nek\tau_-}{m} = \frac{k}{e}\sigma_0$$

$$\lambda_0 = \frac{nk^2T}{m_-}\tau_- = \sigma_0\frac{k^2T}{e^2} \qquad\qquad \psi_0 = \frac{kT}{e}$$

$$\mu = \tfrac{1}{3}nkT\tau_+ \qquad r = \Omega_-\tau_- \qquad M_- = \frac{m_-}{m_-+m_+}$$

$$\Delta_1 = r^4+6\cdot28r^2+0\cdot933, \qquad\qquad \Delta_2 = r^4+16\cdot20r^2+44\cdot3$$

$$\Delta_3 = r^2M_-+9M_-+3\cdot39\sqrt{M_-}+0\cdot32, \quad \Delta_4 = r^2+3\cdot48, \quad \Delta_5 = r^2+12\cdot716$$

$$\sigma^{\mathrm{I}} = \sigma_0\frac{1\cdot93}{2} \qquad\qquad \phi^{\mathrm{I}} = \phi_0 0\cdot777$$

$$\sigma^{\mathrm{II}} = \frac{\sigma_0}{2\Delta_1}(r^2+1\cdot802) \qquad \phi^{\mathrm{II}} = -\phi_0\frac{0\cdot75}{\Delta_1}(r^2-0\cdot966) \qquad (8.12.15)$$

$$\sigma^{\mathrm{III}} = -\frac{\sigma_0}{2\Delta_1}r(r^2+4\cdot382) \quad \phi^{\mathrm{III}} = -\phi_0\frac{2\cdot15}{\Delta_1}r$$

$$\lambda^{\mathrm{I}} = \lambda_0 1\cdot02 \qquad\qquad\qquad\qquad\qquad \psi^1 = \psi_0 3\cdot305$$

$$\lambda^{\mathrm{II}} = 1\cdot25\lambda_0\left[\frac{3M_-+0\cdot566\sqrt{M_-}}{\Delta_3}-\frac{3\cdot566}{\Delta_5}+\frac{5\cdot43r^2+36\cdot1}{\Delta_2}\right] \quad \psi^{\mathrm{II}} = \psi_0\frac{2\cdot5r^2+11\cdot5}{\Delta_4}$$

$$\lambda^{\mathrm{III}} = 1\cdot25\lambda_0\left[\frac{rM_-}{\Delta_3}-\frac{r}{\Delta_5}-\frac{9\cdot28r}{\Delta_2}\right] \qquad\qquad\qquad \psi^{\mathrm{III}} = \psi_0\frac{1\cdot5r}{\Delta_4}$$

$$(8.12.16)$$

In the limit of strong fields (large r) these quantities approach

$$\sigma^{\mathrm{III}} \to \frac{ne^2}{2m_-\Omega_-}$$

$$\psi^{\mathrm{II}} \to 2\cdot5\psi_0$$

$$\lambda^{\mathrm{II}} \to 1\cdot25 \times 0\cdot566 \sqrt{\left(\frac{m_+}{m_-}\right)} \frac{\lambda_0}{(\Omega\tau)_-^2} = 0\cdot707\frac{nkT}{m_+} \frac{\tau_+}{(\Omega\tau)_+^2}k \quad (8.12.17)$$

and

$$p_{yy} - p_{zz} \to \frac{kT}{\Omega_+}S_{yz}$$

$$p_{xy} \to -\frac{kT}{\Omega_+}S_{xz}$$

$$p_{xz} \to \frac{kT}{\Omega_+}S_{xy}$$

$$p_{yz} \to \frac{1}{4}\frac{kT}{\Omega_+}(S_{yy} - S_{zz})$$

The transport coefficients in a magnetic field are surprisingly difficult to investigate. Measurements of the electrical conductivity were mentioned in Chapters 2 and 3 in describing the production of plasma in shock tubes, but the effects of magnetic fields on transport effects are more difficult to determine. Evidence is provided by the experiment of POST, ELLIS et al., in which the plasma profile in a mirror field, as determined by the escaping plasma, had the shape predicted by diffusion theory.

Recently D'ANGELO and RYNN have investigated the diffusion of cold caesium plasma across a strong magnetic field. Theoretical analysis predicts a diffusion coefficient

$$D_\perp = \frac{2\eta kT}{B^2}n,$$

and in the presence of recombination (coefficient α), a radial density distribution $n(r) = K_0(r/R)$, where $1/R = (2\alpha n/D_\perp)^{1/2} = B(\alpha/nkT)^{1/2}$. The plasma was produced by bombarding a hot tungsten plate with caesium atoms from an atomic beam furnace, the caesium ionizing since its ionization potential lies below the tungsten work function; and by holding down the neutral background, 99 per cent ionization was produced. The density was measured by Langmuir probes, the scale R inferred, and plotted against B, proving approximately linear. Numerical agreement requires knowledge of α which is doubtful but $D_\perp$ appeared of the right order.

(b) *The Breakdown of Collective Behaviour—Electron Run-away*

We have so far said little about the relation between a plasma and a neutralized beam of electrons. One constraint on the density is implied by our assumption of screening, since in the absence of collisions the skin depth d is given by $4\pi ne^2 d^2/mc^2 = 4\pi n r_0 d^2 = 1$; while in a magnetic field we have frequently required $nmc^2/B^2 \gg 1$.

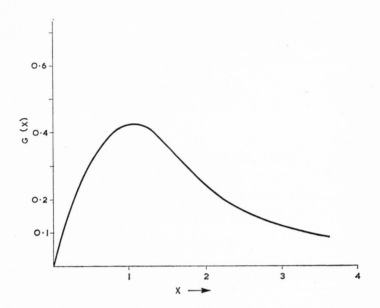

FIG. 8.3. Origin of electron run away. Friction is proportional to $G\,(v/v_\theta)$, for small velocities v, but for $v > v_\theta$ decreases with velocity; hence particles moving rapidly in a strong electric field are unstable against increase in drift speed.

To develop collisionless magnetohydrodynamics, we found it necessary to apply a constraint to the component of the electric field parallel to the electric field $E_\parallel$; namely, that $eE_\parallel/m \ll \sqrt{(\langle v_\parallel^2 \rangle)}/\Omega$ since otherwise the acceleration of electrons along the magnetic field line dominates the behaviour of the plasma, and its cohesive properties are lost.

Even if collisions are important, there is a similar constraint on the parallel electric field, for, if we use eq. (8.3.15) to calculate the drag on an electron we obtain (allowing for the ions)

$$D(v) = \frac{8\pi ne^4 \log \Lambda}{mkT} \left[G\left(\frac{v}{v_\theta^-}\right) + \tfrac{1}{2}G\left(\frac{v}{v_\theta^+}\right) \right] \qquad (8.12.18)$$

and the equations of mean motion for an individual electron takes the form

$$\dot{u} = \frac{e}{m}E - D(u)\left[\frac{\mathbf{u}}{u}\right] \qquad (8.12.19)$$

This permits an equilibrium velocity u_0 for which

$$\frac{e}{m}E = D(u_0) \tag{8.12.20}$$

To investigate the stability of this equilibrium we may linearize eq. (8.12.19) about u_0

$$\delta\dot{u} = \frac{e}{m}E - D(u+\delta u)\frac{u+\delta u}{|u+\delta u|}$$

and for the one-dimensional problem

$$\delta\dot{u} = -\left.\frac{\partial D}{\partial u}\right|_{u_0}\delta u \tag{8.12.21}$$

If $\partial D/\partial u > 0$, an initial disturbance will die away; however, if $\partial D/\partial u < 0$, any departure from equilibrium will grow, and in particular a particle's velocity may increase without limit, thus raising the possibility of electrons streaming through the plasma.

The function

$$G(x) = \left[\frac{2}{\sqrt{\pi}}\int_0^x \exp(-t^2)\,dt - x\exp(-x^2)\right]\bigg/2x^2$$

$$\sim \frac{2}{3\sqrt{\pi}}x$$

for small x

$$\sim \frac{1}{x^2}\times\frac{1}{2}$$

for large x

and G has a maximum for $x \simeq 1$, where its value is $\sim 0\cdot22$. From this it is clear that if the electron drift velocity is large, the electrons may form a beam, and move freely through the plasma.

From eq. (8.12.18) there are two maxima in $D(v)$, one near $v = v_\theta{}^+$, where the electrons are retarded by collisions with ions, and this is clearly the maximum which is important for normal ohmic conductivity where the entire electron gas moves through the ions. The second maximum at $v = v_\theta{}^-$ becomes relevant if electrons are accelerated by local electric fields (i.e. along particular magnetically determined lines and pass through a plasma, not merely an ion gas). In both cases, the critical electric field is approximately given by

$$eE = \frac{8\pi ne^4}{(kT)^2}\log\Lambda\,.\,kT\,.\,G_0$$

or

$$eE\lambda = kT\,.\,G_0 \tag{8.12.22}$$

G_0 being ~ 0.1 for the first case, $v_D = v_\theta{}^+$, ~ 0.2 for the second case $v_D = v_\theta{}^-$, and λ being the mean free path

$$\lambda = \frac{1}{n \cdot 8\pi e^4 \log \Lambda/(kT)^2}$$

A more careful study involving the numerical solutions of the Fokker–Planck equation shows how the runaway beam develops in velocity space, but does not greatly alter the conditions for its appearance.

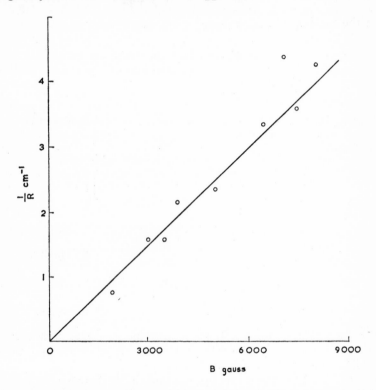

FIG. 8.4. Evidence for classical diffusion. Caesium plasma diffuses across field while ions and electrons recombine. Half width R of diffusion ions is determined by diffusion coefficient, $R^2 \infty D$, but $D \infty 1/B^2$ hence $1/R \infty B$. (d'Angelo and Ryan, *Phys. Fluids* **4**, 275, 1961.)

Runaway electrons plague all containing devices with shearing fields. They make themselves felt by a copious production of X-rays, and have been observed both in the stellerator (see Coor *et al.*) and in pinch devices (see Butt *et al.*). Energies exceed 100 keV, and production is often associated with sudden changes in the current density, and has been blamed for the sudden loss of plasma; for it is believed that the runaway beam may give rise to electrostatic instabilities. Runaways form a major difficulty in plasma containment devices which pursue stability by increasing field shear. Low shear demands low density, while high shear demands high density, and in both cases the ratio of current along the field lines to particle density is high, and runaway can occur. It may be overcome by going to large systems with high density and moderate electric fields, whereupon energy requirements become exorbitant.

(c) Non-analytic Phenomena

Our treatment of the kinetic theory of a magnetized plasma, has with brief exceptions, been developed by expansion in powers of the Larmor radius or $(r_L/B)(\partial B/\partial x)$, but it is conceivable that some phenomena are missed by such an expansion procedure.

One fairly simple dynamical problem can be described exactly. This is the response of a uniform plasma in a uniform field to a small alternating electric field, from which the dielectric behaviour of the plasma can be deduced. The linearized Vlasov equation has the form

$$\left[\frac{\partial}{\partial t} + \mathbf{v}.\boldsymbol{\nabla} + \frac{e}{m}\mathbf{v}\times\mathbf{B}.\frac{\partial}{\partial \mathbf{v}}\right]f^1 = -\frac{e}{m}\mathbf{E}.\frac{\partial f_0}{\partial \mathbf{v}} \qquad (8.12.23)$$

The trajectories specified by the L.H.S. are

$$\mathbf{v} = [v_\parallel, v_\perp\cos(\Omega t+\phi), v_\perp\sin(\Omega t+\phi)]$$

$$\mathbf{x} = \left[x_\parallel+v_\parallel t, x_1+\frac{v_\perp}{\Omega}\sin(\Omega t+\phi), x_2-\frac{v_\perp}{\Omega}\cos(\Omega t+\phi)\right] \qquad (8.12.24)$$

and the solutions become, for $\mathbf{E}(\mathbf{x}, t) = \mathbf{E}\exp(i\mathbf{k}.\mathbf{x}+i\omega t)$,

$$f^1 = -\frac{e}{m}\int_{t'=-\infty}^{t}\mathrm{d}t'\mathbf{E}.\frac{\partial}{\partial\mathbf{v}}f_0\{v_\parallel, v_\perp\cos[\Omega(t'-t)+\phi], v_\perp\sin[\Omega(t'-t)+\phi]\}$$

$$\times\exp\left\{+i(\omega+k_\parallel v_\parallel)\tau+ik_\perp\frac{v_\perp}{\Omega}\times\right.$$

$$\left.\times[\cos(\psi-\phi)\sin\Omega\tau+\sin(\psi-\phi)(1-\cos\Omega\tau)]\right\}$$

where $k = (k_\parallel, k_\perp\cos\psi, k_\perp\sin\psi)$, and $\tau = t'-t$

If f_0 is a function of $v_\perp{}^2$, then the derivatives

$$\frac{\partial f_0}{\partial v} = \{\cos[\Omega(t'-t)+\phi], \sin[\Omega(t'-t)+\phi]\}2v_\perp\frac{\partial f_0}{\partial v_\perp{}^2}$$

and the trajectory integrals may all be reduced to the form

$$\mathscr{I} = \int_{-\infty}^{0}\exp\left\{+i(k_\parallel v_\parallel+\omega)t'\pm i\Omega t'+\frac{ik_\perp v_\perp}{\Omega}\sin\Omega t'\right\}\mathrm{d}t'$$

However, since

$$\exp\left(\frac{ik_\perp v_\perp}{\Omega}\sin\Omega t'\right) = \sum J_n\left(\frac{k_\perp v_\perp}{\Omega}\right)\exp(in\Omega t')$$

the J_n being Bessel functions, the integrals may be carried out as

$$\mathscr{I} = \frac{-i\sum_n J_n(k_\perp v_\perp/\Omega)}{\omega + k_\parallel v_\parallel + \binom{n-1}{n}{n+1}\Omega}$$

In forming such quantities as the induced current, integrals are needed of the form

$$\int f^1 v^n v_\perp \, dv_\perp \, dv_\parallel \, d\phi$$

and integrating over the phase ϕ again produces a series of Bessel functions. From the currents, the dielectric coefficient can be formed. It takes the general form

$$\epsilon_{ij} = 1 - \frac{\omega_p{}^2}{\omega}\sum_n \int dv_\parallel \int dv_\perp v_\perp A_{ij}{}^n(k_\perp v_\perp)B_{jk}(\omega + n\Omega + k_\parallel v_\parallel)$$

$$(8.12.25)$$

where

$$B(x) = \begin{bmatrix} \dfrac{1}{x} & 0 & 0 \\[2mm] 0 & \dfrac{x}{x^2-\Omega^2} & \dfrac{i\Omega}{x^2-\Omega^2} \\[2mm] 0 & \dfrac{-i\Omega}{x^2-\Omega^2} & \dfrac{x}{x^2-\Omega^2} \end{bmatrix}$$

$$A_{ij}{}^n = \sum_m J_n\left(\frac{k_\perp v_\perp}{\Omega}\right)J_m\left(\frac{k_\perp v_\perp}{\Omega}\right)a_{ij}{}^{n,m}$$

$$a_{ij} = a\begin{bmatrix} (\delta_{n,m}+\delta_{n,m+2}+\delta_{m,m-2}) & \dfrac{1}{2i}(\delta_{n,m+2}-\delta_{n,m-2}) & (\delta_{n,m+1}+\delta_{n,m-1}) \\[3mm] \dfrac{1}{2i}(\delta_{n,m+2}-\delta_{n,m-2}) & (\delta_{n,m}-\delta_{n,m+2}-\delta_{n,m-2}) & \dfrac{1}{i}(\delta_{n,m+1}-\delta_{n,m-1}) \\[3mm] (\delta_{n,m+1}+\delta_{n,m-1}) & \dfrac{1}{i}(\delta_{n,m+1}-\delta_{n,m-1}) & \dfrac{b}{a}\delta_{n,m} \end{bmatrix}$$

and

$$a = \tfrac{1}{2}v_\perp \frac{\partial f_0}{\partial v_\perp}, \qquad b = v_\parallel \frac{\partial f_0}{\partial v_\parallel}; \qquad \delta_{m,n} = 0, \qquad m \neq n. \qquad \delta_{m,n} = 1, \qquad m = n$$

The integrals occurring here have denominators of the form $1/(\omega + k_\parallel v_\parallel + n\Omega)$ which must be treated by the Landau procedure. In addition to the Landau form

$$\int \frac{g(t)\,dt}{x-t} = P \int \frac{g(t)}{x-t}\,dt - i\pi g(x)$$

there are singular integrals of the form

$$\int \frac{\Omega g(t)\,dt}{(x-t)^2 - \Omega^2} = P \int \frac{\Omega g(t+x)\,dt}{t^2 - \Omega^2} - \frac{i\pi}{2}[g(x-\Omega) - g(x+\Omega)]$$

which are associated with the cyclotron resonances. The most interesting consequence of this form of the dielectric coefficients is in the appearance of extra resonances at multiples of the cyclotron frequencies.

Evidence for thermal effects on the propagation of r.f. through a magnetized plasma is provided by WHARTON's observations of the first three harmonics of the cyclotron resonance from a hot plasma confined by a mirror field, as described in Chapter 7.

If the plasma is spatially non-uniform a treatment of this kind presents serious difficulties, mainly of a purely geometric kind. However, new physical phenomena appear. In particular, if the magnetic field has a spatial gradient, particles experience a first order drift, $v_D \sim (v_\theta r_L/B) \cdot (\partial B/\partial x)$ and the trajectory integrals must be modified to zero order in the Larmor radius. Instead of $1/(\omega + k_\parallel v_\parallel)$, denominators of the form $1/(\omega + k_\parallel v_\parallel + \mathbf{k} \cdot \mathbf{v}_D)$ appear, and these produce new Landau damping $\sim \exp(\omega/\mathbf{k} \cdot \mathbf{v}_D)^2$, a term that could never be discovered by an expansion in powers of the Larmor radius. If a wave will propagate at a point where $\partial f_0/\partial v$ is positive, this "Landau damping" term may change sign and produce a new instability. Such an instability, the "universal" instability, has been discovered by ROSENBLUTH. It is associated with the ion cyclotron frequency, i.e. arises from the term

$$\int \frac{\partial f_0}{\partial v} \bigg/ (\omega - \Omega + \mathbf{k}_\perp \cdot \mathbf{v}_D + k_\parallel v_\parallel),$$

is oriented along the field line $k_\parallel = 0$, is of short wavelength

$$\lambda \cong r_L(r_L/B)(\partial B/\partial x) \ll r_L,$$

and has the form of a slowly growing oscillation close to the ion cyclotron frequency. Since the wavelength is so small, this instability is almost independent of the macroscopic geometry, and represents one of the "micro-instabilities". Earlier examples of such geometry-independent micro-instabilities have been the two-stream instability, and the anisotropy instabilities. There are further known micro-instabilities associated with the ion and electron cyclotron resonances. The "universal instability" is of particular interest since it may occur whenever the magnetic field varies slightly over a Larmor radius and may be endemic to all confined plasmas.

If this is the case, i.e. if all confined plasmas are subject to instabilities, then the theory presented so far may not be adequate to describe any naturally occurring plasma. It may resemble classical idealized hydrodynamics when used in an attempt to describe turbulent flow. Our present experimental knowledge is too limited for this possibility to be excluded; however, although the agreement with theoretical prediction has been rather limited, there is some evidence that the description sketched in these pages is the appropriate one for some naturally occurring plasmas.

BIBLIOGRAPHY

1. HIRSCHFELDER, J. D., CURTIS, C. F. and BIRD, R. B. (1954). *Molecular Theory of Gases and Liquids*, Wiley, New York.
   GRAD, H., (1958). *Principles of the Kinetic Theory of Gases*. Handbuch der Physik, **12**, Springer, Gottingen.
   CHAPMAN, S. and COWLING, T. G. (1951). *The Mathematical Theory of Non-uniform Gases*, 2nd Edition. Clarendon Press, Oxford.
   GREEN, H. S. (1952). *The Molecular Theory of Fluids*, North Holland, Amsterdam.
   CHANDRASEKHAR, S. (1943). *Rev. Mod. Phys.* **15**, 1.
   ROSTOKER, N. and ROSENBLUTH, M. N. (1960). *Phys. Fluids*, **3**, 1.
   BALESCU, R. (1960). *Phys. Fluids*, **3**, 52.
   BOGOLIUBOV, N. (1946). *J. Phys. U.S.S.R.*, **10**, 265–274.
   Trans. Geophs. Research Directorate A.F.C.R.C. (1959).
   TCHEN, C. M. (1954). *Phys. Rev.* **114**, 394.
   CLAUSER, F. (ed.) (1960). *Plasma Dynamics*
   Ch. 5 BURGERS, J. M. (ed.). Addison-Welsey, Reading Mass.
   LANDAU, L. (1937). *Zh. Eksp. Theor. Fiz.* **7**, 203.
   ROSENBLUTH, M. N., MacDONALD, W. M. and JUDD, D. L. (1957). *Phys. Rev.* **107**, 1.
2. BOHM, D. and GROSS, E. P. (1949). *Phys. Rev.* **75**, 1851.
   BOHM, D. and PINES, D. (1952). *Phys. Rev.* **85**, 338.
   VLASOV, A. (1938). *Zh. Eksp. Teor. Fiz.* **8**, 291.
   LANDAU, L. (1946). *J. Phys. U.S.S.R.* **10**, 25.
3. THOMPSON, W. B. and HUBBARD, J. (1960). *Rev. Mod. Phys.* **32**, 714.
   HUBBARD, J. (1961). *Proc. Roy. Soc.* A, **260**, 114.
   GABOR, D. (1952). *Proc. Roy. Soc.* **213A**, 73.
   ROSTOKER, N. and ROSENBLUTH, M. N. op. cit.
   CHANDRASEKHAR, S. op. cit.
4. SIMON, A. (1961). Proc. of Summer School in Plasma Physics. Risö Report 18, Danish Atomic Energy Agency. Risö Roskilde.
   BUNEMANN, O. (1959). *Phys. Rev.* **115**, 503.
   HAEFF, A. V. (1949). *Proc. Inst. Radio Engineers*, **37**, 4.
   JOHNSON, W. B., McLAINE, C. K. and OLSON, H. N. (ed.) (1959). Proceedings of Conference on Plasma Oscillations, Linde Company, Indianapolis.
   PENROSE, O. (1960). *Phys. Fluids*, **3**, 258.
   AUER, P. L. (1958). *Phys. Rev. Letters*, **1**, 411.
   KARCHENKO, I. F., FAINBERG, Y. B., NIKOLAYEV, P. M., KORNILOV, E. A., LUTZENKO, E. A. and PEDENKO, N. S. (1960). Proc. 4th Int. Conf. on Ionization Phenomena in Gases II. p.671, North Holland, Amsterdam.

DEMIKARNOV, R. A., GEVORKOV, A. K. and POPOV, A. F. ibid, p. 665.

ALLEN, M. A. and KIMO, G. S. (1961). *Phys. Rev. Letters*, **6**, 163.

5. HARRIS, E. R., N.R.L. 4944, Naval Research Lab. Washington.

SPARROW, J. (1960). A.E.R.E. R3301, H.M. Stationery Office.

BENNETT, W. A. (1934). *Phys. Rev.* **45**, 890.

6. HILBERT, D. (1912). *Math. Ann.* **7**, 562.

CHAPMAN, S. and COWLING, T. G. op. cit.

7. CHANDRASEKHAR, S., KAUFMAN, A. N. and WATSON, K. M. (1957). *An. Phys.* **2**, 433,

10. ibid, **5**, 1. (1958).

FERRARO, V. C. A. (1955). *Proc. Roy. Soc.* A238, (310).

BRAGINSKII, S. I. and KAZANTZEV, A. P. (1959). *Plasma Physics and The Problem of Controlled Thermonuclear Reactions*, Vol. IV, p. 24. Pergamon Press, Oxford.

PARKER, E. N. (1957). *Phys. Rev.* **107**, 923.

BRUECKNER, K. A. and WATSON, K. M. (1956). *Phys. Rev.* **102**, 19.

THOMPSON, W. B. (1961). *Rep. Progr. Phys.* **24**, 363.

LÜST, R. (1959). *Forsch. der. Phys.* **7**, 503.

11. ROSENBLUTH, M. N. and ROSTOKER, N. (1959). *Phys. Fluids*, **2**, 23.

KRUSKAL, M. D. and OBERMAN, C. R. (1952). *Phys. Fluids*, **1**, 281.

NEWCOMB, W. (to be published in *Ann. Phys.*).

POST, R. F. and PERKINS, W. A. (1961). *Phys. Rev. Letters* **6**, 85.

12. (a) (b)

KAUFMAN, A. N. (1959). "Proceedings of Les Houches Summer School in Theoretical Physics", Hermann, Paris.

BURGERS, J. op. cit.

CHAPMAN and COWLING, op. cit.

MARSHALL, W. (1958). A.E.R.E. T/R 2247, 2352, 2419, H.M. Stationery Office, London.

VAUGHAN-WILLIAMS, R. W. and HAAS, F. D. (1961). *Phys. Rev. Letters*, **6**, 165.

(c) DREICER, H. (1959). *Phys. Rev.* **115**, 238.

D'ANGELO, N. and RYNN, N. (1961). *Phys. Fluids*. **4**, 275.

(d) BERNSTEIN, I. B. and TREHAN, S. K. (1960). *Nuclear Fusion*, **1**, 3.

BERNSTEIN, I. B. (1958). *Phys. Rev.* **109**, 10.

DRUMMOND, J. E. (1958). *Phys. Rev.* **110**, 293.

RANDLES, J. (1959). A.E.R.E. R3075, R2916, H.M. Stationery Office, London.

GERTSENSTEIN, M. E. (1954). *Zh. Eksp. teor. fiz.*, **27**, 80.

KRALL, N. A. and ROSENBLUTH, M. N. (1961). *Phys. Fluids* **4**, 163.

SOME FORMULAE

MAGNETO-HYDRODYNAMICS

$$\rho D\mathbf{v}/Dt = -\boldsymbol{\nabla}(p+B^2/8\pi) + \boldsymbol{B} \cdot \boldsymbol{\nabla}\boldsymbol{B}/4\pi$$

$$D\boldsymbol{B}/Dt + \boldsymbol{B}\,\mathrm{div}\,\mathbf{v} - \boldsymbol{B}\cdot\boldsymbol{\nabla}\mathbf{v} = \eta\nabla^2\boldsymbol{B}$$

where η is the resistivity in rationalized e.m.u.

Criterion for M.H.D. "typical" behaviour requires

$$M = LB/\eta\rho^{1/2} \gg 1$$

Small displacements $\boldsymbol{\xi}$ about equilibrium satisfy

$$\rho_0\ddot{\boldsymbol{\xi}} = \boldsymbol{\nabla}[\gamma p_0\,\mathrm{div}\,\boldsymbol{\xi} + \boldsymbol{\xi}\cdot\boldsymbol{\nabla}p_0] + [(\mathrm{curl}\,\boldsymbol{B}_0)\times\boldsymbol{Q} + (\mathrm{curl}\,\boldsymbol{Q})\times\boldsymbol{B}_0]/4\pi$$
$$+ \boldsymbol{\nabla}(\rho_0\boldsymbol{\xi})\boldsymbol{\nabla}\phi$$

where

$$\boldsymbol{Q} = \mathrm{curl}\,(\boldsymbol{\xi}\times\boldsymbol{B}_0)$$

is the perturbed field and ϕ the gravitational potential.

Sound Speeds:

$$v = \omega/k,\ c_A{}^2 = B^2/4\pi\rho,\ c_s{}^2 = \gamma p/\rho$$

$$v = \begin{cases} c_A \\ 2^{-1/2}\{c_A{}^2 + c_s{}^2 + [(c_A{}^2+c_s{}^2)^2 - 4c_A{}^2c_s{}^2\cos 2\theta]^{1/2}\}^{1/2} \end{cases}$$

c_A = Alfvén speed
c_s = normal sound speed

Shocks: For transverse shock: the shock Mach, $M = v_s/c_T$, where

$$c_T{}^2 = c_A{}^2 + c_s{}^2$$

$$M^2 = \frac{2}{\gamma+1}\cdot\frac{1 + (c_A{}^2/c_T{}^2)(1-\tfrac{1}{2}\gamma)[(\rho_2/\rho_1)-1]}{(\rho_1/\rho_2) - (\gamma-1)/(\gamma+1)}$$

Rankine–Hugoniot conditions for an oblique shock: if $B_{\parallel}$, $v_{\parallel}$, $\mathbf{B}_{\perp}$ $\mathbf{v}_{\perp}$ are parallel, transverse components of field, velocity, and [] = jump across shock, then

$$0 = [\rho v_\parallel] = [\rho v_\parallel{}^2 + p + B^2/8\pi] = [\rho_\parallel v_\parallel \mathbf{v}_\perp - B_\parallel \mathbf{B}_\perp/4\pi]$$

$$0 = [B_\parallel] = [v_\parallel \mathbf{B}_\perp + \mathbf{v}_\perp B_\parallel]$$

$$0 = [1/2(v_\parallel{}^2 + v_\perp{}^2) + \gamma p/(\gamma-1)\rho + (B_\perp{}^2 - \mathbf{B}_\perp \cdot \mathbf{v}_\perp B_\parallel/v_\parallel)/4\pi\rho]$$

STABILITY

A magneto hydrodynamic system is stable if $\delta W > 0$ where

$$\delta W = \begin{cases} \frac{1}{2}\int\limits_{vac} d\tau\, B_1{}^2/4\pi \\[2ex] + \frac{1}{2}\int ds(\mathbf{n}\cdot\boldsymbol{\xi})^2[\mathbf{n}\cdot\boldsymbol{\nabla}(p+B^2/8\pi)]_a \\[2ex] + \frac{1}{2}\int\limits_{plasma} d\tau\{(Q^2/4\pi) - \boldsymbol{\xi}\cdot\mathbf{j}_0\times\mathbf{Q} + (\gamma p_0\,\text{div}\,\boldsymbol{\xi} + \boldsymbol{\xi}\cdot\boldsymbol{\nabla}p_0)\,\text{div}\,\boldsymbol{\xi} - \\[2ex] \qquad - \text{div}\,(\rho_0\boldsymbol{\xi})\boldsymbol{\xi}\cdot\boldsymbol{\nabla}\dot\phi\} \end{cases}$$

where $[\ ]_d$ = surface discontinuity
and $\mathbf{j}$ is in emu.

Interchange. The volume of a flux tube ϕ is

$$v = \int A\,dl = \phi\int dl/B$$

integrals being carried along magnetic field lines. If on interchange of flux tubes the magnetic energy is unaltered, the change in thermal energy is

$$\delta W_\theta = pv^{-\gamma}\delta v\,\delta(pv^\gamma) = \delta v[\delta p + \gamma p\,\delta v/v]$$

while if the volume of gas is unchanged, the change in magnetic energy

$$\delta W_M = -W_M\delta\phi\delta(\int dl/A)$$

Suydam's necessary condition for the stability of a cylinder,

$$(8\pi p'/Bg^2) + \tfrac{1}{4}r(\mu'/\mu)^2 \geqslant 0, \quad \mu = B_\theta/rBz; f' = df/dr$$

Anisotropy instabilities
"firehose" if

$$p_\parallel > p_\perp + B^2/4\pi$$

"mirror" if

$$\tfrac{1}{6}p^2{}_\perp/p_\| > p_\perp + B^2/8\pi$$

"electrostatic" if $v_D > v_\theta$ (v_D, v_θ, electron drift, thermal, speeds)

$$> \sqrt{(m/M)}v_\theta \text{ if ions cold.}$$

ORBITS

Hamiltonian

$$H = (\boldsymbol{p} - e\boldsymbol{A}/c)^2/2m + e\phi;$$

$\boldsymbol{A}$, ϕ vector, scalar, potentials

Motion *adiabatic* if

$$r_L \partial \log B/\partial x \ll 1$$

adiabatic invariants

$$\mu = v^2{}_\perp/B \qquad \alpha = \oint v_\| \mathrm{d}l$$

In constant fields, another constant is

$$\xi = v^2{}_\| + B\mu - (2e/m)\int E_\| \mathrm{d}l$$

Drifts

$$\mathbf{v_E} = c\boldsymbol{E} \times \boldsymbol{B}/B^2 \qquad \mathbf{v_{\dot{E}}} = c\dot{\boldsymbol{E}}/\Omega B$$

Any force $\mathbf{F}$ acts as a field $\mathbf{F}/c$

$$\mathbf{v_R} = v_\|{}^2 \boldsymbol{b} \times \boldsymbol{n}/R\Omega = v_\| r_L{}^\| \boldsymbol{b} \times \boldsymbol{n}/R; \ r_L{}^\| = v_\|/\Omega$$

$$\mathbf{v_B} = \tfrac{1}{2}v_\perp{}^2 \boldsymbol{b} \times \boldsymbol{\nabla}(\log B)/\Omega = \tfrac{1}{2}v_\perp r_L{}^\perp \boldsymbol{b} \times \boldsymbol{\nabla}(\log B); \ r_L{}^\perp = v_\perp/\Omega$$

R = radius of curvature, $\mathbf{b}$ = unit tangent, $\mathbf{n}$ = principal normal to field lines.

Double adiabatic stress tensor

$$\boldsymbol{p} = p_\perp \mathbf{1} + (p_\| - p_\perp)\boldsymbol{b}\boldsymbol{b}$$

if

$$(\boldsymbol{\nabla} \cdot \boldsymbol{\xi})_\| = \boldsymbol{b} \cdot (\boldsymbol{\nabla}\boldsymbol{\xi}) \cdot \boldsymbol{b}; \ (\boldsymbol{\nabla} \cdot \boldsymbol{\xi})_\perp = \boldsymbol{\nabla}\boldsymbol{\xi} - (\boldsymbol{\nabla} \cdot \boldsymbol{\xi})_\|$$

then

$$\begin{cases} \delta p_\perp = -p_\perp[(\boldsymbol{\nabla} \cdot \boldsymbol{\xi})_\| + 2(\boldsymbol{\nabla} \cdot \boldsymbol{\xi})_\perp] \\ \delta p_\| = -p_\|[3(\boldsymbol{\nabla} \cdot \boldsymbol{\xi})_\| + (\boldsymbol{\nabla} \cdot \boldsymbol{\xi})_\perp] \end{cases} \text{ on displacement } \boldsymbol{\xi}$$

ELECTRICAL PROPERTIES

Dielectric coefficient

$$\epsilon = 1 - (\omega_p{}^2/\omega^2)\phi(\omega/kv_\theta); \ \phi(x) \begin{cases} = x^2 \int \dfrac{\partial f_0/\partial t}{x+t}\mathrm{d}t \text{ (longitudinal waves)} \\[2mm] = x \int \dfrac{f_0}{x+t}\mathrm{d}t \text{ (transverse waves)} \end{cases}$$

where

$$f_0 = \int F(\mathbf{v}/v_\theta)\mathrm{d}(\mathbf{v}_\perp/v_\theta), \quad \mathbf{v} = \mathbf{v}_\perp + (\mathbf{v}\cdot\mathbf{k})\mathbf{k}$$

F being the unperturbed distribution function:

In a magnetic field, the dielectric tensor is

$$\epsilon_{ij} = \begin{pmatrix} 1-\alpha & 0 & 0 \\ 0 & 1-\beta & i\gamma \\ 0 & -i\gamma & 1-\beta \end{pmatrix}$$

where the first row, column represent the field direction

$$\alpha, \beta, \gamma = (\alpha, \beta, \gamma)_+ + (\alpha, \beta, \gamma)_-$$
$$\{\alpha = \omega_p^2/\omega^2, \beta = \omega_p^2/(\omega^2-\Omega^2), \gamma = \omega_p^2\Omega/(\omega^2-\Omega^2)\}_\pm$$

At low frequencies

$$\epsilon \to \begin{pmatrix} -\omega_p^2/\omega^2 & 0 & 0 \\ 0 & 1+c^2/c_A^2 & 0 \\ 0 & 0 & 1+c^2/c_A^2 \end{pmatrix}$$

For a hot manetized plasma, the polarization produced by an electric field **E** is most easily written in circularly polarized form; i.e. with the magnetic field along OZ, write

$$V_\parallel = V_z.\ V_1 = \tfrac{1}{2}(V_x+iV_y),\ V_2 = \tfrac{1}{2}(V_x-iV_y);$$

whereupon the components of the polarization may be written as a sum of terms from each ionic species (electrons and ions), each term itself being a sum of the form

$$\begin{pmatrix} P_\parallel \\ P_1 \\ P_2 \end{pmatrix} = \frac{1}{2}\frac{\omega_0^2}{\omega} \sum_{-\infty}^{n=\infty} \int_{-\infty}^{\infty} \frac{\mathrm{d}v_\parallel}{\omega_n} \int_0^{\infty} \mathrm{d}v_\perp v_\perp \begin{pmatrix} v_\parallel J_n \\ v_\perp J_{n-1} \\ v_\perp J_{n+1} \end{pmatrix} \times$$

$$\left[J_n E_\parallel \frac{\partial f_0}{\partial v_\parallel} + (E_1 J_{n-1} + E_2 J_{n+1})\frac{\partial f_0}{\partial v_\perp} \right]$$

where $(w_n = w+k_\parallel v_\parallel +n\Omega,\ w_0 = $ plasma frequency, $\Omega = $ gyrofrequency (with sign !), $J_n = J_n(k_\perp v_\perp/\Omega)$ is the usual Bessel function of the first kind, and $f_0(v_\parallel, v_\perp^2)$ is the unperturbed distribution function.

If f_0 is anisotropic, a perturbing magnetic field produces a further polarization

17

$$\begin{pmatrix} P_{\parallel}M \\ P_2M \\ P_2M \end{pmatrix} = -\frac{1}{2}\frac{i\omega_0^2}{\omega c}\sum_{-\infty}^{n=\infty}\int_{-\infty}^{\infty}\frac{dv_{\parallel}}{\omega_n}\int_0^{\infty}dv_{\perp}v_{\perp}\begin{pmatrix} v_{\parallel}J_n \\ v_{\perp}J_{n-1} \\ v_{\perp}J_{n+1} \end{pmatrix}\times$$

$$(B_1J_{n-1}-B_2J_{n+1})\left(v_{\perp}\frac{\partial f_0}{\partial v_{\parallel}}-v_{\parallel}\frac{\partial f_0}{\partial v_{\perp}}\right)$$

* More useful than either of these is the dispersion tensor G_{ij}; which results when Maxwell's equations are used to eliminate the magnetic field perturbation. In a coordinate system defined by the propagation vector $\mathbf{k}$, and the unperturbed magnetic field $\mathbf{B}_0$, so that

$$(OX,\ OY,\ OZ)||(\mathbf{k}\times(\mathbf{k}\times\mathbf{B}_0),\ \mathbf{k}\times\mathbf{B}_0,\ \mathbf{k})$$

the resulting equations for $\mathbf{E}$ have the form

$$\begin{pmatrix} (k^2-\omega^2/c^2)E_x \\ (k^2-\omega^2/c^2)E_y \\ k^2E_z \end{pmatrix} = G_{ij}E_j$$

and the dispersion equation giving $w(\mathbf{k})$ becomes

$$Det\left|(k^2-\omega^2/c^2)\delta_{ij}+(\omega^2/c^2)\delta_{iz}\delta_{zj}-G_{ij}\right| = 0$$

If the unperturbed distribution function is Gaussian, i.e.

$$f_0 = \pi^{-3/2}\theta_{\parallel}^{-1}\theta_{\perp}^{-2}\exp-\{[(v_{\parallel}-u)^2/\theta_{\parallel}^2]+(v_{\perp}^2/\theta_{\perp}^2)\}$$

the integrals may be carried out, and G_{ij} written as a sum over the ionic species of terms each in turn being expressed as an infinite sum. Finally, each term in the sum may be written as a product $T_{ij}H_{ij}$ (not summed!), i.e.

$$G_{ij} = \sum_{species} C \sum_{-\infty}^{n=\infty} T_{ij}H_{ij}(n)$$

With the following abbreviations:

$$K = k_{\perp}r_{\perp} = k_{\perp}\theta_{\perp}/\Omega,\quad \omega' = \omega/\Omega,\quad \omega'_n = \frac{\omega+k_{\parallel}u+n\Omega}{k_{\parallel}\theta_{\parallel}}$$

and the following functions
$I_n = I_n(\frac{1}{2}K^2)$, where I_n is the usual Bessel function of imaginary argument;

$$I_n^{(x)} = i^{-n}J_n(x)$$

J_n being the Bessel function of the first kind,

$$\mathscr{I} = \mathscr{I}(\omega'_n) = \pi^{-\frac{1}{2}}\int_{-\infty}^{\infty}dt\frac{\exp-t^2}{\omega'_n+t}$$

$$X = [\omega'_n(\theta_{\parallel}^2/\theta_{\perp}^2)-nk_{\perp}\theta_{\perp}/k_{\parallel}\theta_{\parallel}K]\mathscr{I}-\theta_{\parallel}^2/\theta_{\perp}^2$$

* The inclusion of this form was suggested by M. N. Rosenbluth, to whom (with K. Wilson) it is due.

Then

$$C = \omega_0^2 \, e^{-K2}$$

$$T_{11} = T_{13} = T_{31} = T_{33} = I_n; \quad T_{22} = (k^2 + 2n^2/K^2)I_n - \tfrac{1}{2}K^2(I_{n-1} + I_{n+1})$$

$$T_{12} = T_{21} = T_{23} = T_{32} = I_n - \tfrac{1}{2}(I_{n-1} + I_{n+1})$$

$$H_{11} = \tfrac{1}{2}K^{-2}[(n^2k^2/k_\parallel{}^2) + (nk/k_\parallel) + (\omega'k_\perp{}^2/kk_\parallel)]X$$

$$H_{22} = 1 + X \qquad H_{33} = \tfrac{1}{2}(\omega'/K)^2 X$$

$$H_{12} = -H_{21} = -i[(nk/k_\parallel) + (\omega'k_\perp{}^2/kk_\parallel)]X$$

$$H_{13} = H_{31} = -(\omega'k_\perp/2k_\parallel K^2)[n + (\omega'k_\perp{}^2/k^2)]X$$

$$H_{23} = -H_{32} = -i(k_\perp\omega'/k)X$$

Ohm's law

$$\eta\boldsymbol{j} = \boldsymbol{E} + \mathbf{v} \times \boldsymbol{B} + [\boldsymbol{\nabla}p_- - \boldsymbol{j} \times \boldsymbol{B} - (m/e1)\partial\boldsymbol{j}/\partial t]/ne1 \quad \text{(emu)}$$

n = electron number density.

KINETIC THEORY

Maxwell distribution

$$f(\mathbf{v}) = \begin{cases} n(\pi v_\theta)^{-3/2} \, \exp(-v^2/v_\theta{}^2) \\ n(m/2\pi kT)^{3/2} \, \exp[-(\tfrac{1}{2}mv^2/kT)] \end{cases}$$

Fokker–Planck equation

$$\partial f/\partial t + \mathbf{v} \cdot \boldsymbol{\nabla}f + \boldsymbol{a} \cdot (\partial/\partial\mathbf{v})f = (\partial/\partial\mathbf{v}) \cdot (D f) + (\partial^2/\partial\mathbf{v}\partial\mathbf{v}) : (D f) = \mathscr{I}(f)$$

Landau's F.P.E.

$$\mathscr{I} = 2\pi(e^2/m)^2 \log\Lambda \cdot \partial/\partial v_i \int d^3 v w_{ij}(f'f_{,j} - ff'_{,j})$$

$$f_{,j}(x) = \partial f/\partial x_j, \; w_{ij} = (\delta_{ij} - \hat{\mathbf{g}}_i\hat{\mathbf{g}}_j)/g : \mathbf{g} = g\mathbf{g} = \mathbf{v}' - \mathbf{v}$$

$$\Lambda = (kT/e^2)^{3/2}(4\pi n)^{-1/2}$$

F.P. coefficients for a Maxwellian distribution

$$G(x) = \left(\int_0^x e^{-t^2}dt - x \, e^{-x^2}\right)$$

$$\overline{\sqrt{\pi x^2}}$$

$$\left. \begin{array}{l} D = (kT/m)^{-1} \, G(v/v_\theta) \\ D = v^{-1} \, G(v/v_\theta) \\ D = v^{-1} \, H(v/v_\theta) \end{array} \right\} 8\pi ne'' \log\Lambda \cdot m^{-2}$$

$$H(x) = \frac{2}{\sqrt{\pi}}\int_0^x e^{-t^2}dt - G(x)$$

Transport coefficients
Define

$$\nu_0 = (2kT/m)^{1/2}\, 8\pi ne^4 \log\Lambda (kT)^{-2}$$

$$\nu_- = (6\sqrt{\pi})^{-1}\nu_0,\; r = \Omega/\nu_-\; \sigma_0 = ne^2/m\nu_-$$

$$\Omega_+ = \Omega\cdot m/M;\; e = \text{electron charge (with sign!)}$$

then, (for slow motions)

$$\boldsymbol{j} = \sigma_{\shortparallel}\boldsymbol{D}_{\shortparallel}+\sigma_{\perp}\boldsymbol{D}_{\perp}+\sigma_H\boldsymbol{b}\times\boldsymbol{D}+\phi_{\shortparallel}\boldsymbol{\nabla}T_{\shortparallel}+\phi_{\perp}\boldsymbol{\nabla}T_{\perp}+\phi_H\boldsymbol{b}\times\boldsymbol{\nabla}T$$

$$\boldsymbol{D} = \boldsymbol{E}+\mathbf{v}\times\boldsymbol{B}/c+(ne)^{-1}\boldsymbol{\nabla}p;\; V_{\shortparallel} = (V\cdot\mathbf{b})\mathbf{b};\; V_{\perp} = V-V_{\shortparallel}$$

In strong fields $r \gg 1$

$$\sigma_{\shortparallel} = 0\!\cdot\!8\sigma_0 \qquad \phi_{\shortparallel} = 0\!\cdot\!68\phi_0 = 0\!\cdot\!68k\sigma_0/e$$

$$\sigma_{\perp} = 0\!\cdot\!5\sigma_0 r^{-2} \qquad \phi_{\perp} = 0\!\cdot\!75\phi_0 r^{-2}$$

$$\sigma_H = r\sigma_{\perp} \qquad \phi_H = 2\!\cdot\!13\phi_0 r^{-3}$$

If no Hall current flows

$$\sigma_{\perp eff} = 0\!\cdot\!5\sigma_0$$

Heat flux **q**

$$\mathbf{q} = -\lambda_{\shortparallel}\boldsymbol{\nabla}T_{\shortparallel}-\lambda_{\perp}\boldsymbol{\nabla}T_{\perp}-\lambda_H\boldsymbol{b}\times\boldsymbol{\nabla}T+\psi_{\shortparallel}\boldsymbol{j}_{\shortparallel}+\boldsymbol{\nabla}_{\perp}\boldsymbol{j}_{\perp}+\psi_H\boldsymbol{b}\times\boldsymbol{j}$$

$$\lambda_{\shortparallel} = \lambda_0 = \sigma_0 k^2 T/e^2 \qquad\qquad \psi_{\shortparallel} = 3\!\cdot\!3\psi_0 = 3\!\cdot\!3kT/e$$

$$\lambda_{\perp} = 0\!\cdot\!7(M/m)^{1/2}\lambda_0 r^{-2} \qquad\qquad \psi_{\perp} = 2\!\cdot\!5\psi_0$$

$$\lambda_H = -0\!\cdot\!5\lambda_0 r^{-1}(0\!\cdot\!4+r^2 m/M) \qquad \psi_H = 1\!\cdot\!5\Psi_0 r^{-1}$$

The stress tensor contains

$$\mathbf{p} = (p_0/\Omega_+)[\boldsymbol{b}\times\boldsymbol{\nabla}V-\boldsymbol{\nabla}V\times\boldsymbol{b}]$$

Runaway criterion:
if

$$\lambda_f = (kT)^2/8\pi ne^4\log\Lambda$$

and

$$eE\lambda_f > \left.{\begin{array}{c} 0\!\cdot\!4 \\[4pt] 0\!\cdot\!2 \end{array}}\right\}\, kT\; {\begin{array}{c}\text{a beam}\\[4pt]\text{all}\end{array}}\Big\}\;\text{electrons can run away.}$$

SOME NUMBERS

FUNDAMENTAL CONSTANTS

Electronic charge
$e = 4 \cdot 8 \times 10^{-10}$ esu,

Electronic mass
$m = 0 \cdot 91 \; 10^{-27}$ g

Electronic rest energy
$mc^2 = 511$ keV

Electronic "radius"
$e^2/mc^2 = 2 \cdot 8 \times 10^{-13}$ cm

e/m
$= 5 \cdot 27 \times 10^{17}$ esu/g

Proton/electron mass
$M/m = 1836$
$\sqrt{(M/m)} = 43$

Light speed
$c = 3 \times 10^{10}$ cm/sec

Boltzmann's constant:
$k = 1 \cdot 38 \times 10^{-16}$ ergs/deg

Planck's constant
$h = 6 \cdot 62 \times 10^{-27}$ erg/sec.

1 eV
$= 1 \cdot 6 \times 10^{-12}$ erg $= 1 \cdot 6 \times 10^{-19}$ joules

1 eV
$= kT$ at $T = 11,600°$ K

velocity of 1 eV electron
$= 5 \cdot 93 \times 10^7$ cm/sec

velocity of 1 eV proton
$= 1 \cdot 38 \times 10^6$ cm/sec

If n = electron (ion) number density cm^{-3} W = temperature (eV), B = field (gauss)

Angular frequencies	Lengths	Speeds
Plasma $\omega_p = (4\pi n e^2/m)^{1/2}$	Debye $= v_\theta/\sqrt{2} \cdot \omega_p = (kT/4\pi n e^2)^{1/2}$	Sound $c_s = \sqrt{(\gamma p/\rho)}$ $= \sqrt{(5/6)}v_\theta$
$\omega_p = 5 \cdot 63 \times 10^9 (n)^{1/2}$ $\omega_{p+} = 1 \cdot 31 \times 10^3 (n)^{1/2}$	$\lambda_D = 740(W/n)^{1/2}$	$c_s = 1 \cdot 24 \times 10^6 \sqrt{W}$
Gyro $\Omega = eB/mc$	$r_L = v/\Omega$	Alfvén $c_A = B/\sqrt{(4\pi\rho)}$ $= c\Omega_+/\omega_{p+}$
$\Omega_- = 1 \cdot 76 \times 10^7 B$ $\Omega_+ = 0 \cdot 96 \times 10^4 B$	$r_L = 3 \cdot 37 \times W^{1/2}/B$ $r_{L+} = 145 \; W^{1/2}/B$	$c_A = 2 \cdot 2 \times 10^{11} B/n^{1/2}$
Collision* $\nu_0 = v_\theta \, 8\pi m e^4 \log \Lambda (kT)^{-2}$ $\nu_{0-} = 3 \cdot 1 \times 10^{-5} n \log \Lambda W^{-3/2}$ $\nu_{0+} = 7 \cdot 2 \times 10^{-7} n \log \Lambda W^{-3/2}$	Mean free path $\lambda_f = (kT)^2/8\pi n e^4 \log \Lambda$ $\lambda_f = 1 \cdot 9 \times 10^{12} W^2/n \log \Lambda$	Thermal $v_\theta = (2kT/m)^{1/2}$ $v_{\theta-} = 5 \cdot 95 \times 10^7 \sqrt{W}$ $v_{\theta+} = 1 \cdot 38 \times 10^6 \sqrt{W}$

* Note that the collision frequencies are ill-defined, since cross section varies with velocity. e.g. ν_- used in transport coefficients $= (6\sqrt{\pi})^{-1}\nu_0 \equiv 0 \cdot 16\nu_0$

Spitzer (op. cit.) gives
τ_c "self-collision" time, needed for establishment of thermal equilibrium

among electrons)

$$\tau_c^{-1} = 0.14\nu_0$$

τ_s "slowing down" time for test particle

$$\tau_s^{-1} = 0.38\nu_0$$

τ_e time needed for two assemblies to reach thermal equilibrium

$$\tau_e^{-1} = 0.19\nu_0$$

$$\nu_0 = 8\pi f_1^2 f_2^2 (e^4/m_1 m_2) \log \Lambda [(kT_2/m_1) + (kT_2/m_2)]^{-3/2}$$

Note τ_e electron–electron: ion–ion: ion–electron :: 1:43: 1830

Resistivity

$$\eta_{rat} = c^2/4\pi\sigma = 4 \times 10^8 \log \Lambda \cdot W^{3/2}\text{cm}^2 \text{ sec}^{-1} \text{ (rat. e.m.u.)}$$

$$\eta = 5 \log \Lambda \cdot W^{-3/2}\text{ohm–cm}$$

Depth of penetration: L in cms, t in μ sec,

$$L = (\eta_{rat}t)^{1/2} = 20(\log \Lambda)^{1/2} W^{-3/4}t^{1/2} \quad (\text{ohms, } (\mu \text{ sec})^{1/2})$$

Ratios

$$\Lambda = kT\lambda_D/e^2 = (kT/e^2)^{3/2}(4\pi n)^{-1/2} = 5.1 \times 10^9 W^{3/2}n^{-1/2}$$

$$\log_e\Lambda = 22.3 - 1.15 \log_{10}n + 3.5 \log_{10}W$$

$$r = (\Omega/\nu-) = (6\sqrt{\pi})eB(kT)^2[(2kT/m)^{1/2}8\pi ne^4 \log \Lambda]^{-1}$$

$$r- = 5.8 \times 10^{11}BW^{3/2}/n \log \Lambda$$

$$r+ = 1.3 \times 10^{10}BW^{3/2}/n \log \Lambda$$

SOME FUNCTIONS

	Small	0·2	0·4	0·6	0·8	1	1·5	2	3	4	Large
$x)$	$2x/3\sqrt{\pi} = \cdot 37x$	0·073	0·137	0·183	0·208	0·214	0·175	0·119	0·056	0·031	$\frac{1}{2}x^2$
$x)$	$2G = 0\cdot 75x$	0·149	0·292	0·421	0·534	0·629	0·791	0·876	0·944	0·969	1
$x)$	$x(1-\frac{4}{3}x^2)$	0·39	0·72	0·95	1·06	1·08	0·86	0·60	0·356	0·258	$(1-\frac{1}{2}x^2)/x$
$x)$	$\sqrt{\pi}e^{-x^2}$	1·77	1·5	1·24	0·93	0·65	0·187	0·032	2×10^{-4}	2×10^{-6}	0

$G(x)$ $H(x)$ from Spitzer op. cit.

$$I(x) = \frac{1}{\sqrt{\pi}} \int dt \frac{e^{-t^2}}{x+t} = i\sqrt{\pi} \cdot e^{-x2} + \rho \frac{1}{\sqrt{\pi}} \int dt \frac{e^{-t^2}}{x+t}$$

$$= i\sqrt{\pi}e^{-x^2} + 2e^{-x^2} \int_0^x dt e^{-t^2} = I_i + I_r$$

I from Fried, B.D. and Conte, S.D. (1961) *The Plasma Dispersion Function* Academic Press, New York & London.

AUTHOR INDEX

249

SUBJECT INDEX